Computer Imaging Recipes
in C

Harley R. Myler
Arthur R. Weeks

Department of Electrical & Computer Engineering
University of Central Florida
Orlando, Florida

P T R Prentice Hall
Englewood Cliffs, New Jersey 07632

Library of Congress Cataloging-in-Publication Data

Myler, Harley R.
    Computer imaging recipes in C / Harley R. Myler, Arthur R. Weeks.
        p.   cm.
    Includes bibliographical references and index.
    ISBN 0-13-189879-5
    1. Image processing—Digital techniques.   2. C (Computer program
language)   I. Weeks, Arthur R.   II. Title.
TA1632.M95   1993
621.36'7' 02855133—dc20
                                      92-23501
                                      CIP

Editorial production supervision: *Harriet Tellem*
Cover design: *Ben Santora*
Buyer: *Mary E. McCartney*
Acquisitions editor: *Karen Gettman*
Editorial assistant: *Barbara Alfieri*

Apple and Macintosh are registered trademarks of Apple Computer, Inc.; Epson is a registered trademark of Seiko
Epson Corportion; HP, DeskJet, and LaserJet are trademarks of Hewlett-Packard Company; IBM is a registered
trademark of International Business Machines Corporation; Intel is a registered trademark of Intel Corporation;
Microsoft and MS-DOS are registered trademarks of Microsoft Corporation; PostScript is a registered trademark
of Adobe Systems, Inc.; GIF and Graphics Interchange Format are trademarks of Compuserve Inc.

The publisher offers discounts on this book when
ordered in bulk quantities. For more information, write:
        Special Sales/Professional Marketing
        Prentice-Hall, Inc.
        Professional & Technical Reference Division
        Englewood Cliffs, New Jersey 07632

Printed in the United States of America

10 9 8 7 6 5 4 3 2 1

ISBN 0-13-189879-5

Prentice-Hall International (UK) Limited, *London*
Prentice-Hall of Australia Pty. Limited, *Sydney*
Prentice-Hall Canada Inc., *Toronto*
Prentice-Hall Hispanoamericana, S.A., *Mexico*
Prentice-Hall of India Private Limited, *New Delhi*
Prentice-Hall of Japan, Inc., *Tokyo*
Simon & Schuster Asia Pte. Ltd., *Singapore*
Editora Prentice-Hall do Brasil, Ltda., *Rio de Janeiro*

To Nancy and Krifka

To Dian, Anne, Frank, Kathy, and Frank

Contents

Preface

We wrote his book for scientists, technicians, and students who require knowledge of basic and advanced (though not theoretical) techniques of Computer Image Processing. *Computer Imaging Recipes in C* is a companion to the MS-DOS PC-based UCFImage© Version 4.0 computer image software package, although no specific reference to the software is made until Chapter 12. We have attempted to cover all aspects of imaging from basic characterization and modelling through grayscale and spatial manipulation techniques. Attention has been paid to computer algorithm development and the use of imaging systems in a general way.

This book is arranged by algorithm suite instead of the more common enhancement/restoration/reconstruction format found in other texts. Ordering by algorithm is to allow *Computer Imaging Recipes in C* to be used as a reference guide when developing imaging software systems and solving problems requiring image processing. It is our opinion that this ordering improves comprehension of algorithmic processes in imaging as each suite follows a logical and sequential progression leading from basic techniques of algebraic, geometric, and grayscale manipulations through complex and powerful convolution, spatial frequency, and adaptive filtering methods. The book also contains reference to and descriptions of common image file formats and display technologies as well as a unique appendix that allows rapid look-up of common algorithms and convolution masks.

The UCFImage© computer software imaging system included with the book or available from the authors runs on MS-DOS, 80286 AT Class or better computers with basic VGA display units. Machines of this description may be purchased for less than $1000. The capabilities of UCFImage© are equivalent to software systems costing thousands of dollars that require hardware costing tens of thousands of dollars. The intent of both the book and the software is to put sophisticated imaging capabilities within reach of anyone who can operate a PC and understands basic physical and mathematical concepts. UCFImage© is capable of reading GIF, TIFF, BMP and PCX images[†] as well as raw format data. These capabilities make the program useful to students of electronic media and desktop publishing. TIFF is the recognized format for electronic image scanners, so anyone with access to one of these machines (which start at less than $100) can bring data into UCFImage© for processing.

Computer Imaging Recipes in C can be used as an undergraduate introductory text in image processing as well as a companion text for graduate level students. A single semester

---

[†] GIF (Graphic Interchange Format) is copyrighted by Compuserve, Inc., TIFF (Tagged Interchange File Format) was developed by Microsoft Corp. and Aldus Corp., BMP is copyrighted to Microsoft Corp. and PCX is the image storage format of the PC Paintbrush program by Z-Soft Corp..

offering should be adequate to cover the entire book. Background requirements include algebra, physics, statistics, and basic computer programming. We have omitted any equations or theoretical discussion requiring differential equations or calculus so as to include a wider audience. Specifically, graphic art, computer media, health and biological sciences, and other fields where advanced mathematics are not studied.

We wish to thank our students, Michele Van Dyke-Lewis and David Hefele for their assistance in generating portions of the computer code discussed in this book. We would also like to thank Rahul Dhesi for his software compression system that allows us to include our software with this text.

Harley R. Myler
Arthur R. Weeks

Chapter 1

Image Processing

The processing of images began when nature discovered the advantages of detecting light energy spatially. This approach was no doubt initiated by a creature similar to the *Copilia quadrata*, a copepod that lives in the Bay of Naples. The copilia is a small, transparent crustacean that has a single pair of light receptors that it moves with muscles to form an image. As we move from lower animals to more sophisticated ones, we find that the visual systems increase in capability and complexity. This transition of nature was time dependent; it had to wait for genetic biotechnology to reveal increasingly complex systems at every stage.

Waiting for technology has not been restricted to nature. Modern image processing is considerably different from the first coding of newspaper images in the early 1920's for transmission across transatlantic cables. In the last few years, the improvements and advances in personal computer technology in the form of high-powered microprocessors, large memories and fixed storage devices, and sophisticated high-resolution color displays at reasonable cost has made image processing available to everyone. As little as 5 years ago, systems costing upward of $50,000 were required to perform image manipulation that can be accomplished using personal computer hardware costing less than $1,000. In this book, *image processing* will mean the manipulation of images by a computer to include the acquisition and display of those images.

In the past, due to the high cost of imaging systems and the computers required to manipulate them, image processing was largely an extension of digital signal processing and was performed in the research laboratories of universities, the government, and large corporations. Algorithms were sought to enhance the images acquired by spacecraft and intelligence sources. Imaging algorithms were also developed for use in sophisticated weapons systems, where objects would be acquired, tracked, and recognized. The cruise missile is an excellent example of image-processing state of the art. As the missile flies, a camera mounted in the nose continually scans the ground and compares the image observed to image data stored in its onboard computer. Differences result in course corrections so that the observed scenes are consistent with the required flight path scenes. This is accomplished through the use of image correlation, a technique presented in Chapter 10.

Images returned from the early *Voyager* space probes were often blurry or corrupted with a wide variety of noises. A great deal of research was performed by NASA and the Jet Propulsion Laboratory in Pasadena, California, on algorithms for the removal of degradations and noise from these images. Noise-removal processes fall under the classifications of image *restoration* and *enhancement*. In the case of restoration, an image is processed so as to restore it to a previous condition. In other words, the image was degraded in some way and we wish to remove the degradation. An equivalent situation exists in the restoration of old artwork, where degradation may take the form of dirt and grime that has accumulated on the surface of a painting. Removal of the dirt restores the painting to what is was originally without changing it. Examples of degradation in image processing include defocused lenses on cameras (the Hubble space telescope was launched into orbit in 1990 with this condition) and various electronically sourced noises that give images undesirable random and periodic spots or lines. Chapters 8, 10, and 11 discuss image filtering-processes and address the major forms of image degradation and their removal.

Enhancement is image processing that improves an image for the viewer. Here the criterion for improvement is subjective and depends on preference. The primary techniques for image enhancement are histogram based, or algorithms that modify the distribution of intensities in an image. The contrast control on a television set or computer monitor changes the brightness distribution of the display in a controlled fashion to improve viewing. The contrast of an image can be adjusted in the same way, but with considerably more control, using the histogram modification techniques discussed in Chapter 5.

Medical image processing was the second generation of computer imaging to attract interest and basically began with the *reconstruction* of signal data from various scanning devices capable of generating rays that could pass through tissues. For example, computer aided tomography, or CAT scanning is a process that collects data from a multiple scans of electromagnetic energy at a single point on the body, which are reconstructed into an image of a slice of the body at the position where the scan was taken. Reconstruction techniques have been proposed for the combining of images taken from multiple platforms in space to create a three dimensional picture of missiles and rockets flying above the earth's atmosphere as part of the Star Wars project of the Department of Defense. Reconstruction algorithms require theory and mathematics that are beyond the scope of this book. Medical imaging has also found image *measurement* (see Chapter 6) algorithms useful in the analysis of cell structures and in the tracking of tumor and microorganism growth. Measurement techniques allow the dissection of an image into objects and regions of interest for counting purposes or for further processing. Measurement methods are also important in machine vision applications in which an automated process makes use of data derived from an image, such as recognizing and counting mixed parts on a moving conveyor.

Machine vision, the study of processes that allow machines to see and act on what they see, makes use of almost all the repertoire of image-processing techniques. The most poignant example of this is in factory automation, where robots are used to perform menial or boring assembly tasks. A typical preprocessing algorithm suite might include the following sequence of events (chapters where the appropriate algorithms are covered in this book in parentheses):

1. A camera acquires the image (2).
2. The image is processed to remove lighting variations (10).
3. An enhancement algorithm is applied to improve contrast (5).
4. A spatial filter is invoked to detect the lines in the image (8).
5. The image is binarized (2) and the lines enhanced using morphological filtering (9).

Further processing to detect and recognize specific objects is beyond the scope of this book, and numerous algorithms exist and have been proposed. The successful algorithms operate on very specific objects or classes of objects under tightly controlled conditions or constraints. A general-purpose machine vision system equal to the sophistication of the human visual system has yet to be developed.

Media processing is the latest discipline to affect image processing. This area encompasses sound, text, graphics, and image manipulation by computers to convey information to humans as rapidly, efficiently, and enjoyably as possible. Media systems are in use predominantly in education and by the entertainment industry. The computers used for media processing must have extremely high speed display and input/output subsystems to handle the huge amount of data that must be manipulated from image, graphic, and sound sources. Typically, optical disk storage technology is associated with media processing due to its high storage capacity. Media processing is also associated with graphics-based operating systems such as found on the Apple Macintosh™ computer and on expensive graphics workstations.

The distinction between computer graphics and image processing is an important one that must be understood. Image processing involves the computer manipulation of real scenes acquired from the energy released, reflected, or transmitted from physical phenomena as a spatially distributed signal (the acquisition process is discussed in greater depth in Chapter 2). Computer graphics is the use of the computer to generate, display, and store synthetic renditions of objects. A basic goal of computer graphics research is to synthesize graphic renditions of objects as realistically as possible. This book is restricted to image processing algorithms only, although a number of techniques have been exchanged between these two disciplines.

As computers get smaller and more powerful, the opportunities for image-processing increase. The old saw "a picture is worth a thousand words" has never been more appropriate. In the case of media processing, data are conveyed to the user through multiple channels and modes to (1) speed the information transfer, (2) maintain the attention and interest of the user, and (3) improve the retention of the data. The applications discussed above for image processing indicate that it is important to understand the basic principles behind the computer acquisition, manipulation, display, and storage of images. These processes are discussed in detail in the chapters to follow.

Chapter 2

Image Characterization, Storage, and Display

2.1 Introduction

What exactly is an image? How are images stored and represented in the computer? Is there a difference between image capture, image storage, and image display? These questions are answered through the characterization of images as two-dimensional signal models. We must understand that computer images are representations of electromagnetic energy that may be mathematically manipulated. To do this, we must understand what an image is and where it comes from. Then we may discuss the mathematical and intuitive models that we have of images that allow us to manipulate images intelligently. We then examine methods of capturing images, followed by the techniques and formats used to store images and the ways of getting images out of the computer and displaying them.

We begin this chapter with a discussion of the most advanced visual system known to us, our own. In many ways, computer imaging systems are like our eye and brain; in fact, a great deal of research has been performed and is still underway to create a machine vision system with the sophistication of the human visual system. This chapter is concluded with an examination of computer imaging systems in general, from expensive and complex research laboratory tools to simple personal computer systems.

2.2 Human Visual Perception

The study of human visual perception is important when we talk about images because the human visual system (VS) is the most sophisticated image detection, formation, and analysis system that we know of. The evaluation of the results of image-processing operations is affected by how our visual system responds to image data. The human visual system begins with our eyes, a binocular sensory pair that are capable of imaging both monochromatic and multispectral wavelengths of light. The term *visible spectra* refers to the portion of the electromagnetic spectrum that humans are capable of perceiving (Figure 2.1). In contrast, the visible spectrum for a honeybee begins in the ultraviolet region and stops shortly after the green wavelengths. Other animals, such as reptiles, can image into the infrared regions of the spectra using specialized sensors near their nostrils. Their eyes, in general, are not very high resolution sensors.

The spectrum represents energy waves that exhibit a periodic behavior that can be measured in units of length. The wavelength measures for the visible portion or the spectrum start at 400×10^{-9} meter and end at 700×10^{-9} meter. We can express 10^{-9} meter as *nanometers*(nm) as used in Figure 2.1.

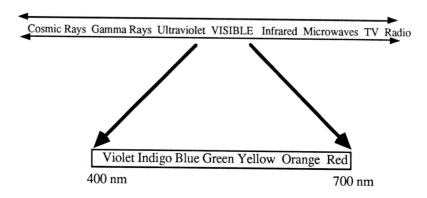

Figure 2.1 *Electromagnetic spectrum and visible spectra.*

We use our eyes to detect the various wavelengths of the visible spectra and format the data into images for interpretation by the brain. The major components of the human eye are the cornea, pupil, lens, retina, and optic nerve. The arrangement and location of these elements is shown in Figure 2.2. The *cornea* forms the outer surface of the eye and is a clear, dome-shaped piece of tissue that performs the initial light-focusing functions. The *pupil* lies at the base of the cornea and consists of a circular sphincter-type muscle that opens and closes to control the overall amount of light passing into the eye. The action is not conscious, but is controlled autonomically in response to brightness and near and distance focusing.

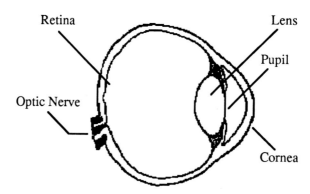

Figure 2.2 *Human eye.*

The pupil covers the *lens*, a dense semicrystalline mass of transparent protein connected to muscle fibers on each lateral side. These muscles constrict and relax to change the shape of the lens from thick (when relaxed) to thin (when constricted). A thick lens bends the light more than a thin lens. For distant objects, the lens is thin as the light rays reflected from a small object (distant objects appear small) require less bending to be focused. Close-in objects fill the field of view and so require greater bending, hence a thicker lens, to be focused properly. The lens action serves to control the focus of light beams entering the eye so that an image is formed over a wide range of object distances. Figure 2.3 illustrates how the lens action does this. At the back of the eye is a dense array of specialized light detecting nerves making up the *retina*. The retina receives the focused image from the lens, converts it to electrical impulses, processes the impulse data and transmits the result to the brain via the *optic nerve*.

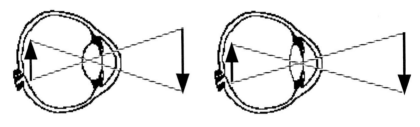

thick lens, close object   *thin lens, distant object*

Figure 2.3 *Lens operation in the human eye.*

The retina consists of approximately 200 million nerve cells having various functions that contribute to the perception of color and monochromatic scenes. The light receptors in the retina are specialized nerve cells called *rods*, for low-intensity colorless vision and *cones*, for color vision. The light-sensing cells output to a complex arrary of nerve signal combining cells. The final output of this combing array constitutes the optic nerve. The number of nerve fibers, or data channels, contained in the optic nerve is at least two orders of magnitude less than the number of sensory cells in the retina. This apparent discrepancy is justified by the combining array that operates to convolve multiple sensor outputs into a single datum. In general, these cells perform a low-pass filtering on the image data detected. This means that the high-frequency components of images, such as edges and lines, are softened and blurred. Retinal processing also takes place between adjacent image sensors in the retina, where cells processing the detected light *laterally inhibit* the output capability of their neighbors. This operates as a high pass filter due to the attenuation that occurs at the highest spatial resolution boundary, that of a single retinal sensory cell. High-pass filtering tends to enhance and sharpen images. The low-pass and high-pass effects of the combining array complement each other and add to the overall capabilities of visual processing in the human visual system. The eye is not a static camera, but rather moves rapidly and detects and processes scenes at a typical rate of 24 pictures per second. The distribution of sensory cells within the retina is not uniform, and the eye moves autonomously to maintain the image of the object of interest at the highest concentration of sensory cells. These aspects further complicate the functional description of the human visual system and are beyond the scope of this book.

The visual system has remarkable dynamic range with respect to light intensity, unlike many animals that are either *photopic* (day vision only, such as most birds) or *scotopic* (night or twilight vision). You may have wondered why almost direct viewing of the illuminated headlamps of an automobile in bright sunlight is not the same as seeing them on a moonless night at the same angle. The ability of the eyes to adjust to widely varying contrast is called *brightness adaptation*. The ability to distinguish between two brightness levels is called *contrast sensitivity* and this is dependent on ambient brightness levels. On a bright sunny day, it is often difficult to see that the headlights of a car are illuminated, but not so at night. Contrast sensitivity curves can be constructed by using a simple contrast test figure such as that shown in Figure 2.4. Here the brightness of the central circular region is varied until a just noticeable difference is detected. The ratio of the change in brightness between the central region and the background and the background itself is called the *Weber Ratio*. The Weber Ratio remains relatively constant over a wide range of background brightness values and is the mathematical expression of brightness adaptation.

Figure 2.4 *Contrast Sensitivity Test.*

In summary, the human visual system is complex and a great deal is still unknown about its function, particularly the mechanisms of visual perception. Since the results of computer image processing are intended for human use, it is important for us to be aware of the basic underlying mechanisms of our visual systems. In short, the eye can be thought of as a camera and the visual portions of the brain as a complex image-processing system.

2.3 Sampling and Quantization

The basic element of a computer image is the *pixel,* or picture element and an image is composed of pixels distributed in a rectangular array. *Sampling* is the process by which a two-dimensional signal, such as a scene captured by a camera, is broken down into a set of pixels. Sources of two-dimensional signals are many and varied. If energy is emitted, reflected or transmitted in two dimensions and a detector exists to capture that energy, then an image can be generated. As an example, take the situation where an object is imaged by a lens as shown in Figure 2.5. Let's now assume that a grid has been applied to the surface that the arrow is imaged on, as in Figure 2.6. The grid represents the spatial sampling of the image of the arrow projected onto the screen. Each individual square of the grid is a pixel. We may now apply an indexing system to the grid so that individual pixels can be identified and discussed. Typically, we start with the upper-left corner of the grid and identify the pixel by its coordinate in column-row order beginning with zero. The notation (0, 0), means the pixel in the zeroth column and the zeroth row, or the upper left corner pixel. Using this convention, Figure 2.7a identifies a number of pixels from the grid shown in Figure 2.6. The coordinate (19, 14) indicates the pixel in the nineteenth column and the fourteenth row and this pixel's value is white. The coordinate (31, 31) is the pixel in the lower right corner, or the last pixel in the image. These coordinates also may be thought of in terms of a *cartesian*, or *X-Y* system as indicated in Figure 2.7b. In this case, the *X* value indicates the column and the *Y* value specifies the row. The range of both *X* and *Y* values is 0 to 31, a total of 32 times 32 pixels for 1,024 pixels in the image.

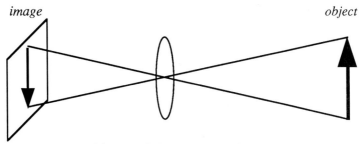

Figure 2.5 *Object imaged by lens.*

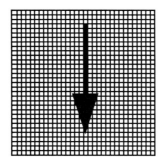

Figure 2.6 *Grid applied to object imaged by lens.*

Each pixel in the image may take on a value that indicates the strength of the signal at its location. If this strength is in terms of lightness, then we have a black and white image. In our arrow picture, we can assign values to each pixel depending on whether a pixel is black (it is part of the arrow) or white (it is not a part of the arrow). Assign the value 0 to black pixels and 1 to white pixels. We can now redraw the arrow image in terms of the values of the pixels, as shown in Figure 2.8, where the circled area of the image has been magnified to show the detail of the arrowhead's tip. The array of 0's and 1's to the right of the magnified inset are the individual pixel values according to our assignment of 1 to a white grid square and 0 to a black grid square. Our range of values is 0 to 1, and we have *quantized* the pixel value to either 1 or

0. The process of *quantization* is the assignment of a meaningful range of values to individual pixels according to the strength of the signal they represent. An image such as the grid arrow with pixel values of only 0 or 1 is called a *binary image*. Binary images are very important for two reasons: (1) they are easy to work with from a computational standpoint, and (2) many of the symbols and graphics that we work with in print are binary images.

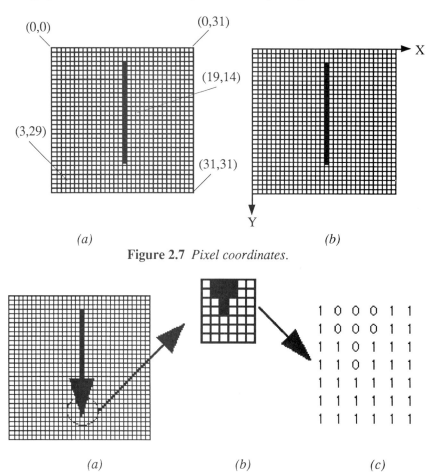

Figure 2.7 *Pixel coordinates.*

Figure 2.8 *(a) Grid arrow, (b) magnified arrowhead, (c) pixel values of magnified head.*

As a further example of a binary image, the letter H in the graphic below has been magnified and applied to a grid to illustrate the sampling and binary quantization of an ordinary printed character:

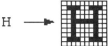

Figure 2.9 (a) is a binary image of the authors at a sampling of (a) 300 pixels/inch, and (b) 150 pixels/inch. The term *dots/inch* is used to describe the resolution of printers and displays. In the case of a binary image, the term is synonymous with pixels/inch, each dot being either a white or black pixel. Note the difference in *spatial resolution* between the two pictures. Spatial resolution is the term used for how small a pixel can be represented by an image and subsequently resolved by a viewer. The more pixels in a given space, the higher the spatial resolution is. When the term resolution is used alone, it generally refers to spatial sampling unless the context indicates otherwise.

(a)   *(b)*

Figure 2.9 *Binary image at (a) 300 pixels/inch, (b)150 pixels/inch.*

Resolution also has meaning with respect to quantization. In the three images shown in Figure 2.10, each has the same spatial resolution, but a different quantization. In Figure 2.10a each pixel may take a value from 0 to 255, with 0 indicating black and 255 indicating white. The center image, Figure 2.10b allows only 16 values for each pixel, 0 to 15, and Figure 2.10c, only 4 values. Even though the spatial resolution (pixels/inch or dots/inch) remained the same, the image becomes coarser as we reduce the number of quantization values or levels.

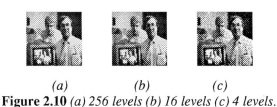

(a)   *(b)*   *(c)*

Figure 2.10 *(a) 256 levels (b) 16 levels (c) 4 levels.*

In a black and white, or monochrome image, the range of quantization values is called the *grayscale* . This term is appropriate because the range begins with black, or zero, and increases to 255, white, with lighter and lighter shades of gray. The individual quantization values are called *graylevels*. Figure 2.11 illustrates the grayscale progression of black to white. The use of 256 levels of gray to describe a pixel's quantization level is important in computer processing of images because the basic unit of computer memory storage is the byte. A byte of data can take on 256 values when considered as a binary number. Recall that our arrow graphic grid was 32 by 32 or 1,024 pixels. If, instead of two values possible per pixel we extended it to 256 values, we would require 1,024 bytes of memory storage, or 1 kilobyte (1K) of memory for the arrow image.

Figure 2.11 *Grayscale.*

In this book, the emphasis will be on what we will call *standard* images that are 512 by 512 pixels in spatial resolution and have 256 levels of grayscale. The pixel values will represent *visible spectrum* intensities. These images require 512 times 512 or 262,144 bytes of storage when in raw format (see Section 2.6) expressed as 256K. The notation for memory storage is based on successive powers of 2. Table 2.1 shows the translation from actual number of bytes to the abbreviated notation. Note that the last entry is 1M in the K notation column. This is read as 1 megabyte, or 1 million bytes of data. A 32-bit (4-byte) 512 × 512 color image requires 1M of storage. These issues are discussed in greater detail in Section 2.6.

Table 2.1 *Abbreviated notation for large powers of 2.*

Bytes	Notation
1,024	1K
2,048	2K
4,096	4K
8,192	8K
16,384	16K
32,768	32K
65,536	64K
131,072	128K
262,144	256K
524,288	512K
1,048,576	1M

Digitization is the term used to describe the conversion of analog, or continuous, signals into computer-usable, or *digital*, form. In Section 2.3, we discussed sampling and quantization, the discrete representation schemes for image data. Recall that sampling describes the spatial distribution of an image, whereas quantization refers to the number of values that a pixel may take. Both of these representations were digital; that is, each element within the range of either image rows and columns (sampling) or pixel values (quantization) had an equivalent unit of measure and the range of values for each was finite. The grid in Figure 2.6 had 32 columns and 32 rows and coordinate values from (0, 0) to (31, 31). Likewise, each pixel took on a value of either 0 or 1. Later, we discussed each pixel as taking on a value between 0 and 255.

The comparison between analog and digital is similar to that between real numbers and integers. Integers take on discrete values (for example, 3, 8, 92), whereas real numbers extend over an infinite range (for example, 1.23, 94.5, 3.1416). The details of the digitization electronics are beyond the scope of this book; however, we can discuss the topic in simple terms and diagrams that will help us further understand the sampling and quantization process.

Almost everyone is familiar with a photocell, a small electronic device that outputs a current that is proportional to any light that is falling on it. A digitizer can take a voltage produced from the photocell current and convert it to a discrete number that may be input to a computer. Digitizers are constrained in the number of values that they can output, and those used for video signals typically have an output of 256 discrete (integer) values. Assume that the output range of the photocell is 0 millivolts (mV) to 512 mV and the output range of the digitizer is 0 to 255. Also assume that the input range of the digitizer is 0 to 512 mV. This means that at 3 the digitizer will output a value of 3 and will not output a 4 until the input reaches 4 mV. In other words, no values in between 3 mV and 4 mV, say 3.6 mV, will be output.

If we now consider an array of photocells arranged like the grid we used for the arrow example, and image an object on the array using a lens, we can construct a computer image by recording the discrete value at each photocell location after digitizing its output. The horizontal and vertical density of photocells determines the spatial sampling and the range of photocell output determines the quantization. This may seem to be a crude example, but it is the basic mechanism of operation of a wide variety of image-generation systems.

2.4 Image Models

As discussed in the previous section, an image is a two dimensional array of values that specifies the strength of a signal at a particular spatial position. When we magnified the tip of the arrow graphic and wrote down the pixel values from the grid we were mathematically modeling the image. We now want to express this concept more formally so that we can input the data into a computer for processing. In Figure 2.12, we have an image on the left represented by a grid that has **N** rows and **M** columns. On the right we have a *matrix* of variables that we will use to represent the image. We want to assign the value of each pixel in the image to a subscripted variable **a**. Note that the row subscripts go from 0 to **N - 1** and the columns range from 0 to **M - 1**.

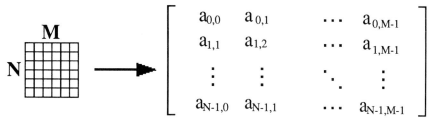

Figure 2.12 *Matrix representation of an image.*

In the computer, a matrix is represented by an array variable, or a variable that contains multiple values that may be accessed using an indexing system. The matrix of subscripted a's would be designated, by common convention, as the array variable **A**. The computer would not use the subscripted variables to identify elements of **A**. Elements are accessed using an indexing scheme, such as **A[2, 3]**, indicating the element in the second row, third column. The indexes **[2, 3]** may be replaced by variables to allow computation of the position of an element in the array. For example, we may encounter **A[x, y]**, where **x** and **y** are variables. If **x = 2** and **y = 3**, then **A[x, y]** accesses the element in the second row, third column, just as before. This is a fundamental programming concept in the manipulation of images in the computer.

Let's return to one of our previous examples and use the array of values from the magnified arrowhead to illustrate this concept further. Recall the array of values. We have seven rows of six columns of values and we can assign them to the array variable **A**, as illustrated in Figure 2.13. The value of **A[3, 2]** will be zero, it is the value of the pixel at the fourth row down in the third column. It is the only zero value in that row. Recall that we start our index numbering with zero. The values of **N** and **M** are 7 and 6, respectively so that the row index varies from 0 to 6 and the column index varies from 0 to 5.

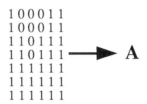

Figure 2.13 *Assignment of values to array variable A.*

Let's examine a simple program to manipulate the arrowhead image. The full image contained 1,024 pixels with 32 pixels in each row and 32 pixels in each column. Assume that a global array variable A has been initialized with the arrowhead image values. The following function will invert the pixel values and leave the "negative" arrowhead image in A:

```
negative_A(){
  int Number_of_Rows = 32,   Number_of_Columns = 32;
  int i,j;

  for( i=0; i< Number_of_Rows; ++i)
      for( j=0; j< Number_of_Columns; ++j)
          if(A[i][j]==0) A[i][j]=1;
          else A[i][j]=0;
}
```

In the function, we vary the value of the row index variable **i** from 0 to 31, the range of rows in the image. For each row in the image, the inner loop variable **j** is varied from 0 to 31, the number of columns in each row. This allows access to every pixel in the image, represented by values of the array variable **A**. The if statement checks the value of the pixel at row **i** and column **j** and makes it 0 if it was 1 and 1 if it was 0. The result of applying this function is shown in Figure 2.14, the original arrow image (with grid) and the result after processing. The grid has been reversed for clarity. The presence of the grid is only to allow easy visualization of the individual pixels in this example, it is obviously not present in the images.

More complex images will have a broader range of pixel quantization and be substantially larger than 32 × 32 pixels. As we normally want to work with images that are 512 × 512 pixels with pixel ranges of 0 to 255, we can modify the program to invert such images. To invert these values, we want to move them to the opposite end of the grayscale (see Figure 2.12). We can do this by simply subtracting each value from 255, so that a pixel that is 0, or black, now becomes 255, or white. A pixel that was a a dark gray, say value 56, now becomes value 199, or light gray. The variables labelled Number_of_Rows and Number_of_Columns each become 512 to accommodate the larger image. We must also modify the program to remove the if statement and simply replace it with the assignment that changes each **A** pixel to its opposite value. The revised function becomes:

```
negative_A(){
        int Number_of_Rows = 512, Number_of_Columns = 512;
        int i,j;

        for( i=0; i< Number_of_Rows; ++i)
            for( j=0; j< Number_of_Columns; ++j)
                A[i][j] = 255 - A[i][j];
}
```

Figure 2.14 *Original arrow image on left, inverted arrow on right.*

We have now replaced each value of **A** with its *arithmetic inverse*, or the value that is opposite to it in the sequence. The function name should be changed to reflect this difference in computation. Figure 2.15 shows an example output of this program. The program is an example of an algebraic operation on an image, or the arithmetic or logical manipulation of the image's pixel values. Algebraic operations are discussed further in Chapter 3.

Up to this point, we have discussed the image model as an array of intensity, or brightness values. In actuality, the pixel value of a standard image is composed of two components, *illumination* and *reflectance*. The concepts of the illumination and reflectance components are illustrated in Figure 2.16. In the figure we see a light source directed toward a cubical object. The illumination (**I**) represents the amount of source light present at the object, and the reflectance (**R**) is the light intensity reflected from the object. Each pixel intensity is the product of these two components.

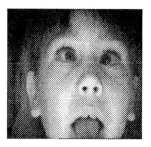 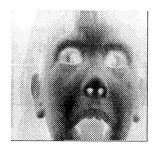

Figure 2.15 *Original image on left, inverted image on right.*

We can access the individual values of illumination and reflectance indirectly by taking the logarithm of the pixel value and performing operations that access the properties of illumination and reflectance. For example, the reflectance component of an image tends to change rapidly from pixel to pixel due to surface effects and the junctures of object groupings. In contrast, illumination changes slowly across an image because it typically issues from a localized source and bathes the image with a steady continuum of light. A *homomorphic filter* (See Chapter 10) accesses these components as variations of spatial frequency.

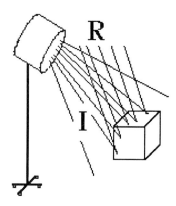

Figure 2.16 *Illumination (I) and Reflectance (R) intensity components.*

2.5 Cameras, Video, and Photographic Systems

The photocell example at the end of Section 2.3 describes the basic construction and function of modern electronic cameras. In this case, we are referring to charge-coupled-devices, or *CCD* cameras. CCD cameras are also referred to as *solid-state* cameras because they employ a dense array of photosensitive electronic elements on a rectangular silicon wafer. The CCD is just one type of solid-state camera, however, the term has gained general acceptance in the industry as a basic nomenclature. The image to be digitized is focused on the wafer using a lens system and the intensity data at the sensor locations are removed and conditioned by specialized electronic circuits. A schematic view of a solidstate camera system is given in Figure 2.17.

The data output from cameras are generally analog and must be digitized by a device called a *frame-grabber*. *Frame* is another word for image and is used when discussing image acquisition and display processes. The term originated with the movie film industry and refers to image sequences, whereas the term image normally implies a single frame, or still picture. The functional details of the frame-grabber are discussed in Section 2.8. Some CCD cameras have built-in digitizers and output discrete data directly. These cameras are expensive due to the complexity of data formatting that must take place prior to output of the image data. In addition to CCD cameras, there are also *metal oxide semiconductor* (MOS) and *charge injected device* (CID) cameras. These represent variations on the type of semiconductor used in the sensing array as well as its configuration. Other types exist, but they are too numerous to list here. If camera selection is a sensitive design issue, then manufacturers data sheets and literature should be reviewed.

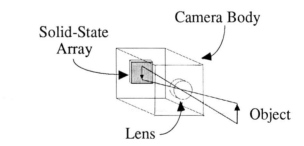

Figure 2.17 *Solid-State or CCD Camera.*

Another basic camera design that is still very much in use is the *vidicon*. A vidicon tube is essentially an elongated vacuum tube that has one end flattened and polished. On the inside of the tube at the polished end is a coating of phosphors, or light sensitive chemicals. When an image is focused on the flat end of the tube, the chemicals react electrically by varying their charge proportionally to the amount of light incident on them. An electron beam is scanned across the phosphor coating from the opposite end of the tube. When the beam strikes a highly charged region of phosphors, a higher current flows than when the beam strikes an area of lessor or no charge. This change in current as the beam is scanned is proportional to the light intensity variations of the image focused at the end of the tube. The primary advantage of vidicon cameras over CCD cameras is in spatial resolution. Vidicons capable of $1K \times 1K$ spatial resolution are available at less than half the cost of a comparable- resolution CCD.

Electronic cameras are generally manufactured with a *C-mount* lens mounting system. The C-mount on the camera is a 1 in. diameter internal thread with 32 threads per inch. Adapters exist to convert C-mount cameras to accept the more popular bayonet-style lens mounts used by the photography industry. This allows the use of more common, less expensive camera lenses, as well as special purpose lenses that may not be available with C-mounts.

An important factor in image acquisition is the speed, called *frame rate*, at which a system can acquire a frame of data. If a camera is connected to a monitor, such as in a closed-circuit television system, the frame rate is in *realtime* if the motion of objects in the camera field of view appears smooth and continuous. For human vision, the rate must be between 22 and 26 frames per second(fps). Standard real-time cameras and imaging systems operate at a 30 fps rate. This is the frame rate of U.S. television receivers and was determined from the 60-cycle alternating current public utility power. If a monochrome camera is generating images that are 512×512 pixels resolution and 256 quantization levels (1 byte per pixel), then a frame rate of 30 fps is approximately 8 million bytes per second of data. As either the resolution or the quantization per pixel in the image increases, the data rate will increase and require extremely highspeed electronic devices to maintain the frame rate.

The decision to use either a solid-state camera or a vidicon depends on many factors that are changing rapidly as the technology improves for both types. Vidicon camera technology is more mature than that of solid-state devices and advances have been slower in recent years. The following summarizes the key design and decision factors for cameras.

•*COST* : Vidicon cameras, all other factors held constant, are much less expensive than solid-state units. Technological history has shown, however, that solid-state devices decrease in cost dramatically over time.

•*INTERFACE:* Solid-state cameras can be purchased with digital output, whereas all vidicons have analog output. As a single factor, however, the increased cost of a discrete solid-state camera generally negates any advantage this factor may have gained.

•*RESOLUTION:* Vidicon cameras are of higher resolution for comparable speed solid-state cameras. Although solid-state cameras are available that match the resolution possible with vidicons, the speed of image acquisition may be considerably slower than real-time rates.

•*SIZE:* Solid-state cameras are always smaller than their vidicon equivalents due to the focusing coils and glass vacuum envelope of the vidicon. The sensing array and lens of the solid-state camera can be mounted in a small package remote from the sensor electronics unit. This is advantageous when the cameras are used in medical or nondestructive testing applications where close spacing is often a factor.

•*SENSITIVITY:* Solid-state cameras typically have less sensitivity than vidicons because of the difficulty of manufacturing an array of sensors to close tolerances. The vidicon technology is mature and has been used extensively in the aerospace field where high-sensitivity cameras are employed in surveillance and monitoring systems. Sensitivity is less of an issue when a camera is used in an indoor, controlled lighting application.

•*CALIBRATION:* Vidicon cameras deteriorate nonlinearly with age and require regular calibration if photometric analyses are performed with the data captured. High-quality, laboratory grade solid-state cameras are shipped with response data and will not degrade over periods as long as 10 years or more.

•*RESPONSE:* Vidicon cameras are faster than their solid-state counterparts in terms of frame-rate. Real-time vidicons with 2048×2048 pixel resolution are obtainable, while solid-state cameras of 1024×1024 pixel resolution can only output data at 6 fps, maximum.

•*DURABILITY:* Vidicon cameras are sensitive to vibration, shock, magnetic fields, and mounting position. None of these factors affects solid-state cameras to any extent.

Video is a catchall term generally used to describe television imaging. In image processing, video refers to the single-dimensional form of the image, or the analog signal that is transmitted by wires. The Electronic Industries Association (EIA) established the RS-170 video standard for television signals in the United States. The EIA also specified the RS-232 standard for serial digital communications in computers. An RS-170 signal produces an image that contains 480 rows (called lines in the television parlance) that are the result of interlacing two frames of 240 rows each. Interlacing means that every other row is scanned, or in the case of displays, output. The time to complete one row is 63.5 microseconds. Each row is restricted to 52.1 microseconds (µs) to cross the horizontal width of the frame and 11.4 µs to return, or retrace, to the start of the next row. The Figure 2.18 illustrates the relationship of interlacing, horizontal scan, and retrace. The odd rows are scanned first from the upper-left corner to the upper-right corner. Retrace means that the scan position jumps from the first row to the third, then the fifth, and so on until the end of the frame. This process takes 1/60th second(s), as does the second set of 240 scans that cover the even rows. The complete frame is scanned in 1/30 s, which gives a frame rate of 30 fps. The number of column pixels is determined by the sampling of the horizontal signal or the number of horizontal sensors available (640 horizontal pixels).

The RS-170 signal is what is presented to the monitor section of a television receiver from the tuner. The tuner accepts a radio frequency (RF) signal from the antenna or a cable service and converts a selected frequency (the channel) into an RS-170 signal that is then displayed (see Section 2.7 for more on display systems). If an electronic camera outputs RS-170 video, the video can be displayed on a television receiver through the use of an *RF modulator*, obtainable at electronics and computer stores. This is a simple electronic device that converts the RS-170 signal into an RF signal so that the television tuner will accept it.

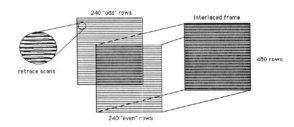

Figure 2.18 *Interlacing, horizontal scan and retrace.*

When RS-170 is augmented with a signal that contains color information, it becomes an NTSC signal. NTSC is an acronym for the *National Television Standards Committee* which determined the standard for color television broadcast in the United States. NTSC video is an enhancement to RS-170 in that a 3.58 megahertz (MHz) carrier is applied to convey the color information. This carrier is transparent to a monochrome television and thus color compatibility with monochrome sets was attained. NTSC is also called *composite* video. An RF modulator will convert an NTSC signal such that a television receiver can display it, and if the receiver is a color set, the display will be in color.

Photographic systems rely on film, a medium by which images are acquired and become permanently stored. Film is of interest to computer imaging because of its long-term storage aspect and the fact that individual frame images do not require complex equipment for viewing. The advantage of movie film is that long sequences of images can be captured and stored for review. Although it is not unusual to find personal computers with hard disks of 100 megabytes, this size disk would hold less than 400 frames of 512×512 monochrome images, or 13 seconds of real-time video. These disks typically have transfer rates of 500 kilobytes per second, far shy of the 8 *mega*bytes per second that is required for real-time video output.

The resolution of film is determined by grain size; grain refers to the silver halide crystals (or other photosensitive compounds) used to detect light intensity and the light-scattering properties of the emulsion that the grains are suspended in. A finer-grain film requires greater exposure time, thus the *speed* of the film, or the time required for the silver halide to convert to silver, depends on grain size and indirectly affects resolution. A high-speed film uses large grains to achieve speed at the expense of resolution. Film manufacturers are continually improving their product using special emulsions and enhancers so that, as time progresses, higher speed films at higher resolutions become available.

A photographic term that is increasingly used in computer imaging is *gamma*, or the slope of the linear region of the film's silver density versus the log of the exposure. Gamma is a measure of film contrast, the steeper the curve, the higher the available contrast is. Gamma can be calculated for both display systems and electronic cameras by plotting the sensitivity of the display phosphors or the camera sensors against the log of the exposure time. Gamma can be modified in some systems by electronically altering the sensitivity of these elements.

Lenses are the primary unit of similarity between photographic systems and imaging systems. Lens selection can be confusing and difficult if one has not had prior experience with photography. A camera lens is selected by its *focal length* and *aperture*. These parameters are important in an indirect way, the focal length of the lens allows calculation of *magnification* and the aperture gives rise to *depth of field*. The focal length of a lens determines its focusing characteristics and is determined in a simple lens from its radii of curvature. Lenses of the type used on electronic cameras always incorporate compound optics, and computation of focal length is complex; however, the focal length is generally printed on the lens case and is the main parameter used in specifying a lens. Assuming a fixed aperture, to compute the magnification of the lens, the following formula is used:

$$m = \frac{f}{D_0 - f}$$

where m is the magnification, f is the focal length and D_0 is the distance from the lens to the object. Magnification is the ratio of image to object size. In the lens system of Figure 2.19, the focal length is 4/3 and the distance of the lens to the object (D_0) is 4 units. This gives a magnification of 0.5. If the object size is 8 mm, then the image size will be 4 mm. The imaging sensor must be large enough to accommodate the image size and the lens should be chosen so that the largest object encountered nearly fills the sensor area because this will give the maximum detail and resolution.

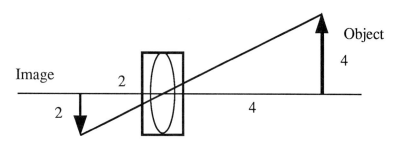

Camera Lens System: *focal length = 4/3*

Figure 2.19 *Lens system example.*

Conversely, the D_0 distance may be calculated from the magnification desired and the focal lengths of available lenses. For example, if the objects to be imaged are parts on an assembly line that are 8 cm in length (approximately 3 in.) and the imaging sensor is 5 mm square, then a magnification factor of one-half (0.5) is required to fit the object imaged by the lens onto the sensor. If the lens has a focal length of 4 cm, then the D_0 distance will be (f/m + f), or 6 cm.

The *aperture* is the size of the lens opening, or entrance pupil, and allows modification of the focal length of the lens. A variable aperture lens is controlled by a mechanical iris that is changed through use of a knurled ring around the outside case of the lens system. Markings on the ring are in *f-stop* units, a numbering that indicates the relative amount of light allowed by the aperture. The term f-number is also used and is synonomous with f-stop. On variable aperture lenses, the aperture control ring is often detented at each f-number setting, hence the term f-stop. The smallest aperture on the lens will be marked with the largest *f* -number, typically 16 or 22. As the numbers get smaller, the aperture opens wider, and each number change increases the amount of light admitted by a factor of 2. As the aperture decreases in size, the D_0 distance increases until the aperture is a pinhole and the effective distance is infinity. The price paid for the increase in distance is the amount of light required to image. This amount depends on the exposure time and will limit the acquisition rate of the sensor. Since this rate is fixed by the sensor electronics, if the aperture is too small, the image will be dark. This indicates that a "faster" lens is required, one with a greater focal length that will allow focus at the greater distance with a larger aperture. The lens will be physically larger.

Aperture has a direct relationship to *Depth of Field*, or the distance that an object can be greater or less than the D_0 distance and still be in focus. Depth of Field determines how small a feature can be resolved and this is important when imaging three-dimensional objects or textures. In Figure 2.20, the lens is focused at D_0, however, object features within the Depth of Field area will remain in focus even though their distance is not equal to D_0.

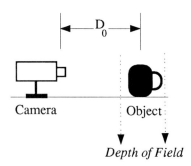

Figure 2.20 *Depth of Field.*

It is important that a camera and lens be selected where the Depth of Field is twice the size of the smallest surface irregularity that must be imaged. This requires that the pixel size of the sensor, the f-stop and the magnification be chosen appropriately. The following equation relates Depth of Field to pixel size (p), f-stop and magnification (m):

$$\text{Depth of Field} = \frac{2 \, p \, f_{\text{stop}} \, (m + 1)}{m^2}$$

As an example of the use of this equation, assume that we have an Elmo model EM-102 CCD camera. This device has a sensor area of 6.39 mm by 4.88 mm partitioned into 570 horizontal by 485 vertical elements. The width of each pixel, 6.39/570, is 0.011 mm and the height, 4.88/485, is 0.010 mm. The vertical depth of field at an f-stop of 16 and a magnification of 0.5 is:

$$\text{Depth of Field} = \frac{2(.010)(16)(0.5 + 1)}{(0.5)^2} = 1.92 \text{ mm}$$

This result means that surface features that vary over 1 mm will be discernible in the image. It also means that an object may move almost 2 mm with respect to the lens and remain in focus.

2.6 Image Storage and File Formats

Storage of images is an increasingly important factor in image processing. As systems are developed that can handle larger images of greater resolution and quantization, the storage problem increases as well. Recall that we defined a standard image as 512×512 pixels, each requiring a data element 1 byte in size. A 40-megabyte disk drive would hold about 150 of these images (40M/0.262M). If these were color pictures, with each pixel requiring 24 bits, or 3 bytes, the disk would only hold 50 images. Standard floppy disks have a capacity of a little over 1 megabyte of storage (for high density drives), meaning that they will hold approximately four standard images.

This discussion has been confined to what is called *raw*, or unformatted, data. The assumption is that each image file on the disk consists of a stream of pixel values, end to end, in row-column order. This is an acceptable method of storing images, however, it has two primary drawbacks. The first is that the program reading the image must know how many bits are contained in each pixel and how many pixels are contained in each column. If our image processing system were to assume that an image file contained a 64×64 pixel image of 1 byte (8-bits) per pixel when it in fact held a 128×128 pixel, 1 byte per pixel image, the results would be as shown in Figure 2.21. The image processor reads the first 64 bytes as the first row and then begins reading the second row in the center of the first row of the original image! The result is a distorted and smeared image that is meaningless. This problem may be easier to visualize using Figure 2.22. Here the stored image is a graphic of a computer and the rows have been abstracted to include a band of pixels. The rows have been halved and the middle image is just the first five half-rows of the stored picture. The image on the right side is the assembled one-quarter image from the first five half-rows. Clearly, the image of the computer is distorted.

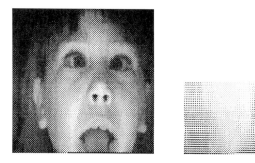

Figure 2.21 *128 × 128 pixel image on left, 64 × 64 pixel image on right.*

Stored Image

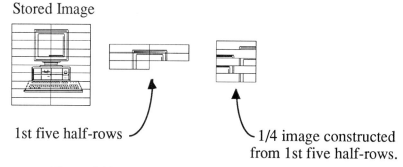

1st five half-rows ⟍   ⟍ 1/4 image constructed
                                                from 1st five half-rows.

Figure 2.22 *Distortion caused by mis-matched image size.*

This problem can be avoided if a number of data bytes at the beginning of the image file are reserved for size information. The program or system reading the image file examines these bytes and reads the remaining pixel data based on the size information determined from this data heading, or image *header*. The image header can be as simple as just the number of rows and columns for an 8-bit monochrome-only system or can contain a great deal of information describing the pixel data in detail. A basic problem with the image header is that the program or system reading the image file must know the exact format of the header in order to read the data correctly. Almost every image-processing system has its own specialized format for the image data. Attempts have been made to standardize image formats and headers, but no one format has emerged as the winner. The most widely accepted image formats for personal computer image processing are the Tagged Interchange File Format (TIFF) and the Graphics Interchange Format (GIF). Both of these incorporate data compression schemes that work to alleviate the second drawback to raw data image files.

As previously discussed, the use of raw data means that no attempt has been made to reduce the size of the data so as to conserve space on the storage medium. An image, admittedly, is a large amount of data; however, in most images many of these data are redundant. Image *compression* schemes take advantage of this redundancy by algorithmically reducing the amount of data required to store the image. As a simplistic example, note the 8 x 8 binary image in Figure 2.23a. Let each white square have a pixel value of 1 and each black square a value of 0. The total number of pixels is 64. If each pixel were to use 1 byte of storage, we would need 64 bytes to store the data, or we could represent the image using the following code: [(18, 1)(4, 0)(4, 1)(4, 0)(4, 1)(4, 0)(18, 1)]. Each number in this code can be represented by a single byte, or 14 bytes total, a savings of over 75%. This scheme is known as *run length encoding*, or RLE. It consists of paired numbers, and in this version the first number in each pair is the number of pixels in the run and the second number is the pixel value for the run. This code is efficient for simple images, but in some cases the code itself can require more data than the image. The image shown in Figure 2.23b requires 35 encoded pairs, or 70 bytes. More effective codes exist, these are always based on the statistics or frequencies of occurrence of pixel values. They also depend on coded symbols that may be represented by less than 1 byte. These methods are beyond the scope of this book, however, a short discussion of two of the most popular schemes follows.

Huffman Coding: this technique requires the frequency of occurrence of each possible value in the data set. In the case of images, the frequency of pixel values is computed. The value with the highest frequency of occurrence is assigned the smallest code, the next higher frequency value gets the next larger code, and so on. This is an extremely efficient technique, but requires the decoding data to be available to the program that reconstitutes the image.

Lempel-Ziv-Welch (LZW): this code scheme is dynamic in that the code is changed based on the values processed in the data stream. It is a modification of the Huffman approach, but does not require analysis of the entire data set to determine the encoding used. Specialized hardware is available that contains custom integrated circuits to perform the necessary calculations for various compression algorithms. These subsystems are used in image-processing systems where large amounts of data must be stored and retrieved rapidly, such as in map analysis and artificial scene generation for flight simulators.

Image formats, as mentioned earlier, are as numerous as the image-processing systems that use them. Typically, the specialized formats used do not encode the pixel data, but simply apply an information header to the data so that spatial resolution, quantization and image source data can be determined by the accessing program. Some imaging systems, often to the frustration of their users, will not read a raw image and will only access a format unique to them. Most modern systems, however, include a raw image read capability. With these systems it is necessary to input the row and column sizes and sometimes the number of bits or bytes per pixel. The image data must be preprocessed to remove the header data, or the system will assume that header bytes are image bytes. Some systems also include an option that allows the user to specify the number of header bytes to skip. For images of unknown header size, the size of the header (if the image is square) may be determined from the file size minus the square of the integer part of the square root of the file size.

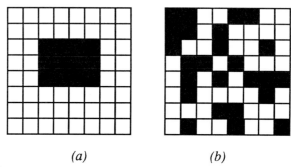

(a)   *(b)*

Figure 2.23 *Binary 8 × 8 image for compression examples.*

The previous discussion assumes that the image format used does not include compressed data. The Graphics Interchange Format (GIF) image pixel data are always compressed, whereas in the Tagged Interchange File Format (TIFF) data compression is optional. The GIF format was developed by the Compuserve Information Service and the copyright to the format is retained by them. GIF files use a relatively simple header that contains the sizes of the image, color lookup tables and fields for identifying image origin. The first 3 bytes of a GIF image are the ASCII format for the letters GIF and this is an immediate identifier for a decoding program that operates on multiple image formats. The next 3 bytes are the ASCII format for the version, a recent one is "87a". The version number allows a decoder to know specifically what features have been incorporated into the format and to decode the image properly. The version was included to ensure that as new information requirements for images emerge, the format can row as well. The actual pixel data of a GIF image are encoded using the Lempel-Ziv-Welch (LZW) scheme mentioned earlier. Appendix A contains the GIF file specification in detail.

The TIFF image file format was developed by Adobe Systems and Microsoft Corporation primarily for the interchange of graphics and imaging data between software programs. TIFF is used extensively by the image scanner industry and desktop publishing systems. It is an extremely complex format and was designed to be easily added to and modified. The term Tagged in its name comes from the use of tags, or pointers, in the format that direct the decoding program or system through a network of data that describes the image. A compressed TIFF file contains data encoded using the Huffman algorithm described earlier. Appendix A contains a more detailed description of the TIFF file format.

To conclude this section, we mention the Apple Macintosh PICT format. PICT images may contain raw pixel data or graphic primitives that describe an image. This format is exceedingly complex, and no known decoders other than those residing on Macintosh™ computers are known to the authors. The popular MacPaint® format, also used by Macintosh™ machines, is easily decoded because all pictures in this format are binary images of 640 × 400 pixels (32K bytes). Each data byte represents 8 pixels on the screen and these bytes are coded using RLE. The format for MacPaint images is also given in Appendix A.

2.7 Image Displays and Hardcopy Output

Image displays are the window by which images are viewed, both before and after processing. By far the largest single classification of displays are the Cathode Ray Tubes (CRTs). The basic monochrome CRT is very similar to the vidicon discussed in Section 2.5 and a greatly simplified cross-sectional schematic is given for it in Figure 2.24. A CRT is a large vacuum tube with a flat front surface, the screen. This area is coated on the inside of the tube with phosphors that glow when an electron beam generated at the tail end of the tube strikes them. The beam is electronically formed and positioned by charged plates and electric coils located midway on the inside and outside of the tube. The tube operates at high voltages and generates considerable heat compared to other electronic components and devices. A number of elements are important in determining the resolution, speed, and capacity of a CRT, such as beam-positioning electronics, phosphor type, envelope shape and other factors that are beyond the scope of our discussion here.

With imaging systems, three factors regarding displays are important: (1) the video standard used, (2) spatial resolution and (3) pixel quantization. The RS-170 standard discussed in Section 2.5 is the most common video signal standard used for imaging displays. It specifies a screen of 480 interlaced lines. This means that the electron beam travels across the screen from left to right, returns to the left side but two lines down, then repeats the process until it reaches the bottom of the screen. It returns to the second line from the top of the screen and repeats the process for every other line. This all occurs in 1/30th s. The net effect is a continuous image.

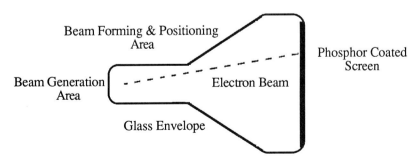

Figure 2.24 *Cross-section of Cathode Ray Tube (CRT).*

The RS-170 standard specifies the vertical pixel resolution as 480 rows, whereas horizontal resolution is determined by the display electronics and the size of the screen phosphors. As the electron beam sweeps across the screen, the number of times it can change intensity is the number of horizontal pixels it will display. This number is generally 512, giving rise to the standard 512 × 480 pixel image. The pixel brightness is determined by the strength of the beam. When it is at low power, the phosphor it strikes will glow weakly, and when at high power, it will glow brightly. The range of intensities that the phosphors and beam can produce depends on how the display was designed and the number of voltages possible from the hardware that converts the digital pixel data into the video signal. Another factor is the screen appearance at the ends of the brightness range, inexpensive displays will not be completely black when the pixel is at its minimum value or paper-white when the pixel is at its maximum value. Also of importance is the flatness of the screen and whether it has a matte finish or is highly reflective. The quality of a CRT often depends on viewer preference, but most often follows a cost scale; the more expensive displays are generally better in all respects. The physical dimensions of the screen are also important. As the size increases, the physical size of the pixels increases as well. On very large screens, an RS-170 signal produces noticeable lines in the image.

The spatial resolution of displays is often specified in dots per inch. Here the dots refer to the pixels possible in a given area of the display. Typically, high-resolution displays are capable of 72 dots per inch that yields approximately 1024 × 1024 pixels on a 19 in. diagonal screen or 640 × 400 on a 12 in. screen. When discussing screen resolutions it is easier to visualize if one remembers that a standard 19" television screen is roughly 40 dots per inch and has a pixel range of 128 gray levels. Computer displays that allow viewing of text documents in "What You See Is What You Get" (WYSIWYG, pronounced *whizzy-wig*) format are generally 72 dots per inch or better.

Synchronization signals are used to control where the electron beam starts and stops on the screen. A display system may have internal synchronization, or sync, where it provides the necessary signals to control the beam or it may require that these signals be generated externally. Most imaging displays, or *monitors*, allow the user to select the type of sync desired. If external sync is used, the video signal may extend beyond the 480 lines of the RS-170 standard and produce a "square" image of 512 × 512, for example. How far a display may go is determined by the design specifications of the display itself. Sync signals are identified separately as horizontal and vertical or together as *composite* sync. Composite sync is a combination of the horizontal and vertical synchronization into a single line. Composite sync signals may also be overlayed onto the video signal itself. If synchronization is not present or corrupted, the screen will display a distorted image that looks twisted if horizontal sync is affected or that rolls if vertical sync is bad. The horizontal and vertical hold controls on most image displays are used to make fine adjustments to the synchronization signals.

The color that the phosphor glows when the electron beam strikes determines the color of the display. White, amber, and green are the most common colors for monochrome displays, however, white is almost always used for image processing. For a CRT display to generate a color image, three electron guns are necessary. Red, green, and blue phosphors are used on the screen to generate the three primary colors. The phosphors are applied in triangular clusters so that each pixel is actual a combination of three small color pixels. The electron guns are aligned and pulsed so that as they scan the screen they strike only the phosphor of their color. The aggregate effect of the color pixel cluster is the color displayed. Figure 2.25 is a graphic representation of how this works. For example, if each pixel in the aggregate of color pixels glows at its maximum intensity, that pixel will appear white. When the pixels in the aggregate are at half-intensity, gray will be displayed. If only the blue pixel is on to its maximum, that aggregate will be blue. If green and red are on, the aggregate will be yellow, and so on.

The number of brightness levels that each pixel in the aggregate can achieve determines the number of colors possible for the display. If each primary color pixel can attain 256 levels, then each aggregate pixel can display over 4 million colors. This means that each pixel will require 1 byte of digital data, and this type of CRT is called a 24-bit (3 bytes) display.

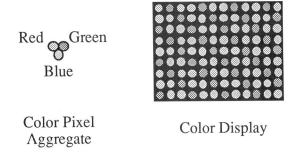

Color Pixel Aggregate

Color Display

Figure 2.25 *Color Pixel and Color Display.*

Computer displays have increased in sophistication over the years and now are capable of serving as imaging monitors. In the early days, a computer display was binary and only output text or primitive graphics. The advent of color displays meant that computers could now display color or monochrome images. A standard computer display capable of 640×400 pixels at 256 colors (such as an IBM VGA or Apple Macintosh color display) can be used to display monochrome color images at a resolution that was previously possible only with expensive and sophisticated imaging systems. Thus complex and sophisticated image-processing algorithms may be experimented with using only the computer itself.

Displays other than CRTs exist, such as gas-plasma and liquid-crystal systems. The gas-plasma display uses the electroluminescence of rare gases to create an image. These displays originally were limited to binary images of a single orange color, but recently multiple graylevel systems have become available. The advantage of the gas-plasma displays is low power and small physical size. They find their most common application in portable computers. Use of gas plasma displays in imaging systems is virtually nonexistent.

Liquid-crystal systems are similar to gas-plasma systems in that they are of low power and small size. These displays use a semisolid crystal that changes its light transmissive or reflective properties according to the amount of electric charge applied to it. Liquid-crystal displays require an external source of illumination, but they are less expensive to manufacture than gas-plasma displays of the same capability.

Hardcopy output of images requires a printing mechanism capable of producing shades of gray or color on paper at the pixel locations of the image to be printed. This can be achieved in a number of different ways. The best, and most expensive, is photographic reproduction, where grayscale is a function of the density of silver halide grains in paper. Photographic reproduction is also possible using thermally sensitive paper. Here the paper is treated with a chemical that turns black with increasing temperature. The degree of change is proportional to the heat applied, so a pixel of value 0 would cause the greatest amount of heat and a white pixel would cause no heat to be used. Thermal printers are most often employed in *facsimile* machines. The disadvantage to thermal images is that the images fade with time. Thermal printers are available to produce color images. These printers apply a colored wax (of the three primary subtractive, or pigment, colors red, yellow and blue) to produce the pictures.

An alternative to photographic methods is *Halftoning*. Halftoning is the method that newspapers use to print images and the term comes from using variable dot sizes to reproduce the illusion of grayscale, or continuous tone. All the pictures in this book have been generated using half-tone techniques. As the distance increases from an image to our eyes, loss of fine detail occurs. This reduction in detail can be used to create varying levels of gray using black dots or shapes, where the smoothness of transition from one gray value to another will depend on the number of dots per inch and the relative size of the dots.

Dithering is the term used in computer graphics to produce halftone effects and is the process by which an image is changed to conform to a specific resolution, either for printing or for video display. An image on disk may be 512×512 by 8 bits resolution; however, if the printer used to print the image has only black and white capability, a problem exists. At each pixel we can print either a white dot or a black dot. A decision must be made as to which value of graylevel is set as the threshold for printing. The image produced will not have the clarity and detail that an image at the full range of grayscale would have. This is illustrated in Figure 2.26: picture (a) has been dithered, while picture (b) has been binarized, where all pixels with a value of less than 128 are set to black, and all pixels above 127 are set to white. Each is printed at 360 dots per inch (DPI) with a printer capable of only black or white and equal-sized dots.

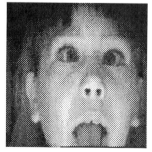 

Figure 2.26 *(a) dithered picture, (b) binary picture.*

A variety of schemes exists for dithering, and a great deal of effort has been expended in algorithms designed exclusively for binary systems such as printers and most computer displays. The simplest approach is to use a fixed pattern to represent each pixel value and to try to configure the pattern to appear as a homogeneous grayscale at a normal viewing distance. This can be accomplished using a set of patterns like those shown in Figure 2.27. Here, 40 patterns are given that vary from all black on the left to completely white on the right. The varying densities of gray are determined by regular patterns of dots.

Figure 2.27 *Simple rectangular dithering scheme.*

An important factor in the selection of a dithering scheme is the dot resolution of the printer (or screen). The higher the resolution, the more patterns that may be used to generate gray levels and the smoother the gray transitions will be. The effect of dot resolution on image quality is shown in Figure 2.28 where the same dithered picture has been reproduced at 300, 144 and 72 DPI.

Image dithering and halftoning is dependent on picture content. This is illustrated in Figure 2.29a to d, where four different techniques are shown. Figure 2.29a is rendered using the *Floyd-Steinberg* algorithm. It is an adaptive process whose dither pattern depends on the value of surrounding pixels, as well as on the pixel being dithered. Figure 2.29b shows the result using an ordered algorithm where the pattern selected depends on a dither matrix that maintains the same spatial resolution as the original image. Figures 2.29c and 2.29d show two different halftone approaches. The first is a 0° halftone and the second is a 53° halftone.

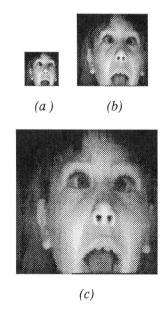

(a)　　　*(b)*

(c)

Figure 2.28 *Printer resolutions, (a) 300 DPI, (b) 144 DPI, (c) 72 DPI.*

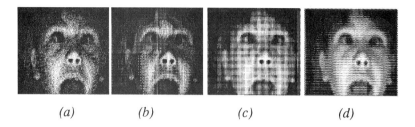

(a)   (b)   (c)   (d)

Figure 2.29 *(a) Floyd-Steinberg Dither (b) Ordered Dither
(c) 0° Halftone (d) 53° Halftone.*

The details of these algorithms are beyond the scope of this discussion, however, Figure 2.30a to d shows the lower-left corner of the image used in Figures 2.29a and b enlarged to illustrate the detail of the dithering schemes. It should be obvious from the enlargements that the Floyd-Steinberg algorithm yields the smoothest transitions in intensities. The image quality is also better, even in the enlarged version. The question may arise as to why one would use the other techniques at all. The answer lies in computer processing time, of the four techniques presented, the Floyd-Steinberg is the most computationally demanding. The halftone techniques can be processed photographically using metal screens in front of enlarging lenses, without computer processing at all. The choice of a dithering scheme depends on the image content, the computer processing available or desired, and the final resolution available for the dithered picture.

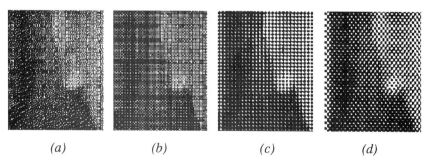

(a)   (b)   (c)   (d)

Figure 2.30 *Enlarged detail of Dithers & Half-Tones from Figure 2.29.*

2.8 Imaging Systems

This chapter is concluded with a discussion of imaging systems in general, although the preceding sections have covered all the basic elements. Figure 2.31 is a block diagram of an image-processing system that one might find in a government or university laboratory. The system begins with the camera to acquire the images desired for processing. The acquisition occurs in a unit called a *frame-grabber*. This unit contains the digitizing hardware that captures a frame of video data and converts it into a digital image. Note that video and data lines have been distinguished in the diagram. The digital image is stored in a *frame-buffer,* which is nothing more than a computer memory. The figure shows four frame-buffers. This number will vary from system to system. Typically, systems with multiple buffers are able to grab images into the buffers in realtime, or at 30 frames per second. This means that a movie can be created from sequences of frames and processing performed on the images as a sequence. The frame-buffer data generally output to an *array processor*, sometimes called a *frame processor*. The array processor is a specialized computer architecture that has been optimized for image-processing algorithms. Image video is output to a display monitor through a *video output controller*. The video output controller is basically a switching device that routes video data through the system. Not shown in the diagram are control lines from the computer to the various parts of the imaging system. The computer is controlled from the terminal and keyboard, and the image-processing functions are controlled from the computer. For example, the computer directs the video output controller to put video from a frame buffer out to the display monitor or the grayscale printer. The computer also serves as the image storage and retrieval system. Mass storage units such as disk and tape drives attached to the computer are used to maintain image libraries and support algorithm development.

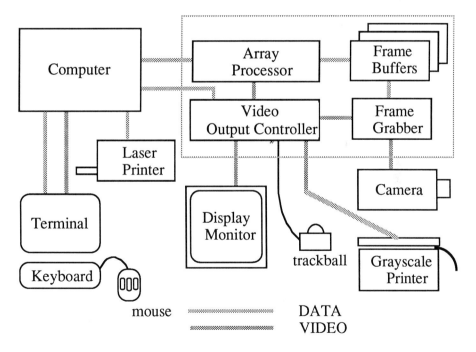

Figure 2.31 *Large-Scale Image Processing System.*

The dotted line in Figure 2.31 surrounds the components of the imaging system that constitute the image processor itself. These items are often enclosed in a separate console from the computer and may exist as a stand-alone device where a computer or terminal is used only to direct the operations of the processor. The image processor may also have high-speed disk units that allow it to store and retrieve image sequences in realtime. Large-scale systems begin at about $50,000 and may cost as much as $500,000 if real-time image storage and retrieval capability is added. Mid-range systems are available that attach to or are embedded in computer workstations. These systems are similar to personal-computer-based systems, but often incorporate the features generally reserved for the high-end systems.

A personal computer imaging system is considerably simpler than a large-scale imaging system. The frame-grabber, frame-buffers and video output controller are all contained on a single add in printed circuit card. The array processor is generally an extra unit, but most systems simply rely solely on the processing capability of the host PC and its math coprocessor. Real-time operation is normally not possible with a PC-based system because of the low data bandwidth of the computer bus. Some systems bypass the computer bus and link extra frame memory and array processing cards with an external bus that attaches across the tops of the units.

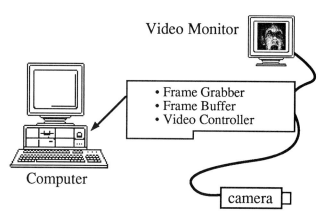

Figure 2.32 *Personal Computer Image Processor.*

Figure 2.32 shows a system diagram of a typical PC-based image processor. In this system, the image processor performs the basic functions of image acquisition and display. Processing of the image takes place in the computer, although some image cards have specialized processing capability built into them for discrete convolution (see Chapter 8) that allows near real-time filtering operations and histogram processes that allow modification of the image brightness distribution (see Chapter 5). Expensive units often include array processors that permit more sophisticated image algorithms to be performed. The primary reason for implementing an imaging system of this type, however, is for image acquisition and display on a small scale. In the past, computer monitors, particularly those on personal computers, did not have the resolution to support image-processing display and so a separate monitor and video system was required. This is no longer the case, because computers with monitors and display cards supporting the IBM VGA video standard are fully capable of allowing display of standard monochrome images of 512 × 512 pixels. If image acquisition is not required, then a basic PC with VGA capability is all that is necessary for almost any image processing algorithm. Chapter 12 discusses UCFImage©, an image processing software system that does not require any image processing hardware and performs a large percentage of the imaging algorithms discussed throughout this book.

Chapter 3

Image Algebra

3.1 Introduction

Once image data have been brought into the computer, they are nothing more than numbers that can be manipulated with all the arithmetic and logic capabilities of the computer. When we use images as variables, we call the operations performed *algebraic*. An algebraic operation can be of one of two types, pointwise or matrix. Both operations can be described by the following annotation:

$$X \; opn \; Y = Z$$

X and Y can be images or scalars (numbers), and Z must be an image. A pointwise operation, *opn*, is performed between each corresponding element of X and Y. The matrix type of operation is more complex and involves a detailed series of steps that will be discussed later. We make an assumption that both X and Y, if images, have the same dimension, or spatial resolution. The equation above, as a linear process, is illustrated graphically in Figure 3.1.

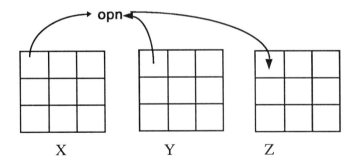

Figure 3.1 *Linear algebraic operation between images.*

Recall that an image is represented as an array of numbers that is spatially arranged in the same way as it was when digitized from the sensor. As an example of a linear algebraic operation, let's say that we have two images of the same scene. In one of the images, we see a

37

room, possibly in a warehouse. In the other image we see the warehouse with a person in the picture. If we let one image be stored in the global image variable X and the other in Y, and we let *opn* be subtraction, then the Z image result of the algebraic operation will be a picture of all 0's (black) with values only at the pixel locations that were different between the X and Y images. We may also assume that the row and column limit variables (Number_of_Rows, Number_of_Columns) are available as globals as well. The C code for this function would be:

```
subtract_XY(){
 int i,j;
 for(i  = 0; i < Number_of_Columns; ++i)
       for(j = 0; j < Number_of_Rows; ++j){
             Z[i,j] = X[i,j] - Y[i,j];
             /* set difference to white */
             if(Z[i,j]<>0)Z[i,j] = 255;
       }
 }
```

This function sets any pixel that is different between the two images equal to white (255). Figure 3.2 illustrates the results of an image subtraction where the second image is subtracted from the first. The first two images of the watch are not only displaced from each other in time, but they also have a small amount of spatial displacement between them. If the camera and the watch had been completely stationary, then only the minute and second hands would have appeared in the third image. The camera was moved slightly from the capture of the first image to the second and, as a result, the difference image shows a faint outline of the edge areas of the watch.

Figure 3.2 *Image subtraction example.*

As a further example of pixel algebra, consider the brightness control of your monitor. This control scales the overall brightness of the display in proportion to its setting. In the same way, we can multiply each pixel in an image by a constant and thus increase or decrease the value and, correspondingly, the overall brightness of the image.

3.2 Arithmetic Operations

The arithmetic operations between images include addition, subtraction, multiplication, and division. In all cases, we replace *opn* in the following expression with the desired operation:

$$X \text{ opn } Y = Z$$

In programming, we need to be careful about overflow and underflow on the results of the operations. Our standard pixel value range is 0 to 255, the values possible in a single byte of data. If the operation produces a number out of this range, we must either scale the entire result set or perform a truncation by which negative numbers are set to zero and large positives are set to 255. The decision is based solely on what is being attempted with the operation. Clearly, the simplest approach is to perform truncation. Graylevel scaling is discussed in Section 5.3, so we will defer explanation of it to that section.

It is important to understand what the operation is doing and when it is appropriate to perform it. As discussed in the introduction to this chapter, image subtraction is useful for detecting differences between image sequences of the same scene. The process is often used in security systems for detecting motion. Table 3.1 summarizes the effects of the four arithmetic operations and when they are useful. These operations can create some unique special effects, however, the effect is difficult to control because the operation takes place on every pixel, regardless of spatial position.

3.3 Boolean Operations

Boolean operations are logical operations performed on the pixels of an image. The standard Boolean operators of AND, OR, and NOT are applied as they were with the arithmetic operations discussed above. Combinations of these operations will yield any boolean function (NAND, NOR, XOR, IOR, and so on), although most imaging software provides XOR because of its transparent masking effect. Boolean operations are easiest to understand in terms of binary images. Since a binary image contains only black and white pixel values, the binary operations will have immediate visual relevance. Examples of elementary Boolean operations are given in Figure 3.3.

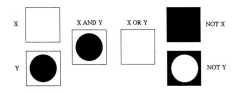

Figure 3.3 *Boolean operations on binary images.*

Boolean operations on grayscale images are more complex in their interpretation. Think of each pixel in terms of its binary representation as 8 bits. The AND operation will cause a dark masking effect where brightness values that are powers of 2 will be preserved only if corresponding values are present in each image. If either image is 0 for a power of 2 level, then that level, and all combinations of brightness that include it, will not be propagated to the result. Those pixels that are 0 will *mask* any value of brightness that the corresponding pixel in the other image represents.

In the case of an OR operation, powers of 2 levels will always propagate through the operation. Any pixels that are 255 will cause a light mask effect to occur in the resulting image.

Table 3.1 *Effects of algebraic operations on images.*

Operation	Effect	Uses
Addition	Z is the sum of brightness values at each pixel in X and Y. If Y is a positive scalar, Z is a brighter version of X; the increase in brightness is equal to Y.	Normalization of brightness
Subtraction	Z is the difference of brightness values at each pixel in X and Y. If Y is a positive scalar, Z is a darker version of X; the decrease in brightness is equal to Y.	Image differences
Multiplication	Z is the product of brightness values at each pixel in X and Y. If Y is a scalar, Z brightness values will be directly proportional to X by the value Y.	Calibration of brightness
Division	Z is the scaling of brightness values at each pixel in X by each pixel in Y. If Y is a scalar, Z brightness values will be inversely proportional to X by the value Y.	Normalization of brightness

3.4 Matrix Operations

Many imaging techniques require that the image be treated as a matrix. This is simply a notational convention and a set of operations that are defined in terms of linear algebra. In the previous sections we applied operations from pixel to corresponding pixel in the image equation. If the operation is addition or subtraction, the matrix operations are identical.

However, if the operation is multiplication, the method discussed in Section 3.2 is called the *dot product*. The dot product is often used to correct for sensor array response problems where a calibration image is generated for which each pixel value is calculated as a multiplicative correction factor. Images acquired by the sensor can be multiplied by the calibration image to remove or attenuate the individual pixel discrepancies and make the image consistent across all pixels. However, when discussing matrix operations, multiplication of images is normally understood to be the *cross product*, or *vector product*.

The cross product of two images is substantially different from the dot product and requires an understanding of vector multiplication. Think of a vector as being a single vertical line (a *row* vector) or horizontal column (a *column* vector) of an image. Profiling (discussed in Chapter 6,) is the process of examining or extracting a vector from an image. Multiplication of a row vector with a column vector results in a scalar, or single-dimensional number. The reason for this is because of the mathematical definition of vector multiplication and we need not explore it further. It is only important here that we understand how it is done. Consider the following example:

$$\text{row vector} \quad \overline{2 \ 2 \ 3 \ 8} \quad \text{column vector} \quad \begin{vmatrix} 4 \\ 3 \\ 7 \\ 1 \end{vmatrix}$$

For vector multiplication, we take the corresponding elements of each vector as we go from left to right on the row vector and top to bottom on the column vector and multiply. We then add each of the sums to obtain the result, which is $(2 \times 4) + (2 \times 3) + (3 \times 7) + (8 \times 1) = 43$. For a 4 by 4 image, there are 4 row vectors and 4 column vectors, yielding a permutation of 16, the number of pixels in the image! If we wish to take the cross product of two images, i.e., the matrix multiplication, we multiply each of the row vectors of the first image by each column vector in the second. Both images must have the same spatial resolution, or *dimension*, both horizontally and vertically. If the images are 4 by 4, then we will have 16 values after the calculations, and these values are the pixels of the resulting image. For example,

$$\begin{bmatrix} 2 & 2 & 3 & 8 \\ ? & ? & ? & ? \\ ? & ? & ? & ? \\ ? & ? & ? & ? \end{bmatrix} \times \begin{bmatrix} 4 & ? & ? & ? \\ 3 & ? & ? & ? \\ 7 & ? & ? & ? \\ 1 & ? & ? & ? \end{bmatrix} = \begin{bmatrix} 43 & ? & ? & ? \\ ? & ? & ? & ? \\ ? & ? & ? & ? \\ ? & ? & ? & ? \end{bmatrix}$$

The first row of the first image multiplies the first column of the second image to yield the first element of the result image under vector multiplication. Note the index for the result is [1, 1]. The index of each element in the result image tells us which row-column pair to multiply to get the value for that pixel. To get the value of the [3, 4] pixel, we would vector multiply the third row of the first image with the fourth column of the second image. A code sample is given of a function that cross multiplies two images that we will call cross_multiply. The function accesses global matrix variables containing the images (X and Y) and storing the result (Z).

```
cross_multiply(){
      for( i = 0; i < Size; ++i)
            for(j = 0; j < Size; ++j)
                  for( k = 0; k < Size; ++k)
                        Z[i][j] = Z[i][j] + X[i][k]*Y[k][j];
}
```

Note that we assume that the result image is full of 0 values at the start. On each cycle of the inner k loop, we multiply the values along the ith row with the values along the jth column and add their product to the z pixel at the i,jth index. The value of k goes from zero to *Size*, the number of rows or columns in the images. The image that results from application of the cross-product algorithm is no longer meaningful as an image to be viewed. The operation is always performed as an intermediate stage of a more complex algorithm, such as inverse filtering. It also plays an important part in matrix division operations.

The division of one matrix (or image) by another is accomplished through the use of the matrix inverse. Calculation of the inverse of a matrix is complex and the inverse does not always exist. It is beyond the scope of this book to discuss how to process the inverse of a matrix, however, for the interested reader a number of advanced imaging texts that discuss the uses of inverse matrices in image processing are included in the Annotated Bibliography. After the inverse has been taken, the cross product is performed between the images, and this results in the matrix division.

Matrix operations on images are important in that mathematics has long studied and analyzed matrices, so that the results of these studies and operations are available to the image researcher and user. Another important aspect of matrix operations on images is their use in the area of mathematics studies known as *image algebra*. This is not to be confused with the title of this chapter. image algebra, as a subfield of mathematics, seeks to define and clarify operations on images as data structures and to standardize image-processing algorithms as mathematical formulae. The reader is invited to consult the references on image algebra included in the Annotated Bibliography if further study in this area is desired.

Chapter 4

Image Geometry

4.1 Introduction

Geometric operations on images involve processes that manipulate the spatial position of pixels. Although pixel values are changed in some geometric manipulations, the primary result is a change in spatial arrangement of the brightness values of the image. The most complex and powerful of the image geometry techniques is that of *warping* (discussed in Section 4.5), or the distortion of an image subject to a constraint of some sort. We mention it here because all of the other techniques discussed in this chapter, with the exception of cutting and pasting, are simplified variations of image warping. The manipulation of image geometry can provide a powerful means of restoring images distorted by camera configuration errors, registering satellite land pictures to maps, and creating stunning special effects.

4.2 Zooming

Zooming and dezooming, or image magnification and demagnification, are processes by which an image is increased or decreased in size. The simplest way to zoom is to duplicate pixel values by an integer number in the X or Y directions, or both. If an image is not zoomed equally in both X and Y, then the *aspect ratio* of the image will be changed. Aspect ratio is the ratio of horizontal to vertical size of pixels in the image. Ideally, we want the ratio to be 1, or properly proportioned. Sometimes we want to create a special effect by distorting the aspect ratio. Figure 4.1 shows a circle with an aspect ratio of 1, less than 1, and greater than 1. Note that the distortion turns the circles into ellipses. This is a common phenomenon observed in computer displays that do not incorporate square pixels. If the pixels are rectangular, a function of the display and drive circuitry electronics, then the aspect ratio of the display will be the height to width ratio of the pixels themselves.

Figure 4.1 *Aspect ratio.*

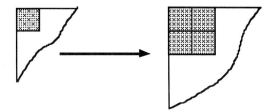

Figure 4.2 *Expansion of pixel by 4 (factor of 2 zoom).*

To zoom an image by a factor of 2, we reproduce each pixel four times, as shown in Figure 4.2. A 256×256 image would become a 512×512 image. Resolution has not been increased, only the size of the image. However, small features will become more noticeable, hence the term *magnification*. We can dezoom, or *demagnify*, using the same technique. There is one small complication. Whereas with the zoom operation we duplicated pixels, with dezooming pixels, and image information, must be discarded. If you are simply reversing a zoom operation, no problem exists. A method sometimes used to attempt to compensate for the loss of data is to take a neighborhood of four pixels and replace them with a single pixel that is the average value of the original four. This tends to give a result that is closer to the original picture in spatial distribution of brightness values.

To zoom (dezoom) by a factor of 4, we use an 8 neighborhood and so on. Figure 4.3 shows the result of dezooming an image by 4 and then by 8 and Figure 4.4 shows the factor of 4 image zoomed back to the original size. The following function zooms an image X by a factor of 2:

```
zoom_X_2(){
     int i,j, m = 0, n = 0;

     /* Z is the zoomed output image */
     for(i = 0; i < Number_of_Columns_of_X; ++i){
          for(j = 0; j < Number_of_Rows_of_X; ++j){
               Z[m][n]     = X[i][j];
               Z[m][n+1]   = X[i][j];
               Z[m+1][n]   = X[i][j];
               Z[m+1][n+1] = X[i][j];
               n = n + 2;
          }
          m = m + 2;
          n = 0;
     }
}
```

The function assumes that the image variables (X, Y and Z) and the row and column limit variables (Number_of_Rows_of_X, Number_of_Columns_of_X) are globals. The **m** and **n** variables are used as doubling indexes for the resultant image. To zoom or dezoom to fractional values, we must employ interpolation algorithms, or algorithms that approximate the correct pixel values based on the reduction or increase in spatial resolution. The most common method is the affine projection algorithm. It is also used for *warping* and is discussed in depth in Section 4.5.

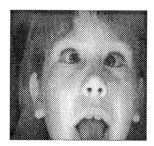

Figure 4.3 *Original image, dezoom factor of 4, dezoom factor of 8.*

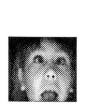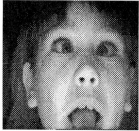

Figure 4.4 *Zoomed image on left, factor of 4 image (from Fig. 4.3) on right.*

4.3 Rotation

Simple rotation of images involves movements of 90° because images are square in shape. Rotations of other than 90° are possible using warping techniques. To rotate an image by increments of 90°, we simply copy row pixels to column pixels in the direction that we wish to rotate. Figure 4.5 illustrates the rotation process. The dashed line region at the top of (a) represents row pixels, they are copied to the left edge column pixels to effect a rotation to the right of 90°. Repeating the operation yields a rotation 180° to the right from the original orientation. The computer code to perform 90° rotation uses three variables, two to sequence normally through the rows and columns of the original image and one to keep track of the target column in the output image.

A function that uses this scheme for rotating an image X 90° to the right into an image Z is given by the following:

```
rotate_90(){
     int i,j,k;

     k  = Number_of_Columns - 1;

     for(i = 0; i < Number_of_Rows; ++i){
          for(j = 0; j < Number_of_Columns; ++j)
               Z[j][k] = X[i][j];
          k = k-1;
     }
}
```

The variables **i** and **j** index across and down through the original image. In the destination image (Z), the **k** variable is set to the highest column value and counts down after each row from the source image (X) is moved by the inner loop.

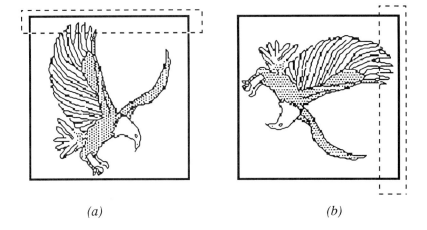

(a)   *(b)*

Figure 4.5 *Rotation example, 90° to the right.*

Note that we rotate one image array (X) into another (Z). We cannot rotate the image onto itself or we will overwrite the existing image data. To perform a 90° rotation to the left, we would start the **k** variable at zero and increment it after each column was copied.

The operations of flipping horizontally and vertically are similar in appearance to rotating, however, they yield the mirror image of the original and are somewhat more difficult to visualize. Figure 4.6 illustrates a horizontal and vertical flip of the eagle graphic shown in figure 4.5. Where we started with the top row of pixels and copied to the right column of pixels for the 90° right rotation, to perform a vertical flip we now start at the bottom row of pixels and copy to the top row. Once again, we use three variables. The first two simply locate the pixel to be copied from the source image (X), while the third variable determines, in this case from the bottom, the row that the pixel is to be copied into. The code segment to perform a vertical flip is given by:

```
flip(){
     int i,j,k;

     k  = Number_of_Rows-1;

     for(i = 0;  i < Number_of_Columns;  ++i){
          for(j = 0;  j < Number_of_Rows;  ++j)
               Z[k][j]  = X[i][j];
     k = k-1;
     }
}
```

A horizontal flip copies the first column of the source image into the last column of the destination image, and so on, until all columns are copied.

Figure 4.6 *Original, horizontal and vertical flips.*
(Note that the flips cannot be obtained by rotation.)

4.4 Cutting and Pasting

In photography, the cropping of pictures and the reassembling of pictures from parts is the equivalent of the geometrical operation of cutting and pasting images. There are three basic ways to cut (and the reverse, paste) image portions. The first and simplest is by using a rectangular region defined by two coordinates. The second, somewhat harder, is to use a geometric figure, such as a circle, ellipse, or a piecewise-linear representation of a regular or irregular polygon. The final and most difficult method is to use a free-form figure generated from a set of spatial coordinates. Coordinates may be entered from the keyboard or input using a *mouse* or a *graphic tablet*. Other spatial coordinate input devices exist that are variations or combinations of these two. For example, a *trackball* is an inverted mouse and a *touchscreen display* is a monitor equipped to operate like a graphic tablet.

To establish a rectangular region, the user can be queried for the coordinates of opposite corners of the desired rectangle. A better approach is to allow the user to specify the corners using a mouse. The program must provide a *cursor*, or graphic indicator, that shows the current location of the mouse and be prepared to record the coordinates of the mouse location when the user presses, or *clicks*, the mouse button. After the first coordinate is entered, the program should indicate this point with a graphic symbol or colored marker. Likewise the second point should be marked. The program may draw connecting lines between the selected corner points that exactly delineate the selected rectangle.

Some systems provide a *rubber-band* marker that delineates the rectangular region. The user positions the mouse to the start point of the desired rectangle and presses and holds the mouse button. A broken line then follows the mouse position as long as the button is depressed and takes the shape of a rectangle between the current mouse position and the point where the button was first depressed. When the button is released, the mouse location at that point becomes the opposite corner of the rectangular region desired.

The program may request coordinates or use mouse entry to describe regions other than rectangles. For example, the first coordinate may describe the center of a circle and the second its radius. Beyond this, more complex regions demand the use of a mouse or other spatial coordinate input device. Figure 4.7 illustrates the progression of complexity in terms of region definition.

Figure 4.7 *Region complexity increases from left to right.*

After a region is defined, the cutting operation is nothing more than a removal of the pixels in the region to a storage buffer. The pixels left within the boundaries of the cut region in the image are replaced by 0's. A distinct advantage of image processing over photography is that the cutting operation may be defined as copying, and in this case the pixels from the first image are left untouched after they have been copied to the storage buffer.

Pasting is the process by which the pixels removed from an image within a defined region are either replaced or repositioned in the same image or copied into a new image. Of issue here is how the pasting takes place with regard to the pixel values present in the destination image. The simplest and most intuitive form of pasting is replacement. The pixels occupying the region in the destination are replaced by the pixels in the storage buffer. Some imaging programs allow algebraic or logical operations to take place, and the details of these operations are discussed in Chapter 3. Figure 4.8 shows an example of defining irregular regions, cutting the regions and pasting them in a new location. The two heads in the left-hand image of Figure 4.8 have been cut using a free-form region and pasted into the image on the right. It is a strange result, but illustrative of the cut and paste process. Note also that the heads have been scaled (zoom/dezoom) to account for size perspective differences.

Figure 4.8 *Example of Cutting and Pasting operation.*

4.5 Warping

Warping is the process by which one image is altered so that the spatial relationship of its objects and features are aligned to another image or a spatial template. The other image is often a map, although warping is now used with shape templates for special effects, where an image is wrapped around a three-dimensional object such as a sphere.

The most common transformation is based on the affine projection, given by the following set of equations:

$$X' = \frac{aX + bY + c}{iX + jY + 1}$$

$$Y' = \frac{dX + eY + f}{iX + jY + 1}$$

X, Y are the old coordinates and X', Y' the new. The coefficients, **a, b, c, d, e, f, i** and **j** are determined from a set of four control points that correspond to the congruency desired between the two images or the selected template. Figure 4.9 is an example of the warping process applied to the binary image of a simple box graphic.

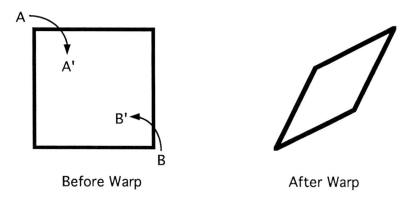

Before Warp   After Warp

Figure 4.9 *Warp example on box graphic.*

In the box example, the point A is warped to A' and B is warped to B'. The affine projection requires that four points be selected to give us the required eight equations to solve for the coefficients. A-A' and B-B' would give us only two sets of X's and Y's; however, we can select two control points that map to their identical spatial locations in each image. This allows us to warp to one, two or three points. In this case, control point A provides us with the first X and Y and A' with the X' and Y'. Control point B provides the second set. The third and fourth point sets in this example are just the opposite corners of the square. Since the corner points do not move, this provides a spatial constraint on the warping function. The final result is the diamond shape. If all points are the same, that is, if X = X' and Y = Y', then the coefficients reduce to an identity matrix. If more than four control points are selected, then a least-squares fit may be used to determine the best values for the transformation.

In practice, a routine for solving simultaneous equations is used to compute the values of the coefficients. Then coordinate X', Y' from the target image is put into the affine transformation equation to get the corresponding value of X, Y from the original image. The gray scale value at X, Y is then assigned to the spatial position indicated by X', Y' in the warped image. The mapping process is easily performed in parallel since each point in the warped result depends only on a single point from the original image.

Using the example of Figure 4.9, assume that the origin is located in the upper-left corner and that the warp-to points are located one-quarter of the diagonal in. Recall that we selected the opposite corners and their corresponding points in the warped image as the other two required points. This will yield the following data set:

Control point 1:	X, Y (0,0) → (2,2) X', Y'
Control point 2:	X, Y (4,4) → (3,3) X', Y'
Control point 3:	X, Y (4,0) → (4,0) X', Y'
Control point 4:	X, Y (0,4) → (0,4) X', Y'

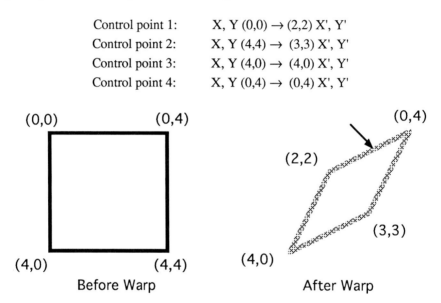

Figure 4.10 *Coordinates of control points before and after warp.*

Figure 4.10 illustrates the spatial relationship of the points between the before and after warp image. When these points are inserted into the affine projection equation and solved for the unknown coefficients, we get the following values:

a =	0.75	e	=	0.75
b =	-0.25	f	=	1.00
c =	1.00	i	=	0.00
d =	-0.25	j	=	0.00

Now choose the X', Y' location (2.5,0.5), which is marked with an arrow in Figure 4.10. This point will map back to (2,0) as expected. The pixel value from the original image at this location becomes the value at the X', Y' location in the warped image. It is important to note that this example is very simple, and in computer images we do not have fractional pixel positions. When fractions in the computations occur, we must round or truncate the values determined. The effects of this process are indirectly proportional to image resolution and decrease as image resolution increases. Figure 4.11 illustrates the application of the diamond shaped warp to an image.

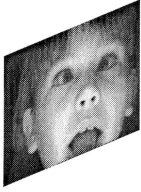

Figure 4.11 *Image warp example.*

Chapter 5

Histogram Techniques

5.1 Introduction

The graylevel content of an image can easily be manipulated to enhance its visual interpretation. The types of enhancements that are available can range from simple graylevel scaling algorithms to the more advanced histogram equalization and specification algorithms. The purpose of graylevel scaling an image's graylevel values is to increase the overall brightness and contrast of an image. Another very common graylevel scaling technique is to find the minimum and maximum graylevel values within an image and to linearly scale this range of graylevels to the minimum and maximum graylevel values used by a particular imaging system. This enables the complete dynamic range of the imaging system to be used. This graylevel modification technique is commonly referred to as *autoscaling*.

Histogram techniques treat the graylevel content of an image as a set of random numbers to modify the histogram of an image. The two histogram techniques that are commonly used are histogram equalization and histogram specification. Both operations are nonlinear and are used to increase the overall contrast and brightness within an image. Histogram equalization uniformly redistributes the pixel graylevel values so that the number of pixels at any one particular graylevel value is about the same for all graylevels within the image. The histogram specification operation modifies the histogram of the original image to a newly specified histogram. With this operation, the dark graylevel pixels within an image can be brightened while the light graylevel pixels can be darkened.

Both graylevel scaling operations and histogram techniques operate on each pixel within an image, changing the pixel's graylevel values. These operations can operate on an entire image or within a local region within an image. It is the goal of this chapter to present to the reader the concepts and algorithms used in graylevel scaling and histogram techniques.

5.2 Computing Histograms

The histogram of an image is simply a set of numbers describing the percentage of pixels within an image that are at a certain graylevel value. Consider an image that contains 256 unique graylevel values in the range from 0 to 255. Each of these values can be described by an 8-bit integer number G_i with the index i indicating the ith graylevel. Fox example, G_{200} equals graylevel value 200 .

Next consider an image with n_t total pixels within the image. For a 512×512 image there is a total of 262,144 pixels. Let n_i be the number of pixels within the image that have the ith graylevel value G_i. The histogram of the image is then defined as a set of M numbers (in this case, since there are 256 graylevel values, M = 256) given by

$$h_i = \frac{n_i}{n_t}, \quad \text{for } i = 0 \text{ to } (M-1),$$ (1)

where M is the total number of graylevel values within the image. For example, consider an $128 \times 128 \times 8$ graylevel image with the distribution of pixels (n_i) given in Table 5.1. The histogram (h_i's) for this image is then computed using Equation 1. The center column in Table 5.1 gives the number of pixels within the image at each graylevel value, while the rightmost column gives the computed histogram values for each graylevel value.

There are several important features of histograms. The first is that each h_i gives the probability of a pixel, $p_r(G_i)$, within an image having the ith graylevel value. The second important feature of histograms is that the total sum of its components equals 1:

$$\sum_{i=0}^{M-1} h_i = 1 .$$ (2)

Another feature, is that the probability of a pixel having a graylevel value less than or equal to the jth graylevel value is the sum of h_i's with i ranging from 0 to j:

Table 5.1 *Example of computing an image's histogram.*

Graylevels	n_i	h_i
0	1028	0.0627
1	3544	0.2163
2	5023	0.3066
3	3201	0.1954
4	1867	0.1139
5	734	0.0448
6	604	0.0369
7	383	0.0234
n_t	16384	

$$P_r(G_i \le G_j) = \sum_{i=0}^{j} h_i , \ 0 \le j < M . \tag{3}$$

And, finally, information about an image can be obtained directly from its histogram. The location of the peaks within the histogram describes the relative brightness of the image, while the width of these peaks gives details about the contrast of the image.

Figure 5.1 illustrates four types of histograms that are typically encountered in images. Assuming that graylevel value 0 is equal to black and graylevel value 255 is equal to white, the histogram given in Figure 5.1a has most of its pixels with graylevel values that are black. This is a result of a dark image. Figure 5.1b, on the other hand, has most of its pixels' graylevel values near 255 showing that this image is a very bright image. In Figure 5.1c, most of the image pixels are located near graylevel value 128, indicating a normal brightness image. In Figures 5.1a, b, and c, most of the pixels are located within a small graylevel region. This is a very common feature in low-contrast images. Figure 5.1d illustrates a histogram of an image that has a normal brightness and a high contrast level. In addition, the pixels within this image are uniformly distributed among all gray-level values.

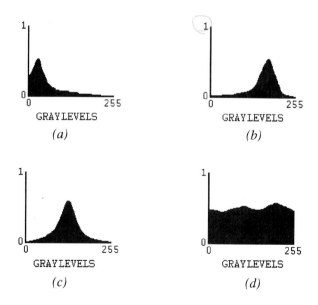

Figure 5.1 *Examples of several types of image histograms.*

To compute the histogram from an image, an array of size equal to the total number of possible graylevels is initialized to zero. Then the image is scanned pixel by pixel, and each time the corresponding pixel's graylevel value is used as an index into an array, this particular array element is then incremented by 1. After the image is scanned pixel by pixel, each value in the array represents the number of pixels at a given graylevel value n_i. To compute the histogram values (h_i's), each value in the array is then divided by the total number of pixels scanned within the image.

Figure 5.2 gives the partial code to compute a histogram for a 128×128 image. The image is assumed to be stored in a two-dimensional array IMAGE[X][Y] that contains 16,384 elements with possible graylevel values ranging from 0 to 255. In addition, a 256-element floating-point array HIST[I] is assumed to be defined and will be used to store the computed histogram. The first part of the program initializes the integer array IHIST[I] to zero. Next, the program scans the image in the horizontal direction line by line and increments the corresponding cell in IHIST[I]. Finally, the histogram array HIST[I] is divided by the total number of pixels scanned. For speed improvement, the integer array IHIST[I] is incremented for each pixel scanned instead of using the floating-point array HIST[I]. Using an integer array instead of a floating-point array requires only integer addition to increment the array, which is much faster than floating-point addition. The floating-point results required for the histogram are computed when IHIST[I] is divided by the total number of points (total). Computing the histogram in this way reduces the total number of floating operations to 256.

```
Histogram(unsigned char IMAGE[][],float HIST[])
    {
    int total;
    int X, Y;
    int I,G;
    int IHIST[255];
    for(I=0; I<=255; I++){
        IHIST[I]=0;
        }
    total=0;
    for(Y=0; Y<=127; Y++){
        for(X=0; X<=127; X++){
            G=IMAGE[X][Y];
            IHIST[G]=IHIST[G]+1;
            total=total+1;
            }
        }
    for(I=0; I<=255; I++){
        HIST[I]= (float)IHIST[I]/(float)total;
        }
    }
```

Figure 5.2 *Partial C code to compute an image histogram.*

To use the partial code given in Figure 5.2 with a different-sized image, the X and Y loops must be changed to the desired X and Y pixel dimensions. Additionally, the integer histogram array IHIST[I] must be changed from an integer to a long integer. This second change in the program is required because there exists the possibility of having one of the n_i's equal to the total number of pixels within the image. For example a 512×512 image with a constant graylevel value of 145 would have all n_i's equal to zero except n_{145} which would be equal to 262,144 (512 times 512).

5.3 Graylevel Scaling

Graylevel scaling remaps the graylevels within an image by applying a transformation function to an image. This transformation function can either be linear or nonlinear. Let $f(x, y)$ define the graylevel at pixel location x, y in an image and P be the transformation function. Then the transformed image is simply defined as

$$g(x, y) = P[f(x, y)] \qquad (4)$$

In Equation 4, the transformation function can be any mapping function. For example, different mapping operations could be applied to different parts of the image. In Equation 5, the graylevel mapping adds a different constant to the image as the locations of the pixels change in the horizontal direction within the image. For $x = 511$, a constant value of 5 is added to all the pixels within the 511th column of the image.

$$g(x, y) = f(x, y) + \frac{5x}{511} \qquad (5)$$

In most cases graylevel mapping of one image into another image depends only on the graylevel values of the pixels within the original image. Under this situation, Equation 4 can be rewritten as a function of the input graylevel values,

$$g = P[f] , \qquad (6)$$

where f is the graylevel value of the input image and g is the output graylevel of the output image. To use Equation 6, the input image is scanned pixel by pixel, and each pixel's graylevel value (f) is replaced with the new graylevel value (g). Consider the linear transformation as described by Equation 7

$$g = c \cdot f + b . \qquad (7)$$

Here the variables c and b take on two important functions. The variable b adjusts the brightness of an image, while c adjusts the contrast of an image.

Figure 5.3 shows several examples of transformation curves for different values of c and b. The horizontal axis gives the input graylevel values, f, while the vertical axis gives the transformed graylevel values, g. As shown in Figure 5.3, if the transformed graylevel values exceed the acceptable graylevel range, the output graylevel values are set to the minimum and maximum allowable graylevels. For an 8-bit imaging system, the graylevel values usually range between 0 and 255. As the variable c is increased, the slope of the transformation curve increases, and as the variable b increases, the minimum graylevel increases. In other words, as the variable b is changed, the transformation curves move up and down in the vertical direction. The effect of changing the variable c (contrast) is equivalent to changing the width of an image's histogram, while changing the variable b (brightness) is equivalent to moving the location of the peaks within the image's histogram.

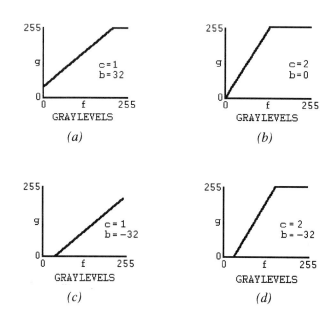

Figure 5.3 *Examples of linear graylevel transformations.*

The linear transformations shown in Figure 5.3 can easily be expanded to nonlinear functions. For example, sometimes it is desired to increase the contrast of the dark regions within an image and at the same time reduce the contrast of the bright regions within an image. A logarithmic transformation of the form

$$g = 31.875 \cdot \log_2(f + 1) \tag{8}$$

shown in Figure 5.4a can be used to enhance the contrast of dark pixels and at the same time reduce the contrast of bright pixels. Another very common nonlinear transformation is shown in Figure 5.4b. With this transformation, the contrast of regions within an image containing pixels with graylevel values close to 128 is increased, and at the same time the contrast of all other graylevel regions is decreased. Typically, nonlinear transformations are used to enhance a given range of graylevel values within an image.

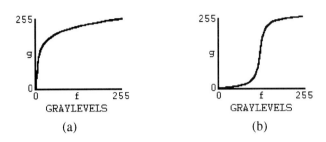

Figure 5.4 *Examples of nonlinear graylevel transformations.*

Another common linear graylevel transformation is to autoscale all the graylevels within an image to the minimum and maximum graylevels used by either the imaging system or the imaging display. The autoscaling operation scales the graylevels within the image to the dynamic range of the system being used. The perceived effect on the image is to increase the overall brightness and contrast of the image. The autoscaling operation is also referred to as *histogram stretching*.

Equation 9 gives the linear transformation for an autoscaling operation for a 256 graylevel imaging system.

$$\text{\textcircled{\tiny{3}}} \quad g = \frac{255}{f_{max} - f_{min}} (f - f_{min}) \tag{9}$$

To use Equation 9, the original image must be scanned pixel by pixel to find the minimum (f_{min}) and the maximum (f_{max}) graylevels within the image. Next, Equation 9 is applied pixel by pixel to the original image, generating a new image that now has a minimum graylevel value of 0 and a maximum graylevel value of 255. In applying Equation 9, it is best that all the arithmetic operations be performed by using floating point arithmetic and converting the final results to an integer number. This reduces the round-off error to only one operation.

Figure 5.5 gives the partial code to implement the autoscaling operation on a $512 \times 512 \times 256$ graylevel image. The partial code given in Figure 5.5 assumes that the image is stored in an unsigned char 512×512 array IMAGE[X][Y] and that this array is passed to the program during execution. The first thing that the program does is scan the image to find the minimum (smin) and the maximum (smax) graylevel values within the image. Next, the program computes the autoscaling coefficient (ascle) and checks to see if ascle is 0. If the variable ascle is 0, a floating-point error will occur during the execution of the autoscaling equation. To prevent this from happening, the variable ascle is set to 1. This is not a major difficulty because if the variable ascle is 0 then the image is simply a constant image and nothing is gained by autoscaling this image. Finally, the image is rescanned, and each pixel's graylevel value within the image is changed to the new autoscaled graylevel value.

The partial code in Figure 5.5 assumes that the desired minimum and maximum graylevel values are 0 and 255, respectively. To change the desired autoscaled graylevel range, the variable graymin must be changed to the minimum desired graylevel value, and the variable graymax must be changed to the maximum desired graylevel value. If the input image's graylevel range is not in the range from 0 to 255, the variables smin and smax must be changed to reflect these values.

```
autoscale(unsigned char IMAGE[][])
        {
        float ascle,graymax,graymin;
        int X,Y;
        int smin,smax;
        smin=255; smax=0;
        graymax=255;
        graymin=0;
        ascle=0..0;
        for(Y=0; Y<=511; Y++){
            for(X=0; X<=511; X++){
                if (IMAGE[X][Y] > smax){
                    smax= IMAGE[X][Y];}
                if (IMAGE[X][Y] < smin){
                    { smin= IMAGE[X][Y];}
            }
            }
        if ((smax-smin) != 0){
                ascle=(float)(graymax-
                graymin)/(float)(smax-smin));}
        else{
        ascle=1.0;}
        for(Y=0;   Y<=511; Y++){
           for(X=0;   X<=511; X++){
           IMAGE[X][Y]=(int)(ascle*(float)(IMAGE[X][Y]
                - smin)+ graymin);
                }
            }
        }
```

Figure 5.5 *Partial C code to autoscale an image.*

5.4 Histogram Equalization

Histogram equalization uniformly redistributes the graylevel values of pixels within an image so that the number of pixels at any one graylevel is about the same. In other words, the histogram for a histogram-equalized image is a uniform histogram. Consider two histograms, one from the original unequalized image, h_{fi}, and one from the equalized image, h_{gi}. The goal is to find a grayscale transformation

$$g = P[f] \tag{10}$$

that yields a uniform histogram for h_{gi}. In other words, all graylevel values are equally likely of occurring within the image.

By definition, in an uniform histogram each bin has the same value or the same probability of occurrence. A uniform histogram of an image with m distinct graylevels yields a probability of any one graylevel value of

$$h_{gi} = \frac{1}{m}. \tag{11}$$

For an image with 256 graylevels, Equation 11 simply reduces to

$$h_{gi} = \frac{1}{256}. \tag{12}$$

The transformation that converts an image to a histogram equalized image is simply a transformation that sums the elements of the histogram from the original image and is given in Equation 13

$$g_i = P(f_i) = (m - 1) \cdot \sum_{j=0}^{i} h_{fi}. \tag{13}$$

Here m is the number of graylevels in the original image and i is the ith graylevel for the equalized image. For example, graylevel g_0 is equal to $(m - 1) \cdot h_0$, and graylevel g_1 is equal to $(m - 1) \cdot (h_0 + h_1)$.

Using Equation 1, Equation 13 can be written in terms of the number of pixels n_{fi} at a particular graylevel value in the original image as

$$g_i = P(f_i) = \frac{m - 1}{n_t} \cdot \sum_{j=0}^{i} n_{fi}, \tag{14}$$

where n_t is the total number of pixels within the original image to be equalized.

To histogram equalize an image, the first step is to compute the histogram of the original image and then compute a new set of graylevels, g_i, as given by either Equation 13 or 14. Next, each pixel within the image is replaced by the new graylevel values. For example, graylevel f_0 is replaced by

$$f_0 = \frac{(m - 1) \cdot n_{f0}}{n_t} \tag{15}$$

Consider the $128 \times 128 \times 8$ graylevel image given in Table 5.1. The first four equalized graylevels are computed as follows:

$$g_0 = 7 \cdot h_{f0}$$
$$g_0 = 7 \cdot 0.0627 = 0.439$$

$$g_1 = 7 \cdot (h_{f0} + h_{f1})$$
$$g_1 = 7 \cdot (0.0627 + 0.2163) = 1.953$$

$$g_2 = 7 \cdot (h_{f0} + h_{f1} + h_{f2})$$
$$g_2 = 7 \cdot (0.0627 + 0.2163 + 0.3066) = 4.099$$

$$g_3 = 7 \cdot (h_{f0} + h_{f1} + h_{f2} + h_{f3})$$
$$g_3 = 7 \cdot (0.0627 + 0.2163 + 0.3066 + 0.1954) = 5.467$$

The last four graylevels reduce to

$$g_4 = 6.264 \qquad g_5 = 6.578$$
$$g_6 = 6.836 \qquad g_7 = 7.000$$

Since only integer graylevels 0 through 7 are allowed, the eight equalized graylevel values must be rounded to the nearest allowed graylevel values.

$$g_0 = 0 \qquad g_1 = 2$$
$$g_2 = 4 \qquad g_3 = 5$$
$$g_4 = 6 \qquad g_5 = 7$$
$$g_6 = 7 \qquad g_7 = 7$$

Since graylevels 5, 6, and 7 are the same, the equalized image for this example reduces to six discrete graylevels. Graylevel values 5, 6, and 7 in the original image will be mapped to the same graylevel value of 7 in the histogram-equalized image.

$$g_0 = 0 \qquad g_1 = 2$$
$$g_2 = 4 \qquad g_3 = 5$$
$$g_4 = 6 \qquad g_5 = 7$$

The distribution of pixels for the equalized image and its corresponding histogram are given in Table 5.2. Pixels with graylevel value 0 stay the same in both the original and the equalized images, while pixels with graylevel value 1 are changed to graylevel value 2. For this example, there will be no pixels at graylevel values 1 and 3 in the equalized image.

In comparing the histogram of the original image given in Table 5.1 to the equalized histogram given in Table 5.2, the reader should notice that the equalized histogram shows that the new pixel graylevels are more uniformly distributed between the dark and bright graylevel values. In Table 5.1, most of the pixels are distributed amongst the dark graylevel values.

Table 5.2 *An example of an equalized image histogram.*

Graylevels	n_i	h_i
0	1028	0.0627
1	0000	0.0000
2	3544	0.2163
3	0000	0.0000
4	5023	0.3066
5	3201	0.1954
6	1867	0.1139
7	1721	0.1050
n_t	16384	

Figure 5.6a shows an image of a set of geometrical shapes with low contrast and brightness. The histogram corresponding to this image is given in Figure 5.6b. From the histogram, it is easy to see that most of the pixels' graylevel values are in the range of 0 to 68. Figure 5.6c shows the histogram-equalized image and in Figure 5.6d is its corresponding histogram. Notice how this image's brightness and contrast have been increased. This can be seen from the range of graylevels present in the histogram given in Figure 5.6d.

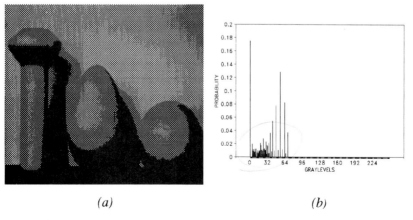

(a)   *(b)*

Figure 5.6 *Example of histogram equalization of a dark image*

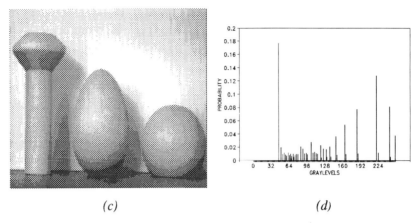

(c)   *(d)*

Figure 5.6 *continued.*

It was stated that the goal of histogram equalization is to uniformly redistribute the graylevel values of the pixels within an image so that the equalized image histogram is a uniform distribution. From Figure 5.6d, even though this histogram is more uniform than the original histogram given in Figure 5.6b, it is not exactly a uniform histogram. There are two reasons why histogram equalization only approximately yields a uniform distribution. The first is that only a finite number of graylevels are present in quantized images. As shown in the previous example, the equalized graylevel values had to be rounded to the nearest realizable graylevel values. The second reason is due to the finite number of pixels that are used to represent an image. To yield an exact uniform distribution, a quantized image must be represented by its equivalent continuous image. In real image-processing systems this is not possible.

```
Histogram_Equalization(unsigned char IMAGE[][])
        {
        int X,Y,I,J,HISTEQ[256];
        float HIST[256], sum;
        Histogram(IMAGE, HIST);
        for(I=0; I<=255; I++){
              sum=0.0;
              for(J=0; J<=I; J++)sum=sum+HIST[J];
              HISTEQ[I]=(int)(255*sum+.5);
              }
        for(Y=0; Y<=511; Y++){
        for(X=; X<=511; X++){
              IMAGE[X][Y]=HISTEQ[IMAGE[X][Y]];
              }
        }
        }
```

Figure 5.7 *Partial C code to perform histogram equalization.*

The partial code to implement histogram equalization on a $512 \times 512 \times 256$ graylevel image is given in Figure 5.7. Again it is assumed that the unequalized image is passed to the program in array IMAGE[X][Y]. The first thing that the program does is call the histogram routine given in Figure 5.2 to compute the image's histogram. Next, the program generates a new integer array HISTEQ[I] of equalized graylevel values. Finally, each pixel within the image (array IMAGE[X][Y]) is transformed to the new graylevel values.

5.5 Histogram Specification

The disadvantage of histogram equalization is that the final histogram cannot be specified and that this histogram is only an approximation to a uniform histogram. Sometimes it is necessary to be able to specify the final histogram. Histogram specification can be used to darken an image or, on the other hand brighten and improve the contrast of an image interactively by specifying the desired histogram.

The histogram-specification algorithm begins by first defining the desired histogram and then equalizing this histogram. Let h_{di} be the ith element of the desired histogram. Then the graylevel transformation required to equalize this histogram is given as

$$s_i = P(d_i) = (m - 1) \cdot \sum_{j=0}^{i} h_{di} \, . \tag{16}$$

The next step is to equalize the graylevel values of the original image as described in Section 5.4, with its transformation summarized here as

$$g_i = P(f_i) = (m - 1) \cdot \sum_{j=0}^{i} h_{fi} \, , \tag{17}$$

The final step is to find the inverse of the graylevel transformation given in Equation 16

$$d_i = P^{-1}(s_i) \tag{18}$$

and to apply this inverse transformation to the graylevel values of the pixels within the equalized image (Equation 17). The inverse transformation given in Equation 18 is found for a particular graylevel by scanning through the elements of g_i and finding which index i yields the closest graylevel value.

Again consider the 128×128 image given in Table 5.1 and then equalized in Table 5.2. Let the histogram h_{di} defined in Table 5.3 be the desired histogram. Using Equation 14, the equalized graylevel transformation values s_i can be found and are given in Table 5.3. The rounded values given adjacent to the exact s_i's correspond to the actual allowed graylevel values. To find the inverse transformation as defined by Equation 16, the closest rounded graylevel value for s_i is located and the corresponding index is found. For example, for a graylevel value of $s_i = 5$ the inverse transformation in Table 5.3 would yield a value of 4.

Table 5.3 *A desired histogram and its equalized values.*

Graylevels d_i	h_{di}	s_i, int $(s_i + 0.5)$
0	0.00	0.00, 0
1	0.00	0.00, 0
2	0.10	0.70, 1
3	0.25	2.45, 2
4	0.30	4.55, 5
5	0.25	6.30, 6
6	0.10	7.00, 7
7	0.00	7.00, 7

The inverse transformation values for the eight possible graylevels for s_i are given by

$$P^{-1}(0) = 1 \qquad P^{-1}(1) = 2$$
$$P^{-1}(2) = 3 \qquad P^{-1}(3) = 3$$
$$P^{-1}(4) = 4 \qquad P^{-1}(5) = 4$$
$$P^{-1}(6) = 5 \qquad P^{-1}(7) = 6$$

In selecting these inverse transformation values, there were two places of ambiguity. The first was in the selection of $P^{-1}(0)$. Either graylevel value of 0 or 1 could have been chosen. The value of 1 was chosen in that it gave the best match to the desired histogram. The second ambiguity was in choosing the value for $P^{-1}(7)$. Either the value of 6 or 7 could have been chosen. Likewise, the value of 6 was chosen in that this yielded the best fit to the desired histogram. In general, the inverse transformation is not single valued, and the final value chosen should be the one that yields the best fit to the desired histogram.

From Section 5.4 the equalized gray values were given as

$$g_0 = 0 \qquad g_1 = 2$$
$$g_2 = 4 \qquad g_3 = 5$$
$$g_4 = 6 \qquad g_5 = 7$$

The final step in the histogram specification algorithm requires that the equalized graylevel values from the original image be mapped using the inverse transformation values.

$$g_0 = 0 \rightarrow P^{-1}(0) = 1 \qquad g_1 = 2 \rightarrow P^{-1}(2) = 3 \qquad g_2 = 4 \rightarrow P^{-1}(4) = 4$$

$$g_3 = 5 \rightarrow P^{-1}(5) = 4 \qquad g_4 = 6 \rightarrow P^{-1}(6) = 5 \qquad g_5 = 7 \rightarrow P^{-1}(7) = 6$$

The final graylevel pixel distribution along with its computed histogram is given in Table 5.4. Notice how the peak of the histogram has moved from graylevel value 2 to graylevel value 4, brightening the image.

Table 5.4 *Histogram of the specified image.*

Graylevels	n_i	h_i
0	0000	0.0000
1	1028	0.0627
2	0000	0.0000
3	3544	0.2163
4	8224	0.5020
5	1867	0.1139
6	1721	0.1050
7	0000	0.0000
n_t	16384	

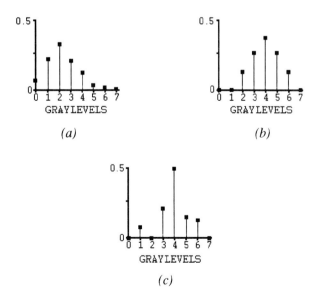

Figure 5.8 *Plots of the(a) original, (b) desired and (c) actual histograms.*

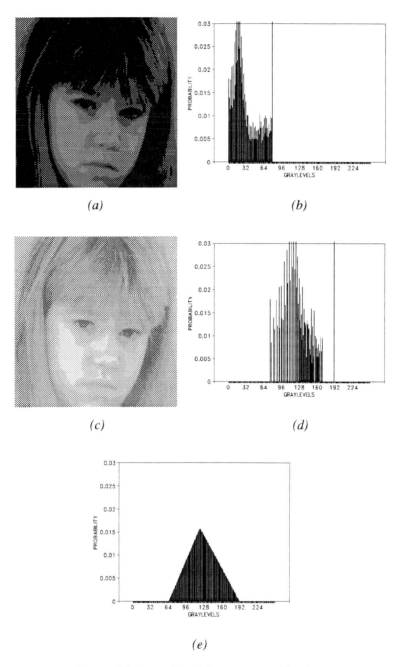

Figure 5.9 *Example of histogram specification.*

Figure 5.8 shows plots for the histogram of the original image (Figure 5.8a) along with plots of the desired (Figure 5.8b) and actual histogram (Figure 5.8c) using the histogram specification-algorithm. In comparing the actual histogram generated from the histogram-specified image to that of the original desired histogram, the two are very similar but not exact. The main reason for the difference, as stated in the previous section, is that there are only a finite number of possible graylevel values and there are a finite number of pixels within the image.

Figure 5.9a is a dark image of a girl's face, and Figure 5.9b is its corresponding histogram. Notice how very little detail can be observed in the girl's hair. Using the histogram-specification technique and the specified histogram given in Figure 5.9e, this image can be lightened so that more details can be seen. The output image from the histogram-specification operation can be seen in Figure 5.9c and its histogram in Figure 5.9d. As can be seen in Figure 5.9c, details of the girl's hair can now be observed. Note that, even though the desired and actual histograms are not identically the same, their approximate shapes are. This is simply due to the fact that histogram specification on a digitized image yields only an approximate result, just like histogram equalization.

```
Histogram_Specify(unsigned char IMAGE[][], float SPEC[])
    {
    int X,Y,I, minval, minj, HISTSPEC[256], J;
    int InvHist[256];
    float sum;
        Histogram_Equalization(IMAGE);
    for(I=0; I<=255; I++){
        sum=0.0;
        for(J=0; J<=I; J++){
            sum=sum+SPEC[J];}
        HISTSPEC[I]=(int)(255*sum+.5);
        }
    for (I=0; I<=255; I++){
        minval=abs(I-HISTSPEC[0]); minj=0;
        for (J=0; J<=255; J++){
            if ( abs(I - HISTSPEC[J]) < minval){
                minval=abs(I - HISTSPEC[J]);
                minj=J;}
            InvHist[I]  = minj;}
        }
    for(Y=0; Y<=511; Y++){
        for(X=0; X<=511; X++) {
            IMAGE[X][Y] = InvHist[IMAGE[X][Y]];}
        }
    }
```

Figure 5.10 *Partial C code for histogram specification.*

The partial code to implement histogram specification on a $512 \times 512 \times 256$ graylevel image stored in the two-dimensional array IMAGE[X][Y] is given in Figure 5.10. It is assumed that the specified histogram is stored in the array SPEC[J] and is passed to the program during execution. This first thing the program does is call the histogram equalization routine given in Section 5.4. Next, the program equalizes the specified histogram, generating its graylevel transformation stored in array, HISTSPEC[I]. Then using a simple search algorithm, the program searches through each element of the array, HISTSPEC[I], generating the inverse transformation array, InvHist[I]. Finally, the program scans the equalized image, remapping each pixel graylevel value using the InvHist[I] array.

5.6 Thresholding

In many applications of image processing it is desired to segment an image's graylevel values into particular subregions. For example, it may be desirable to set the object within an image to a white graylevel, at the same time setting the background to a black graylevel. In many applications, segmenting the graylevel values of an image into two graylevel values is all that is required. This particular two-graylevel image is referred to as a *binary image*.

In Figure 5.11a is a plot of a histogram taken from a white object against a black background. The first peak centered at 50, and the distribution of graylevels about this peak is due to the background, while the second peak centered at 200 is due to the object within the image.

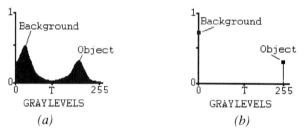

(a)   (b)

Figure 5.11 *Example of thresholding an image using its histogram:*
(a) original histogram; (b) threshold histogram.

To segment this image into two graylevel values of 0 for the background and 255 for the object, the following graylevel transformation is required:

$$g(x, y) = \begin{cases} 255 & \text{if } f(x, y) > T \\ 0 & \text{if } f(x, y) \le T \end{cases}. \tag{19}$$

The threshold value of T is chosen so that the background pixels are set to 0 and the object values are set to 255.

This transformation converts the histogram given in Figure 5.11a to a two-point histogram with graylevel values of 0 and 255 as shown in Figure 5.11b. From Figure 5.11b, the value of the histogram at graylevel 255 gives the percentage of the image that the object pixels occupy. For this example, about 25% of the image contains object pixels.

The concept of thresholding can be easily expanded to multilevel thresholding by a simple modification to Equation 19. For example, it is desired to threshold an image into four discrete graylevels using the three threshold values of T_1, T_2, and T_3. Equation 20 gives the graylevel transformation necessary to perform multilevel thresholding.

$$g(x, y) = \begin{cases} 255 & \text{if } f(x, y) > T_3 \\ 191 & \text{if } T_2 < f(x, y) \leq T_3 \\ 127 & \text{if } T_1 < f(x, y) \leq T_2 \\ 0 & \text{if } f(x, y) < T_1 \end{cases} \tag{20}$$

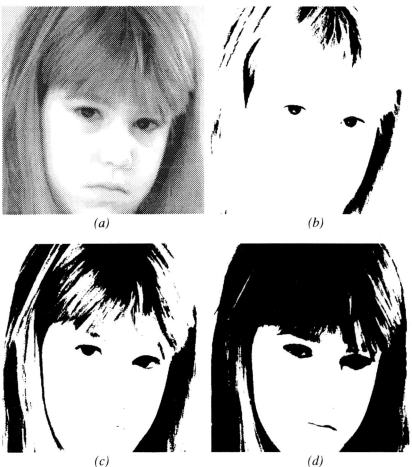

(a) (b)

(c) (d)

Figure 5.12 *Examples of thresholding an image with (a) original image, threshold values (T) of (b) 40, (c) 74, and (d) 105.*

The difficulty of performing thresholding on an image is the selection of the best threshold value(s). In Figure 5.11, if the threshold value were selected as 220 instead of 128, most of the object pixels would thresholded to 0, which is the same value as the background pixels. Several techniques exist in which the threshold values are chosen via some decision about the image. One of the more common adaptive thresholding techniques is that of optimum thresholding. Most of the techniques of adaptively choosing the threshold value are beyond the scope of this book, and the interested reader is referred to any of the more advanced image-processing books given in the annotated bibliography.

Figure 5.12 gives three examples of thresholding an image of a girl's face using threshold values of 40, 74, and 105. As the threshold value is increased from 40 to 105, more details can be seen in the binary image. The girl's eyes and some of the outline of the girl's face are visible using a threshold value of 40. For a threshold value of 74, the complete outline of the face is visible, along with details in the girl's hair. The features of the girl's mouth do not become apparent until a threshold value of 105 is selected.

The partial code to threshold a $512 \times 512 \times 256$ graylevel image into a binary image with graylevel values of 0 and 255 is given in Figure 5.13. The program assumes that the image is stored in array IMAGE[X][Y] and that the desired threshold value is passed to the program in variable THRES. On executing this program, the original graylevel image is replaced by its binary image. To change the output graylevel values from 0 and 255, the variables MINC and MAXC are changed to the desired graylevel values.

```c
Threshold(unsigned char IMAGE[][], int THRES)
    {
    int X,Y;
    int MAXC,MINC ;
    MAXC=255;
    MINC=0;
    for(Y=0; Y<=511; Y++){
        for(X=0; X<=511; X++) {
            if(IMAGE[X][Y]>THRES){
                IMAGE[X][Y]=MAXC;
                }
            else{
                IMAGE[X][Y]=MINC;
                }
            }
        }
    }
```

Figure 5.13 *Partial C code to threshold an image into two graylevel values.*

Chapter 6

Image Measurement

6.1 Introduction

An important aspect in the analysis of imagery is measurement operations. Whenever we are interested in the brightness value of a pixel or set of pixels, we may also be interested in the straight-line distance, in pixels, from one location in the image to another. Image measurement is important when the value of a pixel is related to a particular physical parameter, such as temperature in an infrared image. It also becomes critical when attempting to relate distance on the screen to distance in the real world. Pixels can then be related to distance measures such as millimeters or inches, and measures between screen pixels can relate measures in the scene from which the image was derived.

6.2 Pixel Value and Profiling

Getting a *pixel value* requires knowing the x and y coordinates of the pixel desired. In modern image-processing systems, this is generally done interactively using a mouse, trackball, or arrow keys. A small cursor or other marker is placed on the screen and the user changes its location while the computer outputs the coordinates of the pixel and brightness value. Systems that use a continuously active cursor may provide pixel value data whenever the cursor is within the image area of the screen. The computer code for a pixel value function simply outputs or returns the data value of the image array for any given pixel coordinate. The reverse operation, that of setting a pixel value, may be performed by changing the value of the image array at the given coordinates with a user-selected input.

Image profiling is the process by which a plot of the pixel intensities along a line between two pixels in an image is determined. Profiling is a useful image measure in that it can rapidly allow the user to visualize data changes along a single dimension in the image. An example of a profile plot is shown in Figure 6.1. The original image of computer keys, Figure 6.1a, has a horizontal line that has been selected using a mouse that cuts through the top of the delete, end and page down keys. This line is 340 pixels long and is plotted in Figure 6.1b. The vertical axis of this plot is intensity while the horizontal axis is position. Note that the profile shows the cross-sectional shape of the keys. The dip in intensity on the left side of the plot is where the profile crosses through the *l* in *del*. These plots are useful when attempting to establish parameters for recognition algorithms or when performing data analyses.

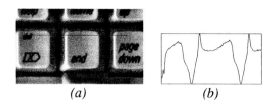
(a) *(b)*

Figure 6.1 *Profiling example: (a) Original; (b) Profile Plot.*

Evaluation of a profile that follows a row or column in an image is very straightforward for a computer routine. One simply selects the two points desired on either the row or column and outputs the pixel values between the points. The problems involved with this are selecting the points and displaying the output. It is beyond the scope of this text to illustrate data input techniques. Most often a program will display the image in question and then activate a routine to place a cursor under mouse or keyboard control. The user indicates the points desired by pressing a mouse button or key when the cursor is positioned. These points are then used as an index range for the image array output. If a diagonal profile is desired, the pixels are determined from the formula for the distance from a point to the line connecting the profile points. If this distance is less than 1, the pixel is considered to be on the line.

6.3 Cluster Analysis

Often a user requires a counting and labeling of objects within an image. If this process is performed automatically, it is called *cluster analysis*. Clusters consist of pixel groupings that are related to one another by a predetermined measure. This measure can be defined as a distance between clusters or a similarity measure such as pixel value, or it may be a complex set of identifiers or *features*. The study of feature analysis and the separation of data sets accordingly is a part of the field of study called *pattern recognition*. If the picture to be processed has been reduced to a binary image, a distance measure is always used.

The simplest automatic approach is to specify a size in pixels that the clusters should be. If we assume a binary image, the clustering algorithm processes each pixel and when one is found that is nonzero, it becomes part of the first cluster and is marked. The next nonzero pixel found is tested to see if the distance between it and the previous pixel is less than or equal to the desired cluster pixel size. If it is, it is marked as a member of the first cluster and the search continues. If it is not, it becomes the first member of the second cluster and is marked accordingly. This process continues until all pixels have been evaluated. The pixels in a binary image are easily marked by setting their pixel values to the cluster number. This procedure allows 254 clusters to be marked in an image where pixel values range from 0 to 255.

The aluster analysis function given on the following page performs the algorithm just described on a binary image.

```
                    /* Cluster Analysis Function */
cluster(){
     int n, i, j, k;

     /* initialize cluster count variable n */
     n=0;

     /* double-loop through each pixel of binary image */
     for(i=0; i < Number_of_Rows; ++i)
          for(j=0; j < Number_of_columns; ++j)
               if(n==0){
               /* only do for 1st cluster */
                    if(Image[i][j] !=0){
                         n=1;            /* 1st cluster found */
                         clustx[1] = j; /* store X coord. */
                         clusty[1] = i; /* store y coord. */

                         /* mark pixel as cluster 1 */
                         Image[i][j] = 1;
                    }
               }
               /* test for membership in all known clusters */
               else if(Image[i][j] != 0){
                    new_clust = 0  /* marker for new cluster */
                    /* compute Euclidean distance */
                    for(k = 1; k <= n; ++k){
                         edist =
                           SQRT((j-clustx[k])²+ (i-clusty[k])²);

                         /* test against cluster size desired */
                         if(edist <= clust_size){
                              /* set pixel to cluster number **/
                              Image[i][j] = k;
                              new_clust = 1;
                              k = n + 1;
                         }
                    }
                    /* add a new cluster */
                    if(new_clust == 0 AND n <= 255){
                         n = n + 1;
                         clustx[n] = x;
                         clusty[n] = y;
                         Image[i][j] = n;
                    }
               }
          }
     }
```

The following variables, with their descriptions, are used in the cluster analysis function.:

```
i,j,k                    Loop variables.
n                        Cluster count variable.
Image[][]                2-D array containing binary image.
Number_of_Rows           Rows in Image
Number_of_columns        Columns in Image
clustx[]                 Temporary storage for x-coordinate
                             of last pixel in cluster [].
clusty[]                 See clustx.
new_clust                Flag for new cluster.
edist                    Euclidean distance.
clust_size               Size of clusters to be found.
```

At the completion of the function, the `Image` array contains pixel values that reflect their membership in the clusters found that meet the criteria of being `clust_size` apart. Clusters of pixels that are larger than `clust_size` size will be partitioned into pieces as they are found in the image. This algorithm is considered primitive, yet it constitutes the basic form for a cluster-analysis program. After the clusters have been marked, measurements may be made on them using the methods to be described in Section 6.4.

6.4 Mensuration

Mensuration is the process where measurement data are calculated for image objects. The simplest measures calculated are geometric parameters. Figure 6.2 illustrates the more common geometric mensuration calculations performed on binary objects within an image. Area is simply the total number of pixels in the object. The height and width are determined from the widest vertical and horizontal dimensions, respectively. The perimeter is the number of pixels along the outer contour of the object. Height to width ratio yields a measure of Cartesian orientation. The height to width ratio along with the perimeter coordinate points can be used to determine a measure of circularity or ovality, that is, how closely the object perimeter is fit to a circle or ellipse.

The centroid of the object may be calculated using the centroid equation:

$$X_C = \frac{1}{A} \sum_{i=1}^{N} X \qquad\qquad Y_C = \frac{1}{A} \sum_{i=1}^{N} Y$$

where X_C and Y_C are the centroids, A is the area of the object, N is the number of pixels in the object, and X and Y are the coordinates of the ith pixel in the object.

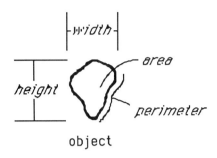

Figure 6.2 *Geometric measurement data.*

A graphic example of the centroid calculation is shown in Figure 6.3. The image consists of 26 × 26 binary pixels. The white object shown consists of 13 pixels, the A value for this example. The coordinates for the object pixels are (9, 4), (8, 5), (9, 5), (10, 5), (7, 6), (8, 6), (9, 6), (10, 6), (11, 6), (8, 7), (9, 7), (10, 7), and (9, 8). The sum of all X coordinates of the object pixels is 9 + 8 + 9 + 10 + 7 + 8 + 9 + 10 + 11 + 8 + 9 + 10 + 9=117 and the sum of all Y coordinates is 4 + 5 + 5 + 5 + 6 + 6 + 6 + 6 + 6 + 7 + 7 + 7 + 8=78. X_C is then 117/13, or 9 and Y_C is 78/13, or 6. These coordinates are indeed the center point of the object, as can be seen from the figure.

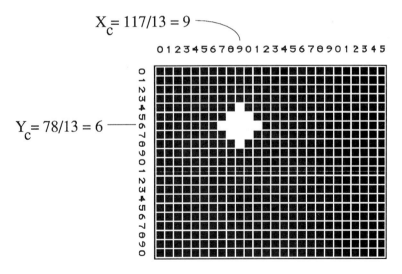

Figure 6.3 *Example of object centroid calculation.*

A C function to calculate the centroid of an isolated binary object in an image is given by:

```
centroid(float *Xc, *Yc){
   int area = 0, i,j;
   *Xc = 0.0;
   *Yc = 0.0;
   for(i = 0; i< Number_of_Columns; ++i)
      for(j = 0; j < Number_of_Rows; ++j)
         if(X[i][j] > 0){      /* test for object */
            /* accumulate X coordinates */
            *Xc = *Xc + i;
            /* accumulate Y coordinates */
            *Yc = *Yc + j;
            /* compute area */
            area = area + 1;
         }
   *Xc = *Xc/area;
   *Yc = *Yc/area;
}
```

If there are multiple objects in an image, a cluster analysis can be applied to separate and flag them. For example, to calculate the centroid of each cluster found using the program in Section 6.3, the following changes would be introduced to the test for the object line from the program above:

```
if(X[i][j] > 0)      /* test for object */
```

This line allows evaluation of the centroid for *any* nonzero object in the image X. We can change the line to test only for objects that are members of a particular cluster by adding the variable, *clust* to the line:

```
if(X[i][j] = clust )/* test for cluster */
```

The routine may now be called for all clusters found in the image by changing the value of the *clust* variable. After each call, the values of *Xc* and *Yc* contain the centroid of the *clust* cluster.

Chapter 7

Color

7.1 Introduction

A very powerful aspect of image processing is the use of color to represent the graylevel values of an image. In this way, certain attributes of an image can be easily visualized. The human eye is much more sensitive to color variations than to graylevel variations. For example, consider the arteries of a human's circulation system. Highlighting the graylevel variations in x-rays of the human circulation system can enhance the visual perception by doctors of various circulatory ailments. This procedure immediately locates and highlights blocked arteries for easy diagnostics. Another use of coloring graylevel images is in aerial photography. The highlighting of roads by colorization enables military analysts to easily locate roads on an aerial map.

The goal of this chapter is to introduce to the reader the color models that are used in color analysis within image processing. Next, these color models will be used to enhance graylevel images in a technique known as pseudocoloring. Finally, color displays and the concepts of palettes will be discussed. This chapter does not deal with color rendering of black and white photographs nor does it deal with color image processing of color images. These are beyond the goal of an introduction to color image processing. However some of the concepts presented here can be easily expanded to color image correction.

7.2 Color Models and Chromaticity

The analysis of color has been undertaken by many scientists and engineers for many years. In the seventeenth century, Sir Isaac Newton showed that a beam of sunlight passing through a glass prism emerged as a rainbow of colors. Newton concluded that white light was made from many different colors. In the late nineteenth century, Clerk E. Maxwell showed that a color image could be created using three color images. He proposed that three basic colors red (R), blue (B), and green (G), mixed in proportions, were all that were needed to create a color image. Maxwell exposed a prize ribbon to three black and white photographic film plates each with a red, blue and green optical filter placed in front of the film plates. Next, he developed and then imaged the three photographic plates on top of each other with the same red, blue, and green filters placed in front of each developed photographic plate. The resulting image was a color rendition of the ribbon. Today these three colors are known as the three primary colors.

In recent years, the visible spectrum observed by Newton and other scientists has been expanded to include x-rays, gamma rays and radio waves. Figure 7.1 shows a diagram of the magnetic spectrum including the visible color spectrum.

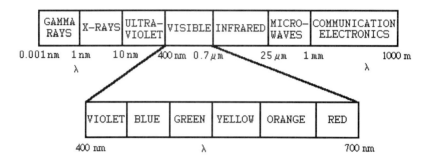

Figure 7.1 *A section of the electromagnetic spectrum.*

Scientists have shown that light can be modeled as an electromagnetic wave traveling at 3×10^8 meters per second (m/s) with a frequency, f, related to its wavelength, λ, by

$$f = \frac{3 \times 10^8 \text{ m/s}}{\lambda} \text{ ,} \tag{1}$$

where the wavelength, λ, is defined in meters. The visible spectrum is usually defined for wavelengths from approximately 400 nm or 0.4 µm to 700nm or 0.7 µm. For longer wavelengths, the visible spectrum is bounded by the infrared part of the spectrum and for shorter wavelengths it is bounded by the ultraviolet part of the spectrum. The visible color spectrum can be divided into six major color bands: violet, blue, green, yellow, orange and red. Table 7.1 shows approximate wavelengths in nanometers for each of the six major color regions given.

Table 7.1 *Approximate wavelengths for the six major color regions.*

Color	Wavelength
Violet	400 - 450 nm
Blue	450 - 480 nm
Green	480 - 550 nm
yellow	550 - 580 nm
Orange	580 - 610 nm
Red	610 - 700 nm

The infrared part of the spectrum has been of interest to researchers and scientists in recent years. A well-known scientist, Max Planck, showed that an object with a temperature, T, radiates a broad band of light energy. The peak wavelength of this light energy is given by

$$\lambda_p = \frac{2895}{T} \quad \text{in } \mu m, \tag{2}$$

where T is the object's temperature in Kelvin (°K) or 273 plus the object's temperature in centigrade (°C).

For a human body, which is at approximately 37°C, the peak radiation wavelength is computed to be 9.34 μm. Even though the human eye cannot respond to this wavelength, electrooptical imaging systems such as forward looking infrared receivers (FLIRS) can image these wavelengths. Hence, in complete darkness to the human eye (no visible light radiant), FLIRS image the temperature variations in the human body or other objects. This is how military pilots flying the latest in the state of the art aircraft can "see" at night.

Sometimes white light sources are referred to as being hotter than other white light sources, and a white light source that has a bluish tint is referred to as a hotter light source than a white light source with a reddish tint. A white light source with a bluish tint has more energy in the blue part of the spectrum than a white light source with a reddish tint. Since blue colors have a shorter wavelength than red colors, the result of solving Equation 2 for the object's temperature, T, yields that the temperature of a bluish tinted white light source is hotter than a reddish tinted white light source.

As stated earlier, the three primary colors of light are red, blue, and green, which are different than the three primary colors for paint. A primary color of light is defined as a color of light that is reflected or transmitted, whereas a primary color of paint is defined as a color that absorbs the primary color of light. The mixture of any two primary colors of light is referred to as a secondary color.

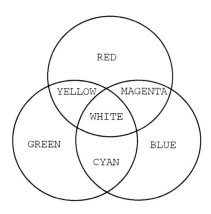

Figure 7.2 *Mixtures of the three primary colors of light.*

Figure 7.2 shows the three primary colors of light and their corresponding secondary colors. The overlapping circular regions represent the mixture of two primary light colors, producing a secondary light color. The three secondary light colors are yellow from the addition of green and red, cyan from the addition of green and blue, and magenta from the combination of red and blue. Mixing equal parts of all three primary colors of light yields white light as shown in the center region of Figure 7.2.

The three primary colors of light and their corresponding secondary colors must be differentiated from the three primary paint colors shown in Figure 7.3. For example, the color that absorbs white light is black. Hence, the center of the three primary colors given in Figure 7.3 is black. The color that absorbs the primary light color green is yellow, yielding a primary paint color of yellow. Color photography uses the primary paint colors in determining a color of a photographic print. This is what should be expected since a primary color on a photographic print is produced by the absorption, not the transmission or reflectance, of light.

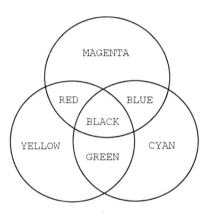

Figure 7.3 *Mixtures of the three primary colors of paint.*

An example of using the additive colors of light to produce a color image is a color television or computer monitor. A color television picture tube contains three different types of phosphorous materials that emit light when bombarded by a stream of electrons. The light colors emitted by the three different types of phosphors are red, blue, and green, the three primary colors of light. The television's picture tube contains three electron gun assemblies that control the electron beams bombarding the various color phosphors. The intensity of the electron beams, which is controlled by electronics driving the red, blue, and green electron guns, determines the intensity of the light emitted by the color phosphors. By modulating the three electron guns with a signal proportional to the desired amounts of red, blue, and green, any mixture of light colors is possible.

Three color characteristics are used to determine one color from another. The first is the *hue* of a color. The hue describes the actual wavelength of the color, for example, blue versus green. The second characteristic is the *saturation* of the color. This is a measure of how pure a color is. It indicates how much white light is added to a pure color. For example, the color red is a pure 100% saturated color, but the color pink is a very low saturated color because of the amount of white in the color. The last characteristic is the *brightness* of a color, which refers to the intensity of the color. The use of a color's hue and saturation is defined as the *chromaticity* of a color. Appendix B shows a picture of the standard CIE chromaticity diagram. The CIE chart is used to determine a color from its hue and saturation values. The percentage of red, blue, and green in a color is known as the color's *trichromatic coefficients*:

$$r = \frac{R}{R+B+G} \tag{3}$$

$$b = \frac{B}{R+B+G} \tag{4}$$

and

$$g = \frac{G}{R+B+G}, \tag{5}$$

where R, B, and G are the amount of red, blue, and green light, respectively. The trichromatic coefficients differ from the actual color intensity values R, B, and G in that the trichromatic coefficients have been normalized between 0 and 1. The sum of the three trichromatic coefficients yields

$$r + b + g = 1. \tag{6}$$

For example, if r = 100%, b = 0%, and g = 0% this color is pure red. On the other hand if r = 60%, b = 15%, and g= 25% then this color is no longer a pure color. To determine the percentage of white present in a color, start by locating the trichromatic coefficient with the lowest percentage value and subtract this value from the other two trichromatic coefficients. The remaining portion of these two trichromatic coefficients becomes the pure color and the common percentage becomes the white portion of the color. Looking at the previous trichromatic coefficients in more detail reveals that 15% of this color is composed of the color white with a pure color hue of 82% red and 18% green.

The trichromatic coefficients are computed from the CIE chart (Appendix B) from the color's hue and saturation. The x axis gives the red, r, while the y axis gives the green, g, trichromatic coefficients. The blue trichromatic coefficient, b, is then computed using Equation 6. For example, the point labelled red in the CIE chart with a wavelength of 625 nm has the following trichromatic coefficients: r = 71%, b = 0%, and g = 29%, yielding a color combination of 0% white and a saturated color hue of 71% red and 29% green.

In many instances a color is represented in terms of its hue (H), saturation (S), and intensity (I) which is called the HSI color model. The HSI color model is a very popular model in that it allows for the manipulation of a color's features in the same manner in which humans perceive color. Figure 7.4 shows the standard HSI triangle with the vertices of the triangle representing the three normalized primary colors (red, blue, green) as given by Equations 3 through 5. At the center of the triangle is the point of equal color, WHITE. At this point, all three of the normalized color components are equal to one-third. The HSI triangle does not give the intensity, I, of the color, but only defines a color's hue and saturation. A color's intensity is given by

$$I = \frac{1}{3}\{R + B + G\} \ . \tag{7}$$

A color's hue, θ, is defined as the angle between the location of a color within the HSI triangle to the line from WHITE to RED. Equation 8 defines a color's hue in terms of its normalized color components as

$$A = \left[\left(r - \frac{1}{3}\right)^2 + \left(b - \frac{1}{3}\right)^2 + \left(g - \frac{1}{3}\right)^2 \right]^{1/2}$$

$$B = \frac{2}{3}\left(r - \frac{1}{3}\right) - \frac{1}{3}\left(b - \frac{1}{3}\right) - \frac{1}{3}\left(g - \frac{1}{3}\right) \ ,$$

$$\theta = \arccos\left[\frac{B}{A\left(\frac{2}{3}\right)^{1/2}} \right]. \tag{8}$$

Whenever b > g, the hue angle, θ, will be greater than 180°. For this case, since the arccos is defined only over the range of 0 to 180°, θ is replaced by 360° – θ.

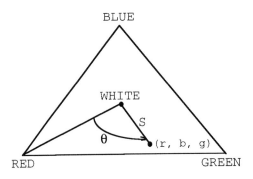

Figure 7.4 *The standard HSI color model triangle.*

A color's saturation is defined as how far the color is located from the center of the HSI triangle. Colors located at the outer edge of the triangle are fully saturated while pastel colors are located near the center of the triangle. The saturation, S, of a color is simply defined as 1 minus 3 times the minimum of the normalized red, blue, and green color components:

$$S = 1 - 3 \cdot \min(r, g, b) \,. \tag{9}$$

7.3 Pseudocolor and Falsecolor

To pseudocolor a graylevel image, the individual graylevels within the image must be mapped to a set of red, blue, and green colors. Fortunately, as will be shown later, many computer graphic display systems provide easy means of performing this mapping.

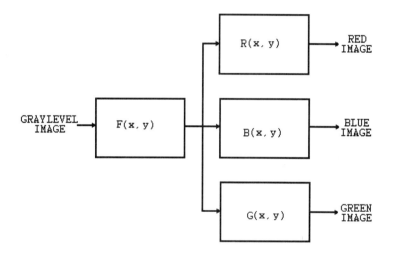

Figure 7.5 *A block diagram that implements pseudocoloring.*

Consider an image with N discrete graylevel values represented by the function F. An image can be considered as a collection of graylevel values given by the function F for all the pixels within the image. Next, this function, F, can be mapped to three functions R, B, and G that produce the output colors red, blue, and green. Figure 7.5 shows a block diagram that pseudocolors an image. The graylevel image F(x, y) is mapped to three images R(x, y), B(x, y) and G(x, y). Each of these images are then used to modulate the red, blue, and green guns of the imaging display's picture tube or CRT.

To display a graylevel image, the mapping functions, R, B, and G, contain the same identical mapping function given by the input graylevel values, F. The three mapping functions can also be used to control the brightness and contrast of the image by modifying all three mapping functions equally. For example, to reduce the contrast of an image R = B = G = 0.5F. The output intensity values of the three images are one half the graylevel values of the input image.

From Figure 7.5, to perform color image processing on color images, three separate images are needed: red, blue, and green. To use the many graylevel image-processing techniques discussed in this book on color images, all three images are processed equally as graylevel images. For example, to spatially filter an image using a mean or median filter, a mean or median filtering operation is performed on each color image separately. Histogram techniques, such as histogram equalization, can be applied to all three images. The example just cited does not limit color image processing to only graylevel operations. Additional algorithms exist that only apply directly to color image processing such as color equalization. Falsecoloring techniques are used to manipulate the colors of a color image, such as changing an image's hue or color saturation similarly to the tint and color controls on a color television.

The concepts used in chapter 5 to threshold an image can also be used to highlight individual graylevel values within an image. For example, to highlight a particular graylevel value T in red, the following equation can be used:

$$g(x, y) \ = \ \begin{cases} R = F: B = G = 0 & \text{for } F(x, y) = T \\ R = G = B = F & \text{elsewhere} \end{cases} \tag{10}$$

In Equation 10, for F(x, y) equal to the desired graylevel value T both the blue, and green images are set to zero or to a low intensity, and the red image is set to the input image's graylevel value. For all other graylevel values, the red, blue, and green images are set equal to the input image's graylevel values, producing a black and white image for these input graylevel values. Equation 10 can be modified for any color desired by simply modifying the three mapping functions. For example, to highlight the graylevel value T in pink,

$$g(x, y) \ = \ \begin{cases} R = F: B = G = 0.2F & \text{for } F(x, y) = T \\ R = G = B = F & \text{elsewhere} \end{cases} \ . \tag{11}$$

The amount of pink is determined by the amount of the input image's graylevel values mapped to the blue and green color images.

Sometimes it is desired to represent graylevel intensities by color wavelengths of the visible part of the spectrum. For example, low graylevel values are represented by blue and high graylevel values as represented by red. As the graylevel values increase from low to high values, this mapping produces colors varying from blue to red. For a 256 graylevel image, the following mapping can be used to implement the transformation that goes from blue white to red.

R = 0,	G = 254 − 4·F,	B = 255,	for 0 ≤ F < 63
R = 0,	G = 4·F − 254,	B = 510 − 4·F,	for 64 ≤ F < 127
R = 4·F − 510,	G = 255 ,	B = 0,	for 128 ≤ F < 191
R = 255,	G = 1022 − 4·F,	B = 0,	for 192 ≤ F < 255 (12)

The 255 graylevel values of the input image F(x,y) have been divided into four equal regions of 64 graylevels. At the beginning of the first region, $0 \leq F < 63$, both green and blue are the dominant colors; but by the start of the second region, $64 \leq F < 127$, blue is now the dominant color. At the start of the third region, $128 \leq F < 191$, green is the dominant color, changing to yellow by the start of the fourth region, for $192 \leq F < 255$. By the end of the fourth region, red is now the dominant color.

Another way of pseudocoloring an image is to highlight an image's edges in color. To implement this pseudocolor mapping, an edge detector is applied to an image. Next, all pixels that are part of the detected edges are flagged. Finally, these pixels graylevel values are mapped to the desired color.

Figure 7.6 gives the partial code to implement an edge-detector pseudocolor mapping on a 512×512 graylevel image stored in the two-dimensional array IMAGE[X][Y]. This program requires a huge amount of storage in that three color images of 262,144-element size are needed to store each color image. The program uses the Sobel edge detector for the detection of edges within the image. After execution of the program, the output color images can then be used to drive a color display.

The program first initializes the two mask arrays, mask1[x1][y1] and mask2[x1][y1], to the coefficient used by the Sobel edge detector. Next, the program computes the gradients in the x and y directions within the image and absolute sums the two together to produce a total gradient stored in variable, EDGE. Finally, the program compares the calculated edge value against a threshold value passed to the program in variable T. If the edge value is greater than the selected threshold value, an edge is determined and the pseudocolor mapping sets the red image to full intensity and the blue and green images to zero intensity resulting in the edge being displayed in the color red. If an edge is not detected, all three colored images are set to the input image.

7.4 Color Displays and Palettes

Figure 7.7 shows the difference between three common types of display systems presently in use. The dimensions given in Figure 7.7 of the image storage memory are for explanation purposes only. Many other display systems are available with higher pixel resolution and more graylevel values. Figure 7.7a shows a 512×512 pixel black and white display system with 256 different graylevel values. This display system is sometimes referred to as an RS-170 display system. The system contains 262,144 bytes of digital memory that store the image to be displayed. The output of the display memory drives a digital-to-analog converter that produces an analog voltage compatible with the black and white display.

A pseudocolor display system is shown in Figure 7.7b. This imaging system has only one image storage area of size 512×512 pixels by 256 graylevels, requiring 262,144 bytes of memory. The output of the image memory is mapped through three Look-Up-Tables (LUTs) of 8 bits each. The LUTs are used to map each of the 256 graylevel values to the colors red, blue, and green. The output of the LUTs drives three digital-to-analog converters that become the red, blue, and green inputs to the color display.

```
Pseudo_edge(unsigned char IMAGE[][],int RED[][],int
BLUE[][],int GREEN[][],int T)
    {
    int X,Y, x1, y1, mask1[3][3], mask2[3][3];
    int GX, GY, EDGE;
    mask1[1][1]=-1; mask1[2][1]=-2; mask1[3][1]=-1;
    mask1[1][2]= 0; mask1[2][2]= 0; mask1[3][2]= 0;
    mask1[1][3]= 1; mask1[2][3]= 2; mask1[3][3]= 1;
    mask2[1][1]=-1; mask2[2][1]= 0; mask2[3][1]= 1;
    mask2[1][2]=-2; mask2[2][2]= 0; mask2[3][2]= 2;
    mask2[1][3]=-1; mask2[2][3]= 0; mask2[3][3]= 1;
    for(Y=1; Y<=510; Y++){
        for(X=1; X<=510; X++) { GX=0; GY=0;
            for(y1=-1; y1<=1; y1++){
                for(x1=-1;  x1<=1; x1++){
    r       GY += mask1[x1+2][y1+2]*IMAGE[X+x1][Y+y1];
            GX += mask2[x1+2][y1+2]*IMAGE[X+x1][Y+y1];
                }
            }
                EDGE=abs[GX]+abs[GY];
            if (EDGE  > T){
    RED[X][Y]=255; BLUE[X][Y]=0; GREEN[X][Y]=0;
            }
            else{
                RED[X][Y]=IMAGE[X][Y];
                BLUE[X][Y]=IMAGE[X][Y];
                GREEN[X][Y]=IMAGE[X][Y];
                }
            }
        }
    }
```

Figure 7.6 *Partial C code to implement pseudocolored edges within an image.*

The LUTs presented in Figure 7.7b are implemented using three 256 bytes by 8 bits digital read/write memory devices. This memory is used to hold the mapping coefficients for the three primary light colors. For example, if a red image is desired, the bits controlling the blue and green colors are set to zero in the blue and green LUTs. The bits controlling the red color are set equal to the input image's graylevel values in the red LUT.

A pseudocolor display is not a true-color display system. It gives the user the capability of choosing a subset of colors from a huge assortment of colors. For the system shown in Figure 7.7b, 16 million possible color combinations can be created via the LUTs. Color images that are limited to only 256 colors can be displayed with this system. Techniques exist that compress the colors of images to 256 total colors so that they may be displayed using a pseudocolor system.

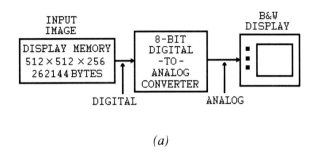

(a)

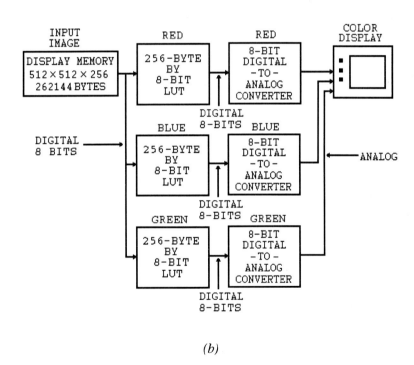

(b)

Figure 7.7 *Examples of common imaging systems: (a) black and white display system (b) pseudocolor display system; (c) true-color display system.*

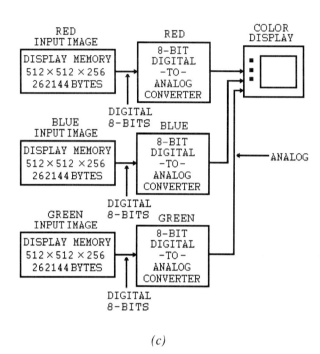

(c)

Figure 7.7 *continued*

Since only 256 graylevel values are able to be displayed at any one time, only 256 colors out of the 16 million colors can be seen at any one time on the display monitor. The possible colors that can be created are referred to as the *color palette* of the display system. This name comes about from the similarity between the choice of colors via the LUTs and that of a painter's color paint palette. LUTs are commonly referred to as the *color palette table*. Of the three types of display systems presented in Figure 7.7, the pseudocolor display system is the most common display system presently available in image-processing systems and most low-end computer graphic systems. The VGA graphics display card used in many MS-DOS compatible computers uses the same approach as Figure 7.7b except the output of the LUTs is 6-bits instead of 8 bits and the digital-to-analog converters are 6-bit devices. This limits the choice of possible colors to 262,144, with only 256 of these colors being displayed at any one time.

The Figure 7.7c is the block diagram for a true-color display system. What separates a true-color display system from a pseudocolor display system is that there are three input image memories, one for each primary color. Each image memory contains the appropriate color intensity value for each of the three primary colors for every pixel within the image. In this way, true-color viewing of a color image is possible. For the block diagram in Figure 7.7c, each color image pixel can have one out of 16 million possible colors. With computer memory devices becoming cheaper, more imaging systems are becoming available that support true-color capability which is also known as a 24-bit color system.

Chapter 8

Spatial Filters

8.1 Introduction

Spatial filters are basically *discrete convolution* filters, or filters that convolve one image with another. The filter image is typically very small with respect to the target image and is called a *convolution mask* (see Section 8.2). The simplest definition for convolution without resorting to complex mathematical constructs is that it is an operation that copies one image at each pixel location of another while allowing for the effects of all pixel values in the area where the copy takes place. This is accomplished by a multiplying, adding, and shifting operation, hence the term *convolve*, which means to roll, twist, or coil together. Convolution can occur when signals, such as images, are modified by optical, electronic, or nervous systems. The modification of signals in this way yields desirable results when the outcome extracts information that would not be obtainable otherwise, such as in an edge-detection process. Undesirable results occur when a signal is distorted by a defocused lens, and this too is a convolution process.

Convolution is a reversible process, and this chapter explores how it can be used to enhance images by extracting or improving information indicators such as edges, remove noise from images, and mitigate the effects of undesirable distortions. The importance of discrete convolution cannot be underestimated as it is a process that lends itself to high speed computation with parallel processors. Convolution allows a large ensemble of processes to be performed simply and efficiently with spatial filters. As a final note, convolution must be distinguished from *correlation*, which is a comparison operation using the same multiplying, adding, and shifting processes as convolution. The difference is that convolution involves signals that have been reversed in time, and the distinction is only important when considering time-varying signals, or images as time-varying signals, which we will not do.

Spatial filters incorporate *local*, or *neighborhood*, operations on pixels. In other words, the computations affecting a particular pixel in an image involve the value of that pixel and its neighboring pixels and not pixels elsewhere in the image. This is in contrast to the filters based on spatial frequency (Chapter 10). Spatial frequency is a global property of an image, so the values of all pixels are incorporated in each computation on a single pixel value. It will be shown how the computations for a wide variety of very effective and interesting filter operations are accomplished with nothing more than a simple loop and an arithmetic sum of products operation.

8.2 Convolution Masks

Consider two sets of numbers, the first set has only one element and can be written as {3}. The second set has seven elements and is written as {0, 1, 2, 3, 2, 1, 0}. If we multiply the elements of the second set with that of the first set, we get {0, 3, 6, 9, 6, 3, 0}. This procedure is defined as vector multiplication by a scalar and you may recall it in a different form from Section 3.4. Now modify the first set and add two more elements to get {1, 3, 1}. If we now try to multiply the second set by the first, we encounter a dilemma. Do we perform the multiplication so that the result increases in dimension, such as {0, 0, 0, 1, 3, 1, 3, 6, 3, ...} or do we select one of the three elements of the first set as a multiplier? Assume that we do not wish to expand the dimension of the result, yet we want to include all values of the multiplier. A solution might be to align the two sets, multiply the corresponding elements, add the results, and use the sum as the new value at the aligned position. Then the aligned position is changed by shifting the multiplier to the right and performing the process of multiplying and adding at the new position. If this approach is taken, a simple example will suffice to show how the process works.

In the following sequence of seven tables, the first row, A, of each table contains the large set, {0, 1, 2, 3, 2, 1, 0} while the second row, B, contains the small one, {1, 3, 1}. Each table in the sequence shows the small set at a different position as it is shifted with respect to the large set. The third row, A*B, shows the discrete convolution, which is the result of multiplying each element of the small set with its corresponding element in the large set, adding the three values, and placing the sum at the aligned position, the center of the B set.

1. Center value of B set aligned to first value of A set. Convolution result A*B is 1, placed at position corresponding to center of B set, missing values assumed to be zero.

A		0	1	2	3	2	1	0	
B	1	3	1						
A*B		1							

2. Set B shifted by one position. Convolution result A*B is $(0 \times 1) + (1 \times 3) + (2*1) = 5$.

A		0	1	2	3	2	1	0	
B		1	3	1					
A*B		1	5						

3. Set B shifted by one position. Convolution result A*B is $(1 \times 1) + (2 \times 3) + (3*1) = 10$.

A		0	1	2	3	2	1	0	
B			1	3	1				
A*B		1	5	10					

4. Set B shifted by one position. Convolution result A*B is $(1 \times 2) + (3 \times 3) + (2*1) = 13$.

A		0	1	2	3	2	1	0	
B				1	3	1			
A*B		1	5	10	13				

5. Set B shifted by one position. Convolution result A*B is $(3 \times 1) + (2 \times 3) + (1*1) = 10$.

A		0	1	2	3	2	1	0	
B					1	3	1		
A*B		1	5	10	13	10			

6. Set B shifted by one position. Convolution result A*B is $(2 \times 1) + (1 \times 3) + (0*1) = 5$.

A		0	1	2	3	2	1	0	
B						1	3	1	
A*B		1	5	10	13	10	5		

7. Set B shifted by one position. Convolution result A*B is $(1 \times 1) + (0 \times 3) + (0*1) = 1$ (Missing values assumed to be zero)

A		0	1	2	3	2	1	0	
B							1	3	1
A*B		1	5	10	13	10	5	1	

7 reveals the final result of the discrete convolution operation, the set {1, 4, 8, 10, 8, 4, 1}. The importance of this result is the difference between the convolved result, A*B, and the large set, A. The peak at the center of the data has become steeper. This is more obvious if we plot the set data, as is shown in Figure 8.1.

The small set is called a *convolution mask* because it is passed over a set of data and effects a change. Other terms used are template, window and filter. *Template* refers to the fact that the result will have a large value at the position where the mask and the data set are equal. *Window* describes the action of the mask as a passage that takes a data set from one set of values to another, and *filter* describes the action of various masks (as we will see later) that restrict or remove data of a specific shape or value.

The values of the convolution mask are not restricted to positive values, if the mask had been {-1, 3, -1} the result shown in Figure 8.2 would have been obtained. Now the mask has left the original signal intact except in the region of the peak value, where it has exaggerated it.

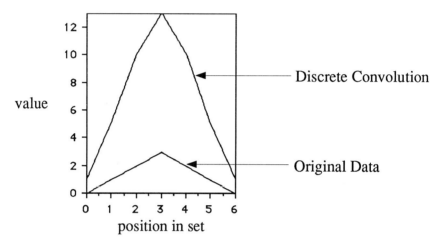

Figure 8.1 *Plot of original data set and convolution with {1, 3, 1}.*

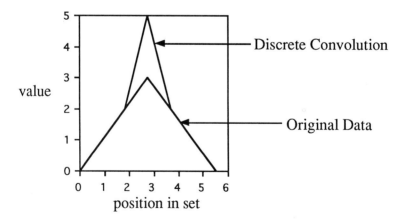

Figure 8.2 *Plot of original data set and convolution with {-1,3,-1}.*

The transition from a single-dimensional set to a two-dimensional set is straightforward. Consider the following matrices:

$$
\begin{bmatrix}
5 & 8 & 3 & 4 & 6 & 2 & 3 & 7 \\
3 & 2 & 1 & 1 & 9 & 5 & 1 & 0 \\
0 & 9 & 5 & 3 & 0 & 4 & 8 & 3 \\
4 & 2 & 7 & 2 & 1 & 9 & 0 & 6 \\
9 & 7 & 9 & 8 & 0 & 4 & 2 & 4 \\
5 & 2 & 1 & 8 & 4 & 1 & 0 & 9 \\
1 & 8 & 5 & 4 & 9 & 2 & 3 & 8 \\
3 & 7 & 1 & 2 & 3 & 4 & 4 & 6
\end{bmatrix}
\qquad
\begin{bmatrix}
-2 & -1 & 0 \\
-1 & 0 & +1 \\
0 & +1 & +2
\end{bmatrix}
$$

The 8 by 8 matrix on the left will be considered the image and the small 3 by 3 matrix on the right the convolution mask. With the single dimensional sets, the mask set was overlaid onto the larger set, the corresponding values in each set were multiplied together, and the products were summed and used as the value for the convolution at the set position corresponding to the center value of the mask. Recall that the convolution result was the same size as the large set. This will also be the case for the two-dimensional process. Figure 8.3 illustrates this overlay process with grids. By convention, the convolution usually starts in the upper-left corner of the image where the center value of the small grid (the mask) will multiply the first value of the large grid (the image). The mask elements that overhang the image will multiply zero; however, we can also wrap the mask around to the other side and perform what is known as a circular convolution. For the purposes of this book, circular convolutions will not be performed. The remaining values of the mask multiply their corresponding values in the image, and the products are summed. The result is then placed in the convolution image at the upper-left position, as shown in Figure 8.4 using the matrix values given earlier.

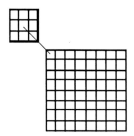

Figure 8.3 *Convolution mask applied to image.*

Subsequent operations require that the mask be shifted one position to the right until all values of the first row of the convolution result have been determined. The mask is then moved to the first value of the second row, and the process is repeated until all rows and columns of the convolution are computed. Note that this mask has negative values in it and is negative symmetric about the right diagonal axis. This mask performs a shadow operation when convolved with an image because it increases the brightness values across one side of a three-pixel band and decreases values along the other side. The orientation is diagonally across the image, giving a shadow effect. The convolution of this mask with an image of a lens cap is shown in Figure 8.5. The effect of the shadow mask is seen as an exaggeration of the three dimensional features of the cap.

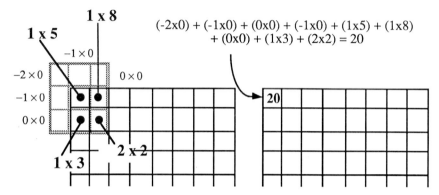

Figure 8.4 *First value computed in convolution of data sets.*

Figure 8.5 *Original image on left, image convolved with shadow mask on right.*

Convolution of images is not restricted to 3×3 masks. Since convolution is a local operation in which computations that affect pixel relationships in the image are confined to the mask size, the overall effect of the convolution is independent of mask size as long as masks are small. Also, convolution operations are easily performed using parallel processing techniques, and this approach is severely degraded when mask size approaches the image size. Programming the discrete convolution is relatively easy, the most difficult part is keeping track of the indexes. Figure 8.6 shows the relationship of column (**i**) pixels and row (**j**) pixels in a three by three image region for a given center value at coordinate (**i, j**).

[0][0] i−1, j−1	[0,1] i−1, j	[0][2] i−1, j+1
[1][0] i, j−1	[1][1] i, j	[1][2] i, j+1
[2][0] i+1, j−1	[2][1] i+1, j	[2][2] i+1, j+1

Figure 8.6 *Index relationships in a 3 × 3 image region.*

A C program segment to compute a simple discrete convolution is given next. It convolves a 3 × 3 mask with an M × M image to give an M × M convolved result. The evaluation of the convolution ignores a single pixel edge around the image to avoid an error by trying to access a negative array index.

```
for(i = 1; i < M-2; ++i)
   for(j = 1; j < M-2; ++j)
      Result[i][j] = Image[i-1][j-1] * mask[0][0] +
                     Image[i-1][j+1] * mask[0][1] +
                     Image[i-1][j]   * mask[0][2] +
                     Image[i][j-1]   * mask[1][0] +
                     Image[i][j]     * mask[1][1] +
                     Image[i][j+1]   * mask[1][2] +
                     Image[i+1][j-1] * mask[2][0] +
                     Image[i+1][j]   * mask[2][1] +
                     Image[i+1][j+1] * mask[2][2];
```

This program may be easily modified to accommodate larger masks. To do this, the mask array would be increased in dimension and the necessary multiplications added to the inner loop. To avoid negative index problems, the loop ranges would also have to be changed. In this example, a single pixel edge around the image is left out of the convolution computation, if our mask increased in size to 5 × 5, we would incur a two-pixel edge loss, and so on, as the size of the mask was increased. It is a convenience to make the dimensions of the mask odd so that the mask always has a center pixel. This is not required because masks with even dimensions may be computed by selecting a pixel position in the mask to serve as the compute point. This issue gains significance when discussing discrete convolution in a signal processing or optics-sense, where physical systems are most often modeled with a symmetric point spread distribution.

A final consideration in the computation of convolution masks is the scaling of data. The data value computed by a mask may exceed the maximum value of a pixel, which is normally

255. The image data structure used to store the convolution (Result[i][j] in the program above) must accommodate the maximum possible value or arithmetic overflow will result. A simple alternative is to compute the value of the convolution and truncate it to 255. Also, computations involving the high-pass filters will often result in negative values. If a byte-sized variable (such as is often used for image data structures) is set equal to a negative result, the final pixel value will be incorrect. The simple alternative here is to set all negative results equal to zero. These simple solutions may eliminate important results from many images by destroying the dynamic range of the computation. It is recommended that a scaling operation be applied to the final image. Scaling techniques are discussed in Section 5.3 and in Appendix A.

8.3 Edge-detection Filters

Edge detection is an important initial step in many computer vision processes because edges contain the bulk of information within an image. Edges are comprised of high-spatial -frequency information and so filters that detect edges are also high-pass filters. Consider the image of a white square on a black background shown in Figure 8.7a. If we plot the profile of intensities horizontally across the center of this picture, we obtain a plot such as that shown in 8.7b. Moving from left to right along the x axis of this plot takes us through the sharp transition from black to white at the edge of the square, across the top of the square, and then down the far side in another sharp transition, this time from white to black. Note the use of the term sharp. This word implies high frequency when we compare the terminology to that used in sound (or music) processing. Sound is nothing more than a single-dimensional signal, much like the profile plot given through the center of our picture. If our goal is to detect the vertical edge on the left side of the square, we can accomplish this using a high-frequency spatial convolution mask such as that given in Figure 8.8. In regions of the image that contain identical pixel values, the sum of products will equal zero so that all *homogeneous* image regions will be removed. As the mask is processed over the image, when pixel values transition from low to high (as with a left vertical edge), the convolution will output its maximum value. The highest values in the result image will be given to the left-sided edges.

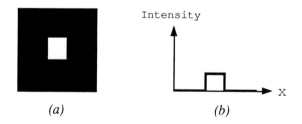

(a)   *(b)*

Figure 8.7 *(a) Image of white square on black. (b) Center profile plot.*

$$
\begin{array}{ccc}
-1 & 0 & +1 \\
-2 & 0 & +2 \\
-1 & 0 & +1
\end{array}
$$

Figure 8.8 *Left vertical edge detector mask..*

An example of this filter applied to an image is shown in Figure 8.9. The areas of the image that decrease in intensity toward the right in the original Figure 8.9a are darkened, while those edges that increase towards the left have increased in intensity Figure 8.9b. If the filter is flipped vertically so that the values in the first column are positive while those in the third become negative, then the filter will favor edges increasing from the right, as seen in Figure 8.9c. Clearly, these masks are directional in nature. It is not hard to visualize similar masks for top, bottom, left and right diagonal edges. The mask given is more commonly known as one of the *Sobel* masks, which are distinguished by the values 1, 2, and 3.

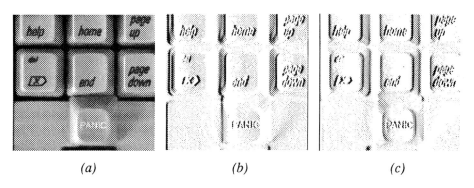

| (a) | (b) | (c) |

Figure 8.9 *(a) Original Image, (b) Left (c) Right*

We can combine the value computed from the mask in Figure 8.7 with its horizontal counterpart using the formula

$$
S = \sqrt{V^2 + H^2},
$$

where S is the edge strength, V is the vertical convolution value, and H is the horizontal value. Figure 8.10 shows the result of this processing applied to the image of Figure 8.9a. These computations are possible because the operator pair yields a pair of values that constitutes a *vector*, or multidimensional element. The formula for S is the standard form for determining the magnitude of a vector, which we have called the *edge strength*.

A vector also has a direction, and in this case, the direction of the edge is computed using the formula

$$
D = \tan^{-1}\left(\frac{V}{H}\right)
$$

where D is the edge direction in *radians*, and V and H are the convolution values. The image computed by using this formula is not useful in a direct observation sense. This is because each pixel value represents an angle, not an intensity. The image is useful in machine vision processes that seek to compile as much information as possible about a scene. Edge direction may be used to confirm edge linking operations or be included in feature analysis.

Figure 8.10 *Sobel edge detector.*

An edge operator that is nondirectional, or rotationally insensitive, is the *Laplacian*. A Laplacian mask is basically a second-derivative operator or an operator that computes the rate of change of an edge as it varies in intensity across the image. The Sobel is a first-derivative operator that computes the rate of change of an edge, or the gradient. Although the Laplacian is nondirectional, it is highly susceptible to noise. Figure 8.11 shows the effects of the three Laplacian masks given in Figure 8.12 as applied to the image in Figure 8.9a.

```
                                     -1 -1 -1 -1 -1 -1 -1 -1 -1
                                     -1 -1 -1 -1 -1 -1 -1 -1 -1
                                     -1 -1 -1 -1 -1 -1 -1 -1 -1
                                     -1 -1 -1  8  8  8 -1 -1 -1
                  -1 -1 -1 -1 -1      -1 -1 -1  8  8  8 -1 -1 -1
                  -1 -1 -1 -1 -1      -1 -1 -1  8  8  8 -1 -1 -1
   0 -1  0        -1 -1 24 -1 -1      -1 -1 -1 -1 -1 -1 -1 -1 -1
  -1  4 -1        -1 -1 -1 -1 -1      -1 -1 -1 -1 -1 -1 -1 -1 -1
   0 -1  0        -1 -1 -1 -1 -1      -1 -1 -1 -1 -1 -1 -1 -1 -1
     (a)               (b)                     (c)
```

Figure 8.11 *Laplacian Masks (a) 3×3 (b) 5×5 (c) 9×9.*

To summarize, edge-detection filters are high-pass filters with the edges in an image representing the high spatial frequencies. These filters are also called sharpening filters as they improve the presence of lines. Another term used is edge-enhancement filters. The distinction between edge enhancement and edge detection is determined from the purpose for which the filter is employed. If the filter is used to improve edges for human evaluation, then that is enhancement. If the filtering is used as a preprocess to a machine vision system, then that usage is detection. These filters are characterized by negative values in the mask that compute the difference between pixel values as the convolution takes place. Hence, the derivative, or gradient, which is rate of change, is computed.

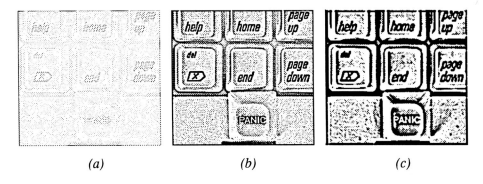

(a)   *(b)*   *(c)*

Figure 8.12 *Effects of Laplacian Masks (a) 3×3 (b) 5×5 (c) 9×9.*

8.4 Mean and Median Filters

A *mean* spatial filter is one that replaces a pixel value with the average (or mean) value of the pixels in a given neighborhood. The median filter replaces the pixel with the median or middle value of its neighborhood. The mean filter is easily implemented with the masks shown in Figure 8.13.

$$\begin{bmatrix} \frac{1}{9} & \frac{1}{9} & \frac{1}{9} \\ \frac{1}{9} & \frac{1}{9} & \frac{1}{9} \\ \frac{1}{9} & \frac{1}{9} & \frac{1}{9} \end{bmatrix} \qquad \begin{bmatrix} \frac{1}{25} & \frac{1}{25} & \frac{1}{25} & \frac{1}{25} & \frac{1}{25} \\ \frac{1}{25} & \frac{1}{25} & \frac{1}{25} & \frac{1}{25} & \frac{1}{25} \\ \frac{1}{25} & \frac{1}{25} & \frac{1}{25} & \frac{1}{25} & \frac{1}{25} \\ \frac{1}{25} & \frac{1}{25} & \frac{1}{25} & \frac{1}{25} & \frac{1}{25} \\ \frac{1}{25} & \frac{1}{25} & \frac{1}{25} & \frac{1}{25} & \frac{1}{25} \end{bmatrix}$$

Figure 8.13 *Mean spatial filter masks.*

As an example, consider the following pixel neighborhood:

$$\begin{matrix} 7 & 7 & 7 \\ 7 & 16 & 7 \\ 7 & 7 & 7 \end{matrix}$$

The result of using the 3×3 mask from Figure 8.13 in the discrete convolution program given earlier would be the same as computing

$$(\frac{1}{9} \times 7 + \frac{1}{9} \times 7 + \frac{1}{9} \times 7 + \frac{1}{9} \times 7 + \frac{1}{9} \times 16 + \frac{1}{9} \times 7 + \frac{1}{9} \times 7 + \frac{1}{9} \times 7 + \frac{1}{9} \times 7) = 8.$$

This result, 8, is the average of the pixel values in the neighborhood. The overall effect of this filter is to smooth the image by reducing pixel values, that is, image intensities in areas where a difference in values exists. This has the opposite effect of the edge-detection filters, where the goal of the filter is to accentuate differences. For this reason, the mean filter is a low-pass filter. This filter does not disturb regions where pixels are identical or close in value. Recall that the edge-detection filters replaced these regions with zero. Figure 8.14 shows the effect of the masks given in Figure 8.13. Note that the lettering in the image of Figure 8.14a becomes increasingly blurred as the mean filter becomes larger. The graphics, however, are relatively unaffected because they contain large expanses of similar pixel values.

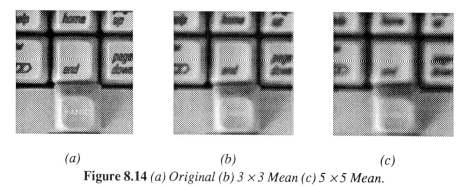

        (a)   *(b)*   *(c)*
Figure 8.14 *(a) Original (b) 3 × 3 Mean (c) 5 × 5 Mean.*

The *median* spatial filter cannot be computed from a convolution mask, but, rather, the pixels within the neighborhood must be sorted in intensity value and the middle, or median, selected.

In the example neighborhood from before,

$$\begin{array}{ccc} 7 & 7 & 7 \\ 7 & 16 & 7 \\ 7 & 7 & 7 \end{array}$$

the median value is 7. We can convert the neighborhood into a set of numbers, moving from the top left to the bottom right and get $\{7, 7, 7, 7, 16, 7, 7, 7, 7\}$. Now, order the set by increasing value and get $\{7, 7, 7, 7, 7, 7, 7, 7, 7,16\}$. The middle value is 7. The median filter is very effective in removing pixel values that are greatly different from the rest of the neighborhood, as shown in this example. Where the mean simply attenuated the center pixel from 16 to 14, the median removed it and replaced it with a value closer to that of the neighborhood. Figure 8.15 shows the effects of a median filter. The median shows much less smoothing on the lettering than the mean. When the filter mask is over an edge, the filter selects the middle value and that value must be either one side of the edge or the other. In the case of the mean, the edge is smoothed and consequently blurred.

(a)   *(b)*   *(c)*

Figure 8.15*(a) Original (b) 3 × 3 Median (c) 5 × 5 Median.*

8.5 Enhancement Filters

The term *enhancement* refers to the improving of an image based on some subjective criterion that is typically determined by human observers. This is in contrast to the term *restoration*, which is the recovery of image data based on an objective criterion that is evaluated against a known or estimated degradation function. Spatial enhancement filters may be categorized as either sharpening filters to remove blurs or smoothing filters to remove noise. The previous two sections discussed examples of both types: the edge detectors work to sharpen images and the mean and median filters have a blurring effect. Sharpening masks are high-pass filters and smoothing masks are low-pass filters. We can now state two very simple rules to follow when generating sharpening and smoothing filter masks:

- Masks whose values are all positive and whose sum is equal to 1 will have a *smoothing* effect on pixel intensities.

- Masks whose values include negative numbers and whose sum is equal to 0 will have a *sharpening* effect on pixel intensities.

This can be visualized using the plots shown in Figure 8.16. The first indicates a function with very sharp peaks, the slopes of the various peaks are steep. The second plot is the smoothed version of the first, its slopes are less steep and the peaks have been rounded. The final plot shows the differences between the first two, that is, how data have been added in the smoothing process or removed in the sharpening process.

Two factors will affect the application of these rules. The first is the selection of the mask values. The larger the values, the more effect the mask will have on the overall contrast of the image. The second consideration is the size of the mask. As mask size increases, the localized effect will broaden so that pixels farther away from the center pixel will contribute to the filter. This effect was readily seen in Figure 8.13, where the 5×5 mean filter introduced a substantial amount of blurring with respect to the 3×3 mean. Figure 8.17 shows a set of four enhancement masks that conform to the rules given above (the smoothing masks are scaled by the sum of their elements), and their effects on an image is shown in Figure 8.18.

Figure 8.16 *Sharpening and smoothing example.*

$$\begin{bmatrix} 1 & 2 & 1 \\ 2 & 4 & 2 \\ 1 & 2 & 1 \end{bmatrix} \qquad \begin{bmatrix} 1 & 1 & 1 & 1 & 1 \\ 1 & 4 & 4 & 4 & 1 \\ 1 & 4 & 12 & 4 & 1 \\ 1 & 4 & 4 & 4 & 1 \\ 1 & 1 & 1 & 1 & 1 \end{bmatrix} \qquad \begin{bmatrix} -1 & -1 & -1 \\ -1 & 9 & -1 \\ -1 & -1 & -1 \end{bmatrix} \qquad \begin{bmatrix} 0 & -1 & 1 & -1 & 0 \\ -1 & 2 & -4 & 2 & -1 \\ -1 & -4 & 13 & -4 & -1 \\ -1 & 2 & -4 & 2 & -1 \\ 0 & -1 & 1 & -1 & 0 \end{bmatrix}$$

(a) $\qquad\qquad$ (b) $\qquad\qquad$ (c) $\qquad\qquad$ (d)

Figure 8.17 *Enhancement masks (a) 3×3 smooth (b) 5×5 smooth (c) 3×3 sharpen (d) 5×5 sharpen.*

The smoothing masks yield a soft blurring of the image, while the sharpening masks enhance the lines and edges. This is most clear in the area of the lettering. The sharpening filters are useful for clarifying fine detail in a corrupted or blurred picture. The smoothing filters are used when an image contains noise. Most noises appear as single pixel spots on the picture that can either be smoothed out or, in some cases, eliminated altogether. The choice of an adequate enhancement mask is generally through experience and trial and error. Appendix D may be useful in your choice of a mask for a particular enhancement problem.

3 x 3 smooth

5 x 5 smooth

3 x 3 sharpen

5 x 5 sharpen

Figure 8.18 *Effects of masks from Figure 8.17.*

Chapter 9

Morphological Filtering

9.1 Introduction

In chapter 8 various types of spatial filters were discussed, including the mean and median filters. Each of these filters manipulated the graylevel content of an image without any regard to the geometrical shapes of various objects within the image. Usually, the final goal of image processing is to segment the objects within an image for object recognition and identification. The image-processing steps required prior to pattern recognition and identification usually include spatial filtering of the image to remove noise from the image, thresholding of the graylevel image to produce a binary graylevel image, and then morphological filtering of the image for geometrical shape decomposition.

Morphological filters operate on objects within an image by manipulating an object's geometrical shape. The goal of morphological filters is to smooth the contours of the objects and to decompose an image into its fundamental geometrical shapes. Morphological operations can be separated into two categories. (1) binary morphological filtering of binary images, and (2) graylevel morphological filtering of graylevel images.

Four basic types of binary morphological filtering operations are available: erosion, dilation, opening, and closing. Each of these filters uses a mask or structuring set to determine the geometrical filtering process. The *erosion filtering* operation reduces the geometrical size of an object, while the *dilation filtering* operation enlarges an object's geometrical size. However erosion filtering is not generally a reversible operation. Two other morphological filtering operations include the opening and closing filters. An *opening filter* is simply an erosion filter followed by a dilation filter, and a *closing filter* is a dilation filter followed by an erosion filter. Two other important morphological operations are outlining and skeletonization. Morphological *outlining* is used to find the contours of objects, while *skeletonization* is used to find the medial axis transform or skeleton of an object.

The goal of this chapter is to introduce the reader to the concepts of binary morphological operations and their use in image processing. Those interested in a discussion on graylevel morphological filtering should consult, *Nonlinear Digital Filters Principles and Applications* by I. Pitas and A. N. Venetsanopoulos listed in the annotated bibliography. Before any discussion of binary morphological filtering can continue, the reader must be introduced to the concepts of using set theory to describe objects within an image.

9.2 Set Theory Background

The approach taken here is to introduce the reader to the various properties obtained from set theory and how to apply these properties directly to objects within images. These properties will be a foundation in the development of binary morphological filters.

The concepts behind set theory are very simple. The concept of a *set* is the grouping of objects or elements together in a common collection. The grouping can be a function of some common attribute among all elements in the set. For example, the collection of records an individual might own is considered to be a set. The collection of all Christmas records in this record collection is also a set. In particular, the set of Christmas records is a *subset* of the total collection.

In mathematics, it is very useful to consider numbers as sets. Let the symbol R represent all possible real numbers that can exist. Then the number A = 1.2, must be a member or element of R, denoted by $A \in R$. The real numbers R can range from $-\infty$ to $+\infty$, indicating that there is no boundary for the set R. Since the set R contains no boundaries, it is referred to as an *open set*. Next, consider the complement of R, (R^C), every element that is not a member of R. Since the set R contains all real numbers, then the complement of R must contain no real numbers. In other words, the complement of R must be an empty set containing no members. An empty set is often called a *null set* and is denoted by the symbol $\varnothing$.

For example, consider the set X of the following integer numbers

$$X = \{1, 2, 3, 4, 5, 6, 7, 8\} \quad . \tag{1}$$

Then the set Y = {1, 4, 5} is a subset of the set X, denoted by $Y \subset X$. It could have also been stated that the number 1 is an element of the sets X and Y, $1 \in X$ and $1 \in Y$.

The set of all integer numbers is denoted by the set I and is also a subset of the set of real numbers R, $I \subset R$. A set of numbers, X, ranging from 0 to 15 is given in Equation 2.

$$X = \{0, 1, 2, 3, 4, 5, 6, 7, 8, 9, 10, 11, \ 12, 13, 14, 15\} \tag{2}$$

This set can then be divided into three subsets A, B, and C as follows

$$
\begin{aligned}
A &= \{1, 3, 11, 15\} \\
B &= \{2, 4, 8, 10 \} \\
C &= \{5, 6, 7, 9, 12, 13, 14\} \quad .
\end{aligned}
\tag{3}
$$

Given the definition in Equation 3, then $A \subset X$, $B \subset X$, and $C \subset X$. From Equation 3, the common feature of set A is that each of its members is an odd number, and the common feature of set B is that each of its members is an even number. The complement of subset A, A^C, is all numbers that are a member of set X and are not a member of set A.

$$A^C = \{2, 4, 5, 6, 7, 8, 9, 10, 12, 13, 14\} \tag{4}$$

Two fundamental properties of set theory are the *intersection* ($\cap$) and the *union* ($\cup$) of sets. The union of sets combines the member of sets together forming a new combined set. The intersection of sets is a new set that only contains members that are common to all sets. Consider a new set D that is the union of sets A and B given in Equation 3.

$$D = A \cup B$$
$$D = \{1, 2, 3, 4, 8, 10, 11, 15\} \tag{5}$$

From Equation 5, the set that is the union of sets A and B contains all the elements from both sets. The intersection of A with B yields the null set $\emptyset$, because there are no elements that are common between both sets. Equation 6, gives two new subsets A and B obtained from the set X given in Equation 2.

$$A = \{0, 3, 6, 9, 10, 14, 15\}$$
$$B = \{0, 1, 3, 5, 9, 11, 12\} \tag{6}$$

The intersection of sets A and B yields

$$A \cap B = \{0, 3, 9\} \tag{7}$$

and the union of sets A and B is

$$A \cup B = \{0, 1, 3, 5, 6, 9, 10, 11, 12, 14, 15\} \ . \tag{8}$$

The union of sets follows the associative and commutative laws of algebra in that the order in which the sets are combined does not make a difference. Stated in another way, given the three sets A, B, and C, then the associative law states that

$$A \cup B \cup C = (A \cup B) \cup C = A \cup (B \cup C) \tag{9}$$

and the commutative law states

$$A \cup B = B \cup A \ . \tag{10}$$

The intersection of sets also follows the associative and commutative laws of algebra. Again, for the intersection of sets, the order in which the sets are operated on does not make a difference. The associative law yields

$$A \cap B \cap C = (A \cap B) \cap C = A \cap (B \cap C) \tag{11}$$

and the commutative law gives

$$A \cap B = B \cap A \ . \tag{12}$$

To illustrate these two laws, consider the following three sets: A = {1, 2, 6, 9}, B ={1, 3, 8, 9}, and C = {1, 4, 5, 9}. Then A $\cup$ B $\cup$ C is given by

$$
\begin{aligned}
A \cup B \cup C &= [\{1, 2, 6, 9\} \cup \{1, 3, 8, 9\}] \cup \{1, 4, 5, 9\} \\
&= \{1, 2, 3, 6, 8, 9\} \cup \{1, 4, 5, 9\} \\
&= \{1, 2, 3, 4, 5, 6, 8, 9\}
\end{aligned}
\tag{13}
$$

or

$$
\begin{aligned}
A \cup B \cup C &= \{1, 2, 6, 9\} \cup [\{1, 3, 8, 9\} \cup \{1, 4, 5, 9\}] \\
&= \{1, 2, 6, 9\} \cup \{1, 3, 4, 5, 8, 9\} \\
&= \{1, 2, 3, 4, 5, 6, 8, 9\} \ .
\end{aligned}
\tag{14}
$$

The intersection of sets A, B, and C is given as

$$
\begin{aligned}
A \cap B \cap C &= [\{1, 2, 6, 9\} \cap \{1, 3, 8, 9\}] \cap \{1, 4, 5, 9\} \\
&= \{1, 9\} \cap \{1, 4, 5, 9\} \\
&= \{1, 9\}
\end{aligned}
\tag{15}
$$

or

$$
\begin{aligned}
A \cap B \cap C &= \{1, 2, 6, 9\} \cap [\{1, 3, 8, 9\} \cap \{1, 4, 5, 9\}] \\
&= \{1, 2, 6, 9\} \cap \{1, 9\} \\
&= \{1, 9\} \ .
\end{aligned}
\tag{16}
$$

Another important identity is the equality identity which states that set A is equal to set B when

$$A = B \qquad \text{if } A \subset B \text{ and } B \subset A \ . \tag{17}$$

Two other useful identities commonly referred to as De Morgan's laws are

$$(A \cup B)^c = A^c \cap B^c \quad \text{and} \quad (A \cap B)^c = A^c \cup B^c \ . \tag{18}$$

The last identity that will be presented is the difference between two sets, A − B. The difference between two sets means to remove the elements of set B from set A. For example, let set A = {1, 2, 6, 9}, and set B ={1, 3, 8, 9} then (A − B) = {2, 6}. Another way of writing the difference between two sets is

$$A - B = A \cap B^c = A - (A \cap B) \quad . \tag{19}$$

The concepts of set theory presented in the previous pages for one-dimensional numbers can easily be expanded to include two-dimensional numbers. The set of all two-dimensional real numbers will be denoted by R^2, and the set of all two-dimensional integer numbers will be denoted by I^2. In image processing, pixels are represented by two-dimensional integer numbers giving the location of the pixel within the image and by a one-dimensional number indicating the pixel's graylevel value. For binary images, the graylevel values of pixels will only be allowed to take on two values, 1 for an object's pixels and 0 for the background pixels. In this way, to describe an object pixel, only its coordinates are needed. The collection of pixels given by their the two-dimensional coordinate numbers will be used to form a set describing an object.

Before describing objects within images using set theory, a few examples using two-dimensional real numbers are appropriate. The collection of two-dimensional real numbers can be used to represent any geometrical shape. Venn diagrams are usually used as a geometrical representation of two-dimensional sets. Figure 9.1 shows a Venn diagram with two geometrical sets (objects) A and B. The total space of two-dimensional real numbers is given by R^2.

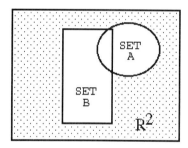

Figure 9.1 *Venn diagram for two sets A and B.*

The union of set A with set B is shown in Figure 9.2a, and the intersection of set A with set B is shown in Figure 9.2b. From the Venn diagrams, it becomes clear that the intersection of two sets is simply the area of overlap, and the union of the two sets is the combined area of both sets.

The difference of set B from A (A − B) using Equation 19 is easily derived using Venn diagrams. Figure 9.3a shows the Venn diagram for B^c, which is all the area given for R^2 minus the area of set B. Figure 9.3b shows the intersection of A and B^c which is A − B. In Figure 9.3b, the area that remains for set A − B is the portion of set B that overlaps set A removed from set A.

Expanding on this example further, the Venn diagram given in Figure 9.4 shows the regions of (A − B) and (B − A) for the sets A and B. From this figure, the union of set (B − A) with the set (A ∩ B) is equal to set B and likewise the union of set (A − B) with set (A ∩ B) is equal to set A.

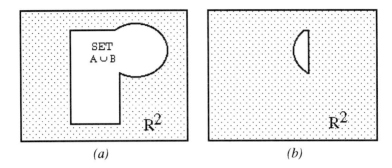

(a)   (b)

Figure 9.2 *Venn diagrams for (a) the union of set A with B and (b) the intersection of set A with B.*

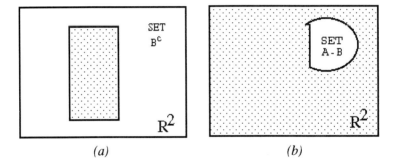

(a)   (b)

Figure 9.3 *Venn diagrams for the set Bᶜ and the difference set A − B.*

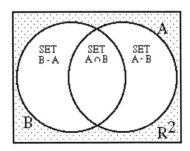

Figure 9.4 *Venn diagram showing the regions (A − B) and (B − A).*

Consider the three sets represented by the geometrical shapes of a triangle (A), a square (B), and a circle (C) given in the Venn diagram in Figure 9.5. It is obvious from this figure that set A is a subset of set B (A $\subset$ B), set B is a subset of set C (B $\subset$ C), and all three sets are a subset of R^2. From this diagram several properties can be derived. The first, is that the union of set A with set B is simply equal to set B, and then the intersection of set A with set B is equal to set A. In general,

$$B = A \cup B \qquad \text{if } A \subset B \qquad (20)$$

and

$$A = A \cap B \qquad \text{if } A \subset B \ . \qquad (21)$$

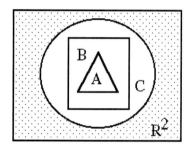

Figure 9.5 *Venn diagram for three geometrical sets.*

The use of Venn diagrams to represent two-dimensional sets provides the easy understanding of how geometrical objects can be represented by sets. In digitized images though, the continuum space R^2 is replaced by the integer space I^2. The values of x and y describing the location of a pixel within an image usually only takes on integer values. Let X be the set of numbers describing the possible pixel locations in the horizontal direction, and let Y be the set of numbers describing the pixel locations in the vertical direction in an image. Next, let the variables x and y be the location of a pixel within the image at its horizontal and vertical location. Then, if the pixel is an element of the image given by the sets X and Y, x $\in$ X and y $\in$ Y. For example, to describe a 512 $\times$ 512 image, the sets X and Y must contain all integer numbers in the range of 0 to 511. Then for every pixel location within the image the variables x and y must be an element of the sets X and Y, respectively.

Figure 9.6 shows a 5 $\times$ 5 binary image with two objects defined by the sets A and B. Object pixels take on the graylevel value of 1, and background pixels take on the value of 0. The pixels describing the two objects can be separated into two sets A and B as A = {(0,0), (0,1), (1,0), (1,1)} and B = {(3,3), (3,4), (4,3), (4,4)}. From this image, the intersection of object A with B yields the null set, $\varnothing$.

X Direction.

		0	1	2	3	4
	0	1	1	0	0	0
Y	1	1	1	0	0	0
Direction	2	0	0	0	0	0
	3	0	0	0	1	1
	4	0	0	0	1	1

Figure 9.6 *A 25 × 25 pixel binary image with two objects.*

Next, consider the image given in Figure 9.7a which shows two objects A and B. For clarity, the graylevel values of 1 for each object have been replaced by the letters A and B to indicate the two objects. The sets A and B of pixels describing each object is given as A = {(0,2), (1,0), (1,1), (1,2)} and B = {(1,2), (1,3), (1,4), (2,2)}. Object A appears to be the bottom-right corner of two line segments, and object B looks as if it is the upper-left corner of two line segments. Some interesting results can be obtained using the various set operations. The intersection of the two objects A ∩ B is the one pixel at location (1,2). This pixel could be interpreted as the corner pixel from the two line segments for both objects A and B. Let C be a new object representing the union of the two objects A and B shown in Figure 9.7b. Note how the geometrical interpretation of this object is different from the two objects shown separately in Figure 9.7a. No longer does the image appear to have two objects that are corners of two line segments, but the image appears now to have two line segments intersecting each other at right angles.

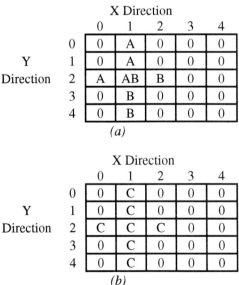

X Direction

		0	1	2	3	4
	0	0	A	0	0	0
Y	1	0	A	0	0	0
Direction	2	A	AB	B	0	0
	3	0	B	0	0	0
	4	0	B	0	0	0

(a)

X Direction

		0	1	2	3	4
	0	0	C	0	0	0
Y	1	0	C	0	0	0
Direction	2	C	C	C	0	0
	3	0	C	0	0	0
	4	0	C	0	0	0

(b)

Figure 9.7 *Two 25 × 25 binary images of two overlapping objects.*

Using mathematical notation, an object A within a binary image is described by

$$A = \{a: f(a) = 1, a=(x, y), x \in X, y \in Y\} \tag{22}$$

and its background by

$$B = A^c = \{a: f(a) = 0, a = (x, y), x \in X, y \in Y\} \ . \tag{23}$$

What Equations 22 and 23 are telling the reader is that the variable, a, is a function of two variables, x, and, y, that are both elements of the sets X and Y. The sets X and Y are all the possible horizontal and vertical locations that a pixel can have within an image. The function f(a) describes the graylevel values of the object and background within the image. Finally, the sets A and B are the collection of pixels for the object and background, respectively.

9.3 Morphological Erosion and Dilation

The two fundamental morphological operations are erosion and dilation and are based upon two set operations, Minkowski set addition and subtraction. Figure 9.8a is a plot of a square object located in the two-dimensional space R^2, and in Figure 9.8b is a plot of a point located on the vertical axis.

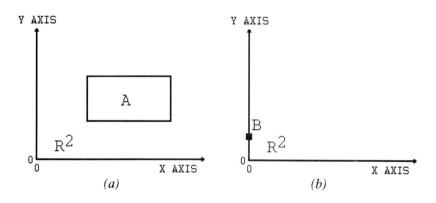

(a)   *(b)*

Figure 9.8 *Two objects A and B shown in two-dimensional space R^2.*

Let A be the set denoting the square object with all its elements denoted by the two-dimensional variable a. Next, let B be the set containing the one point and the two-dimensional variable b used to describe this point. The Minkowski addition of set A with B, given by the symbol ⊕, is

$$A \oplus B = \{ \, t \in R^2 \colon t = a + b, a \in A, b \in B \} \; . \tag{24}$$

Equation 24 states that all the elements, a, of the object A are added to all the elements, b, of object B to form a new set of elements, t. To determine the contour of the new object, only the contour pixels for objects A and B must be considered. From this simple example, the object A is moved vertically in the +Y direction by the distance that point b is located from the origin. Figure 9.9 shows the results of the Minkowski set addition.

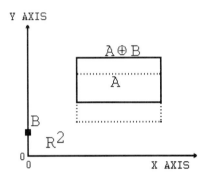

Figure 9.9 *Minkowski addition of two sets A and B.*

Figure 9.10 shows a new set B containing two points placed symmetrically about the vertical axis. The idea of Minkowski addition given in Equation 24, can now be expanded to include this new set B. Minkowski addition of point b_1 moves the square shown in Figure 9.8a up in the vertical direction, while point b_2 moves the square down in the vertical direction. Since both of these points are elements of the set B, the union of the individual Minkowski additions results in the total Minkowski addition of set B with A and is given in Figure 9.11. Figure 9.11 shows that the new dilated object has been expanded vertically in both directions. When the set B is replaced by its symmetric set about the origin, Minkowski addition is referred to as *morphological dilation.* The word dilation is used because, as shown in Figure 9.11, the new object has been enlarged or dilated. In addition, the set B has been given a special name and is called a *structuring set.* The dilation operation described by Equation 24 is referred to as "the object A dilated by the structuring set B."

Figure 9.12a shows a circular structuring set B with a radius of r. The dilation of the square object given in Figure 9.8a is shown in Figure 9.12b. The effect of the circular structuring object B is to expand dimensions of the square by the radius r in all directions. The dilation of the corners of the square is of special interest. Adding all the elements from set B to the four corner points yields four circles centered at these corners. The outer parameters of the circle become the new contour of the dilated object. If a square structuring element of dimension 2r were used, the square in Figure 9.8a would be still be expanded by r in all directions, but the corners of the dilated object would remain square. Figure 9.13a shows a square structuring object, and Figure 9.13b shows the dilated results.

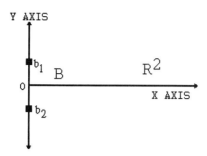

Figure 9.10 *Structuring set B with two elements.*

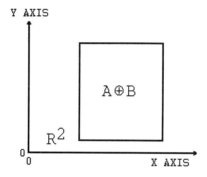

Figure 9.11 *Dilation of the object given in Figure 9.8a with the structuring element given in Figure 9.10.*

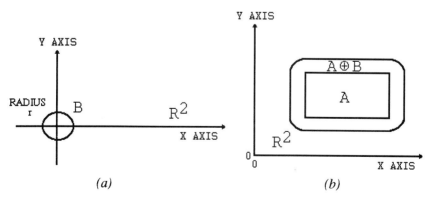

Figure 9.12 *The dilation of a square by a circle.*

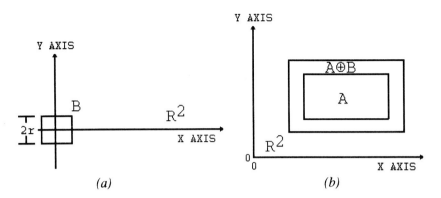

Figure 9.13 *The dilation of a square by a circle.*

The dual of Minkowski addition is Minkowski subtraction, and if the symmetric structuring set about the origin is used, this operation is known as *morphological erosion*. Minkowski subtraction is defined as

$$A \ominus B = (A^c \oplus B)^c \qquad . \tag{25}$$

To obtain the Minkowski subtraction given in Equation 25, the complement of object A is found, and this object is dilated by object B. Next, the dilated object is complemented, yielding the final Minkowski subtraction results. Again, consider the square object given in Figure 9.8a and the structuring set B given in Figure 9.10. The complement of object A is all points outside the square, and the dilation of this object with the two-point structuring set reduces the vertical height of the square hole by the distance between the two points b_1 and b_2. The final Minkowski subtraction result is obtained by taking the complement of this reduced square hole to obtain a reduced vertical square, as in Figure 9.14.

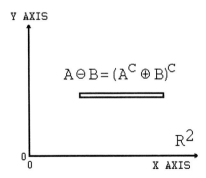

Figure 9.14 *Minkowski subtraction of the object given in Figure 9.8a and the object given in Figure 9.10.*

The erosion of a square given in Figure 9.8a and by the circular structuring object given in Figure 9.15a is shown in Figure 9.15b. The effect of the erosion on the square is to reduce the dimension of the square by the diameter of the circle in all directions.

There are several important properties of erosion and dilation. The first is the translation property. This property states that, if an object is translated in the R^2 or I^2 space and then eroded or dilated, that this is equivalent to first eroding or dilating the object and then translating the object to its new coordinates. The property of scale states that the final eroded or dilated shape of an object is only a function of its shape, not of the size of the object. The size of the original object determines only the final size of the eroded or dilated object. Another property of importance is the increasing property. The increasing property states that an eroded or dilated object preserves an object's size. For example, if object A is a subset of object B, then the eroded or dilated object of object A will also be a subset of the eroded or dilated object of object B. This identity guarantees that the relative size of an object remains the same after a morphological erosion or dilation operation.

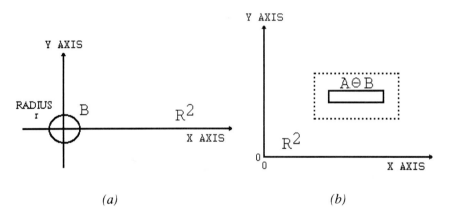

(a)   (b)

Figure 9.15 *The square object given in Figure 9.8a eroded by a circular structuring set given in Figure 9.15a.*

Both the erosion and dilation operations follow the commutative and associative algebraic laws. For example, the commutative law for dilation is

$$A \oplus B = B \oplus A \qquad (26)$$

and for erosion it is

$$A \ominus B = B \ominus A \quad . \qquad (27)$$

The associative law for dilation is given as

$$A \oplus (B \oplus C) = (B \oplus A) \oplus C \tag{28}$$

and for erosion it is

$$A \ominus (B \ominus C) = (A \ominus B) \ominus C \tag{29}$$

The distributive property of dilation simply states that the union of two objects A and C that is dilated by the structuring set, B, is equivalent to dilating each object individually and then finding the union of the two dilated objects.

$$(A \cup C) \oplus B = (A \oplus B) \cup (C \oplus B) \tag{30}$$

This property was used in finding the dilation of the square object in Figure 9.8a with the two-point structuring object given in Figure 9.10. Each point was dilated separately and then both objects were combined.

For erosion, the distributive property is written as

$$(A \cup C) \ominus B = (A \ominus B) \cap (C \ominus B) \tag{31}$$

which is equal to the intersection of the two individual objects eroded separately. Equation 31 could have been used to find the erosion of the two-point structuring function given in Figure 9.10 with the square given in Figure 9.8a. The erosion of the square by structuring point b1 moves the square up in the vertical direction, while the erosion of the square by b2 moves the square down vertically. The intersection of these two eroded squares yields a new square that is reduced drastically in its vertical dimension, as shown in Figure 9.14.

Suppose the structuring set B_t can be decomposed into a set of smaller structuring elements B_1 through B_N in the following manner

$$B_t = B_1 \oplus B_2 \oplus B_3 \oplus \cdots B_N \quad . \tag{32}$$

The dilation of an object A by B_t is simply the dilation of the object A by each one of the structuring elements B_1 through B_N as described by Equation 33.

$$A \oplus B_t = (\cdots(A \oplus B_1) \oplus B_2) \oplus B_3) \oplus \cdots B_N) \tag{33}$$

For erosion, Equation 33 is replaced by

$$A \ominus B_t = (\cdots(A \ominus B_1) \ominus B_2) \ominus B_3) \ominus \cdots B_N) \tag{34}$$

To perform dilation and erosion on an image is different from performing dilation and erosion in the continuous space R^2. The main difference is that the structuring set and the images are represented by discrete pixels. To illustrate how dilation is accomplished on an image, consider the structuring set given in Figure 9.16a and the image of a square given in Figure 9.16b. Assume that the origin of the structuring set, $x = y = 0$, is located at the pixel b_2.

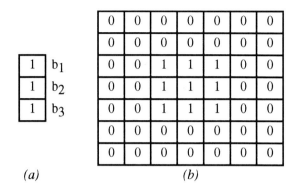

(a)   *(b)*

Figure 9.16 *Three-pixel structuring Set and a 7×7 image of a square object.*

Equation 30 can be used to separate the total dilation operation into three separate dilation operations each using the elements b_1, b_2, and b_3. The dilation of the square by b_1 simply moves the square vertically up one pixel, while the dilation of the square by pixel b_3 moves the square down by one pixel. The pixel b_2 simply leaves the square unchanged. Combining these three images to obtain the union of the three dilated objects yields a new square that has been expanded vertically one pixel in the up and down directions. Figure 9.17 shows the output of the total dilated image. If the structuring set given in Figure 9.16 is rotated by 90° so that the three elements are now horizontal, and this new structuring set is applied to the square image in Figure 9.16, the square would expand by two pixels in the horizontal direction.

0	0	0	0	0	0	0
0	0	1	1	1	0	0
0	0	1	1	1	0	0
0	0	1	1	1	0	0
0	0	1	1	1	0	0
0	0	1	1	1	0	0
0	0	0	0	0	0	0

Figure 9.17 *The dilated image obtained from Figure 9.16.*

1	1	1
1	1	1
1	1	1

Figure 9.18 *A 3 × 3 square structuring set.*

0	0	0	0	0	0	0
0	1	1	1	1	1	0
0	1	1	1	1	1	0
0	1	1	1	1	1	0
0	1	1	1	1	1	0
0	1	1	1	1	1	0
0	0	0	0	0	0	0

Figure 9.19 *The dilated image obtained using the structuring set given in Figure 9.18.*

The structuring set in Figure 9.18 yields the same results as if the structuring set in Figure 9.16 were first used, followed by its 90° translated structuring set. The net effect is to expand the square in all directions by one pixel. Figure 9.19 shows the dilated image of the square expanded in all directions.

The erosion of the square image given in Figure 9.16b by the three structuring elements b_1, b_2, and b_3 given in Figure 9.16a, yields a new image of a square, with the dimensions of the square reduced by two pixels in the vertical direction. Figure 9.20 shows the output of the eroded image. If the original square is eroded by the square structuring set given in Figure 9.18, the final eroded image reduces to a single pixel in the center on the 7 × 7 image.

0	0	0	0	0	0	0
0	0	0	0	0	0	0
0	0	0	0	0	0	0
0	0	1	1	1	0	0
0	0	0	0	0	0	0
0	0	0	0	0	0	0
0	0	0	0	0	0	0

Figure 9.20 *The eroded image obtained using the structuring set in Figure 9.16.*

Figure 9.21 shows several examples of structuring sets used in morphological erosion and dilation. The first structuring set is a discrete approximation to a circle while the last two structuring sets perform erosion and dilation only in the vertical or horizontal direction. The example of dilating the square in all directions, given in Figure 9.19, was discussed first by dilating the square in the vertical direction, followed by the dilation of the square in the horizontal direction using the masks shown in Figure 9.21. The same dilated image could have been obtained using the 3×3 square structuring set also shown in Figure 9.21. Then by Equation 32, the decomposition of a 3×3 square structuring set must be the three-element horizontal and vertical structuring sets.

So far nothing has been said about how to automatically perform dilation or erosion on an image. Consider a mask that represents the desired structuring set that is moved throughout the image pixel by pixel. This is the same technique used to perform spatial filtering. This time, though, only pixels within the mask region with mask elements equal to 1 will be used to compute a maximum value. This maximum value will replace the center pixel's graylevel value that the mask is centered over. Since the images of interest for binary morphological filtering are binary images, the possible outputs for the maximum filter are 0 or 1. The morphological dilated image will be the output of this maximum filter. The morphological erosion filter is obtained by replacing the maximum filter with a minimum filter. The minimum filter works exactly the same as the maximum filter, except that the minimum value is used instead of the maximum value.

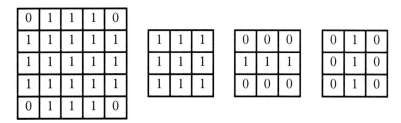

Figure 9.21 *A circle, a square, a horizontal and a vertical structuring set.*

For example, using the square 3×3 structuring set given in Figure 9.18 as the mask for the maximum filter on the square image in Figure 9.16 yields the same dilated image as given in Figure 9.19. As the mask is moved horizontally from left to right, the second-row pixel's graylevel values will change from 0's to 1's. Figure 9.22 shows an example of a 3×3 image under the 3×3 square mask. Since all elements of the 3×3 square mask are 1, all pixels within the mask are used in the computation of the maximum graylevel. From Figure 9.22, the maximum value is computed to be 1 and the center pixel is replaced by this value.

For morphological erosion, the minimum filter is used in connection with the structuring mask. An example of this filter is shown in Figure 9.23. In this example, the center pixel element is set to zero. If the minimum filter along with the 3×3 square structuring mask is used on the square image in Figure 9.16, the resulting image is the same as the eroded image; a single pixel located in the center of the 7×7 image.

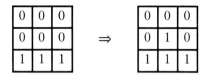

Figure 9.22 *An example of using the maximum filter for dilation.*

0	0	0
1	1	1
1	1	1

$\Rightarrow$

0	0	0
1	0	1
1	1	1

Figure 9.23 *An example of using the minimum filter for erosion.*

```
Dilation(unsigned char IMAGE[][],int MASK[][],
     unsigned char Filter[][])
     {
int X, Y, I, J, smax;
for(Y=2; Y<=509; Y++){
     for(X=2; X<=509; X++){
           smax=0;
           for(J=-2; J<=2; J++){
                 for(I=-2; I<=2; I++){
                 if(MASK[I+2][J+2] ==1){
                    if (IMAGE[X+I][Y+J] > smax){
                          smax= IMAGE[X+J][Y+J];}
                     }
                  }
               }
           FILTER[X][Y] =smax;
           }
        }
     }
```

Figure 9.24 *Partial C code to perform morphological dilation on a binary image.*

Figures 9.24 and 9.25 give the partial code to implement morphological dilation and erosion using a 5×5 structuring mask on a 512×512 binary image. Both programs assume that the input image is passed to the program in the two-dimensional array IMAGE[X][Y] and that the graylevel values for the binary image are 0 (black) and 255 (white). Also, the 5×5 structuring array is passed to the program in MASK[I][J] and the allowed value for the mask array elements is 0 or 1. Upon completion, the output image is stored in the two-dimensional array FILTER[X][Y] with graylevel values of 0 (black) and 255 (white). For the dilation filter, the maximum value is computed using all pixels within the 5×5 region whose mask elements are

1. The erosion filter performs identically to the dilation filter, except that the minimum value is computed for the nonzero mask elements and stored in the output image array FILTER[X][Y].

```
Erosion(unsigned char IMAGE[][], int MASK[][],
  unsigned char Filter[][])
    {
    int X, Y, I, J, smin;
    for(Y=2; Y<=509; Y++){
        for(X=2; X<=509; X++){
            smin=255;
            for(J=-2; J<=2; J++){
                for(I=-2; I<=2; I++){
                if(MASK[I+2][J+2] ==1){
                    if (IMAGE[X+I][Y+J] < smin){
                        smin= IMAGE[X+J][Y+J];}
                    }
                }
            }
            FILTER[X][Y] =smin;
        }
    }
}
```

Figure 9.25 *Partial C code to perform morphological erosion on a binary image.*

9.4 Morphological Opening and Closing

Morphological opening and closing operations on an image are used to geometrically filter the contours of objects. For example, small narrow openings and small outward bumps can be reduced by an opening operation. The closing operation on an object will fill small inward bumps and small holes on the object's contour. The net effect is that opening and closing operations result in new geometrical objects in which the contours have been filtered. By definition, morphological opening is erosion followed by dilation and is given by

$$\text{open}(A, B) = (A \ominus B) \oplus B \quad . \tag{35}$$

Morphological closing is the dual of the morphological opening operation and is defined as dilation followed by erosion

$$\text{close}(A, B) = (A \oplus B) \ominus B \tag{36}$$

Since these two operations are duals of each other

$$\text{close}(A, B) = \text{open}(A, B)^c \tag{37}$$

and

$$open(A, B) = close(A, B)^c \ . \tag{38}$$

Several important properties of opening and closing should be mentioned. The first is that, once an object is either opened or closed, then opening or closing the object a second time with the same structuring set yields the same results as the first opening or closing of the object. Both opening and closing obey the increasing law. If the object A is a subset of the object C then opening or closing of both objects yields two new objects; where the new object generated from object A will be a subset of the new object generated from object C.

Consider the object given in Figure 9.26b and the structuring object given in Figure 9.26a. Figures 9.27a and b shows the results of opening and closing of the object. Figure 9.27a shows how the opening operation has smoothed the portion of the object labeled A and has rounded all the outside corners. Note how the closing operation has rounded the inside corners of section A of the object and almost completely removed the small inward section labeled B. This is the same as stated earlier; the opening operation removes small outward bumps and the closing operation removes small inward bumps.

The partial codes to implement opening and closing are quite simple. To open an image, the erosion partial code in Figure 9.25 is called, followed by the dilation partial code given in Figure 9.24. For the closing operation, the dilation partial code is executed first, followed by the erosion partial code. Using the partial codes for dilation and erosion given in Figures 9.24 and 9.25 requires that after the first operation the output image stored in array FILTER[X][Y] be transferred to the array IMAGE[X][Y], since both programs expect the image to be filtered to be stored in array IMAGE[X][Y] upon execution.

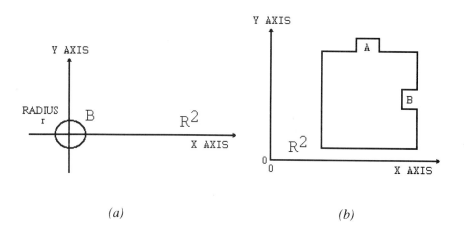

(a)   *(b)*

Figure 9.26 *An example of using opening a closing on an object.*

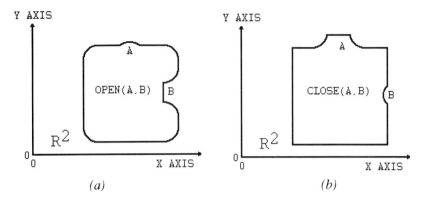

Figure 9.27 *Opening and closing of the object given Figure 9.26b.*

9.5 Morphological Outlining

Morphological outlining or contour detection is the process of removing all of an object's pixels except those pixels that lie on the contour of the object. Two types of morphological outline detectors are available. The outside contour detector and the inside contour detector. The outside contour detector produces a contour that borders the outside edge of the object's contour, and the inside contour detector produces a contour that borders the inside edge of the object's contour. Another name for a contour detector is an edge detector. The advantage of using a morphological contour detector for detecting edges is that these detectors are more immune to noise than the standard edge detectors such as the gradient, Robert's and Sobel edge detectors. Figure 9.28a shows a binary image of the symbol X, and Figure 9.28b shows its respective contour.

(a) (b)

Figure 9.28 *An example of an image's outline or contour.*

Consider an object, A, eroded by a fine structuring object, B, and that this eroded object is subtracted from the original object. The result is a new object containing elements that border the inside contour of the original object. The inside contour detector is defined as

$$C_i = A - (A \ominus B) \tag{39}$$

The minus symbol implies the difference between the two sets, not the normal definition of algebraic subtraction. Equation 39 was used to generate the contour given in Figure 9.28b with the width of the structuring set B determining the width of the contour.

The outside contour detector is an object dilated by a small structuring set subtracted from the original object:

$$C_o = (A \oplus B) - A \quad . \tag{40}$$

The widths of the inside and outside contours depend on the width of the structuring element B. Given a square structuring element of size d the width of the contour will also be d.

Recall the dilation example of the 3×3 pixel square given in Figure 9.16 and dilated with the structuring set given in Figure 9.18. Using Equation 40 yields a new image containing a one-pixel wide contour surrounding the outside of the original image. Figure 9.29 shows the final computed contour image.

0	0	0	0	0	0	0
0	1	1	1	1	1	0
0	1	0	0	0	1	0
0	1	0	0	0	1	0
0	1	0	0	0	1	0
0	1	1	1	1	1	0
0	0	0	0	0	0	0

Figure 9.29 *The outside contour detection for a square object.*

Likewise, the inside contour could have been computed by first eroding the 3×3 pixel square, which yields one pixel left in the center of the 7×7 image. This eroded image can then be subtracted from the original image to yield the inside contour as shown in Figure 9.30. Even though this image at first does not appear to be the actual contour of the original square which is now lying on the inside edge of the square, this is simply due to the small pixel resolution of the square. Clearly, an eroded image subtracted from its original image must border on the inside contour of the original image.

The partial code to implement a one-pixel wide inside contour detector for a 512×512 binary image is given in Figure 9.31. The program expects the input image to be stored in the array IMAGE[X][Y] and to already have been binarized to the graylevel values of 0 and 255. The program also assumes that a graylevel value of 255 is the object's graylevel value. Upon execution of the program, the outline image is stored in array FILTER[X][Y]. The first thing the program does is set the structuring array MASK[I][J] to a 3 × 3 square. Next, the program calls the erosion program given in Figure 9.25. The program then subtracts the eroded image stored in array FILTER[X][Y] from the original image leaving the final results in FILTER[X][Y]. The outside contour detector is implemented by calling the morphological dilation program given in Figure 9.24 and replacing the equation

$$FILTER[X],[Y] = IMAGE[X][Y] - FILTER[X][Y] \tag{41}$$

with

$$FILTER[X][Y] = FILTER[X][Y] - IMAGE[X][Y] . \tag{42}$$

Equation 41 is another way of stating Equation 39, and Equation 42 is another form of Equation 40.

0	0	0	0	0	0	0
0	0	0	0	0	0	0
0	0	1	1	1	0	0
0	0	1	0	1	0	0
0	0	1	1	1	0	0
0	0	0	0	0	0	0
0	0	0	0	0	0	0

Figure 9.30 *The inside contour detection for a square object.*

```
Inside_contour(unsigned char IMAGE[][],unsigned char
     Filter[][])
     {
     int X,Y, I, J, MASK[5][5];
     for(J=0; J<=4; J++)
          for(I=0; I<=4; I++) MASK[J][I]=0;
     MASK[1][1]=1; MASK[1][2]=1; MASK[1][3]=1;
     MASK[2][1]=1; MASK[2][2]=1; MASK[2][3]=1;
     MASK[3][1]=1; MASK[3][2]=1; MASK[3][3]=1;
     erosion(IMAGE, MASK, Filter);
     for(Y=0; Y<=511; Y++)
          for(X=0; X<=511; X++)
               FILTER[X][Y] =IMAGE[X][Y] -FILTER[X][Y];

     }
```

Figure 9.31 *Partial C code to perform morphological outlining on a binary image.*

9.6 Morphological Skeletonization

The goal of many image processing applications is to classify unknown objects within an image. To use all of the pixels within an object for the identification process adds an enormous amount of complexity to the object identification process. One way to decompose an object into a set of unique characteristics that can be used for object identification is to find the skeleton of the object. The skeleton of an object represents a geometrical shape that is uniquely defined by the original shape of the object.

The mathematical derivation of skeletonization of an object is due to H. Blum. He called the transformation from an object to its skeleton the medial axis transform (MAT). Conceptually, Blum proposed to treat the area within an object as a grass field. Then he proposed starting a grass fire at the contour of the object and letting the fire burn toward the center of the object. The points at which the fire lines crossed and are then extinguished are known as the medial axis of the object. Figure 9.32a shows the image of the symbol X and Figure 9.32b shows its medial axis transform. Note how much less information (number of pixels) is needed to describe the medial axis of this object as compared to its original image.

(a)   *(b)*

Figure 9.32 *An example of an image's skeleton.*

Consider the 3×3 square structuring set, B, given in Figure 9.10. The nth erosion of object A by B can then be written as

$$E_n(A) = A \ominus nB \ . \tag{43}$$

The nth-order difference between the eroded image, $E_n(A)$, and the opening of the eroded image by the structuring set B_1, open($E_n(A)$, B_1), can be defined as

$$K_n(A) = E_n(A) - \text{open}(E_n(A), B_1), \quad \text{for } n = 0 \text{ to } N - 1 \ , \tag{44}$$

where the structuring set B_1 is defined in Figure 9.33. The skeleton of object A becomes the union of all N terms of $K_n(A)$. The number of times $K_n(A)$ is implemented is until the nth erosion of object A by nB yields the null set $\varnothing$.

0	1	0
1	1	1
0	1	0

Figure 9.33 *A 3×3 structuring set for skeletonization of an object.*

Figure 9.34 shows the image of a 5×5 square object within a 7×7 image. Figures 9.35a and b shows the first and second erosion of the 5 by 5 square with the 3×3 square structuring set B. The third erosion yields the null set defining N = 2. Figures 9.35c and d show the opening of the original object and the first eroded object given in Figure 9.35a. It should be mentioned that the opening of the single-point eroded object in Figure 9.35b yields the null set $\varnothing$. Finally, Figures 9.35e, f, and g shows the results of $K_0(A)$, $K_1(A)$, and $K_2(A)$.

0	0	0	0	0	0	0
0	1	1	1	1	1	0
0	1	1	1	1	1	0
0	1	1	1	1	1	0
0	1	1	1	1	1	0
0	1	1	1	1	1	0
0	0	0	0	0	0	0

Figure 9.34 *A 7×7 image of a 5×5 square.*

Figure 9.35h shows the union of the three images $K_0(A)$, $K_1(A)$, and $K_2(A)$, which is the medial axis transform of a 5×5 square object. For large irregularly shaped objects, the structuring set B_1 can be replaced by the 3×3 square structuring set B reducing Equation 44 to

$$K_n(A) = E_n(A) - \text{open}(E_n(A), B), \quad \text{for } n = 0 \text{ to } N - 1 \ . \tag{45}$$

A better approximation is to increase the size of the medial axis transform to a two-pixel width and use the first structuring set given in Figure 9.21 as an approximation to a circular structuring set B with a radius of two pixels.

0	0	0	0	0	0	0
0	0	0	0	0	0	0
0	0	1	1	1	0	0
0	0	1	1	1	0	0
0	0	1	1	1	0	0
0	0	0	0	0	0	0
0	0	0	0	0	0	0

(a)

0	0	0	0	0	0	0
0	0	0	0	0	0	0
0	0	0	0	0	0	0
0	0	0	1	0	0	0
0	0	0	0	0	0	0
0	0	0	0	0	0	0
0	0	0	0	0	0	0

(b)

0	0	0	0	0	0	0
0	0	1	1	1	0	0
0	1	1	1	1	1	0
0	1	1	1	1	1	0
0	1	1	1	1	1	0
0	0	1	1	1	0	0
0	0	0	0	0	0	0

(c)

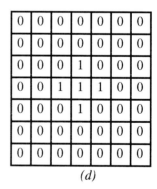

0	0	0	0	0	0	0
0	0	0	0	0	0	0
0	0	0	1	0	0	0
0	0	1	1	1	0	0
0	0	0	1	0	0	0
0	0	0	0	0	0	0
0	0	0	0	0	0	0

(d)

Figure 9.35 *An example of skeletonization of a 5 × 5 pixel square object.*

0	0	0	0	0	0	0
0	1	0	0	0	1	0
0	0	0	0	0	0	0
0	0	0	0	0	0	0
0	0	0	0	0	0	0
0	1	0	0	0	1	0
0	0	0	0	0	0	0

(e)

0	0	0	0	0	0	0
0	0	0	0	0	0	0
0	0	1	0	1	0	0
0	0	0	0	0	0	0
0	0	1	0	1	0	0
0	0	0	0	0	0	0
0	0	0	0	0	0	0

(f)

0	0	0	0	0	0	0
0	0	0	0	0	0	0
0	0	0	0	0	0	0
0	0	0	1	0	0	0
0	0	0	0	0	0	0
0	0	0	0	0	0	0
0	0	0	0	0	0	0

(g)

0	0	0	0	0	0	0
0	1	0	0	0	1	0
0	0	1	0	1	0	0
0	0	0	1	0	0	0
0	0	1	0	1	0	0
0	1	0	0	0	1	0
0	0	0	0	0	0	0

(h)

Figure 9.35 *continued.*

The partial code to implement the morphological skeletonization algorithm on a 512 × 512 binary image with graylevel values of 0 and 255 is given in Figure 9.36. The program assumes that the input image is stored in the two-dimensional array IMAGE[X][Y], and the output image is stored in SKELETON[X][Y]. The first thing the program does is set the 5 × 5 mask for the circular structuring set given in Figure 9.21. Next, the program clears the output array SKELETON[X][Y] to zero. The program continues until the eroding of the input image results in all its pixels being cleared to zero. This condition is checked via the variable pixel_on. In the while loop, the image is first opened via an erosion followed by a dilation operation. The opened image stored in array FILTER[X][Y] is then subtracted from the input image implementing Equation 45. For the first subtraction, this is equivalent to n = 0 in Equation 45. The difference image is then combined with the output image stored in SKELETON[X][Y]. If every pixel within difference image is 0 then no more erosions are necessary and the variable pixel_on is set to false. The last operation the program does before it loops through another iteration is erode the input image stored in IMAGE[X][Y] as required by Equation 45.

The skeletonization partial code given in Figure 9.36 has a huge storage requirement. The three two-dimensional arrays IMAGE[X][Y], FILTER[X][Y], and SKELETON[X][Y] each require 512 × 512 elements. Other skeletonization algorithms exist that use a mask and a set of conditional statements to perform the skeletonization operation. These algorithms execute faster than the morphological skeletonization algorithm presented here. One such algorithm can be found in *Digital Image Processing* by Rafael Gonzalez and Paul Wintz given in the annotated bibliography.

```
Skeleton(unsigned char IMAGE[][],unsigned char
  SKELETON[][])
      {
      int X,Y,I,J,MASK[5][5],pixel_on,false,true,pixel;
      unsigned char FILTER[512][512];
      true=1; false=0; pixel_on=true;
      for(J=0; J<=4; J++)
          for(I=0; I<=4; I++) MASK[J][I]=1;
      MASK[0][0]=0;MASK[0][4]=0;MASK[4][0]=0;MASK[4][4]=0;
      for(Y=0; Y<=511; Y++)
          for(X=0; X<=511; X++)SKELETON[X][Y]=0;
          while(pixel_on==true){ pixel_on=false;
              erosion(IMAGE,MASK,FILTER);
              dilation(FILTER,MASK,FILTER);
              for(Y=0; Y<=511; Y++)
              for(X=0; X<=511; X++){
                  pixel=IMAGE[X][Y]-FILTER[X][Y];
                  SKELETON[X][Y]=SKELETON[X][Y]| pixel;
                  If(pixel==255)pixel_on=true;}
              erosion(IMAGE, MASK, IMAGE);}
      }
```

Figure 9.36 *Partial C code to perform morphological skeletonization on a binary image.*

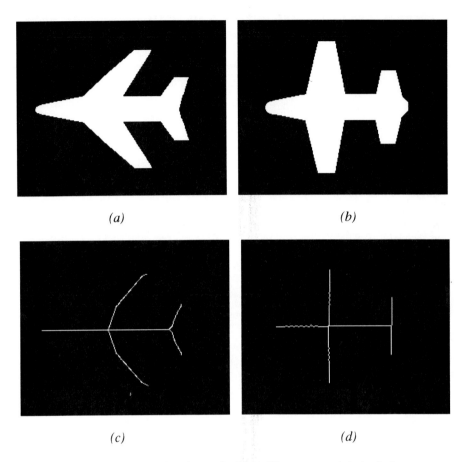

(a)   *(b)*

(c)   *(d)*

Figure 9.37 *An example of two airplane silhouettes and their skeletons.*

Figure 9.38 shows the effectiveness of using skeletonization for airplane silhouette identification. Figures 9.36a and b show two different airplane silhouettes, and Figures 9.37c and d shows their respective skeletons. Note the difference between the two skeletons, in particular, the angle between the cross member of the main wing assembly and the plane's main body.

The material presented in this chapter represents the major body of techniques used in binary morphological filtering. Other morphological techniques include decomposition of an object into a subset of fundamental shapes. These shapes may include circles, rectangles, and even triangles. Once a subset of geometrical shapes has been determined, these shapes can be used to identify the object. Further discussion on shape decomposition is given in *Nonlinear Digital Filters Principles and Applications* by I. Pitas and A. N. Venetsanopoulos, listed in the annotated bibliography.

Chapter 10

Spatial Frequency Filtering

10.1 Introduction

Spatial frequency filtering of images is based on the manipulation of the frequency components contained within an image. By modifying an image's frequency components, periodic noise can be removed, edges can be enhanced and the overall image can be softened or sharpened. To find the spatial frequencies contained within an image, the discrete Fourier transform (DFT) is used. The DFT is a decomposition of an image into a set of sine and cosines with the frequency and amplitude of each representing the spatial frequencies within an image. In this chapter the reader will first be introduce to the discrete Fourier transform as a means of decomposing a one-dimensional function into a set of sine and cosine functions. Next, the one-dimensional DFT will be expanded into two dimensions and applied to image enhancement.

The mathematical formulation of a function as a series of sine and cosine functions was first developed by the french mathematician Baptiste Joseph Fourier (1768 - 1830). Fourier used a sine and cosine series expansion to describe heat conduction and the temperature distribution along an infinite heat conducting sheet. Since then, Fourier's work has been applied to many problems dealing with frequency analysis. Fourier transforms have been applied to electrical signals to analyze their frequency content thus allowing for electronic filtering of these electrical signals. Fourier transforms have also been applied to stock market data so as to find any periodic down- or upturn in the market. Fourier transforms and their properties are widely used in image processing to enhance and restore images.

Since the Fourier transform is a decomposition of a function or an image into sine and cosines a good place to start in the development of the Fourier transform is to define both the sine and cosine. A sine function as a function of distance X is defined as

$$f(X) = A \cdot \sin(2\pi f X + \theta) \tag{1}$$

The amplitude of the sine wave is given by the variable A and its frequency is given by the variable f. The starting point shift, also known as a phase shift, is described by θ. Figure 10.1 is a typical plot of the sine function given in Equation 1 for $\theta = 0$ and 45°.

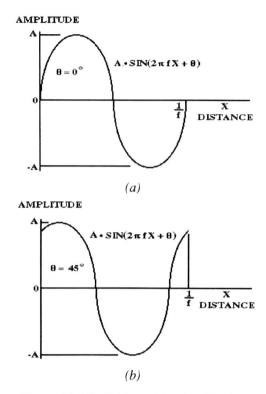

(a)

(b)

Figure 10.1 *Definition of the sine function.*

The frequency of the sine function describes how many times the sine wave repeats itself within a given distance. For example, if f = 1000 cycles/millimeter, then the sine function repeats 1000 times within a distance of 1 mm. The concept of frequency can be easily expanded to an image by observing the spatial detail within the image. Figure 10.2 illustrates the concept of spatial frequency. Figure 10.2 shows a periodic set of stripes for two different spatial frequencies. The periodic rate of the stripes shown in Figure 10.12a is 25 complete periods in 2 inches or 12.5 cycles/in. The image in Figure 10.2b contains 2.8 cycles/in and thus has a lower spatial frequency component than the periodic image given in Figure 10.2a.

The other variables used to describe a sine function are: the amplitude A, which describes the maximum deviation of the sine, and the phase θ which determines the starting point of the sine. As shown in Figure 10.1b, for θ = 45°, its sine function leads the sine function for θ = 0°. For θ = 90° degrees, a special identity is obtained:

$$A \cdot \cos(2\pi fX) = A \cdot \sin(2\pi fX + 90°) \qquad (2)$$

The sine and cosine functions given in Equations 1 and 2 are the two basic functions that are used in defining other types of periodic functions. Fourier showed that the sum of the sine and cosine functions as defined by Equations 1 and 2 could be used to describe a periodic function of the form $f(X) = f(X + T)$, where T is the distance for one complete period. A periodic function is any function that repeats after a given distance. Both the sine and cosine functions as defined by Equations 1 and 2 are periodic over the distance of 1/f.

(a)   *(b)*

Figure 10.2 *Comparison of spatial frequency.*

The one-dimensional Fourier series describing $f(X)$ in terms of a series of sines and cosines is defined as

$$f(X) = \sum_{n=-\infty}^{\infty} F(nf_0)[\cos(2\pi nf_0 X) - j\sin(2\pi nf_0 X)] \tag{3}$$

$$F(nf_0) = \frac{1}{T} \int_0^T f(X)[\cos(2\pi nf_0 X) + j\sin(2\pi nf_0 X)]\, dX \tag{4}$$

where $j = \sqrt{-1}$ and $f_0 = 1/T$ is the fundamental frequency of the function $f(X)$. $F(nf_0)$ in Equation 4 is the amplitude of the sine and cosine components of $f(X)$ at the frequency nf_0. It should also be noted the integral given in Equation 4 is over the period of $f(X)$. Since the variable n is an integer, the frequency terms occur at discrete locations and are multiples of the *fundamental frequency* f_0.

Equation 4 shows that the frequency components $F(nf_0)$ contain both real and imaginary terms. The integral in Equation 4 can then be separated into two integrals describing the real and imaginary components of $F(nf_0)$;

$$F_r(nf_0) = \frac{1}{T} \int_0^T F(X)[\cos(2\pi nf_0 X)]\, dX \tag{5}$$

$$F_i(nf_0) = \frac{1}{T} \int_0^T F(X)[\sin(2\pi nf_0 X)]\, dX \tag{6}$$

Given the real and imaginary frequency components as defined in Equations 5 and 6, the magnitude and phase for each frequency term can be found.

$$|F(nf_0)| = \sqrt{\{F_r(nf_0)\}^2 + \{F_i(nf_0)\}^2} \qquad (7)$$

$$ang[F(nf_0)] = \arctan\left[\frac{F_i(nf_0)}{F_r(nf_0)}\right] \qquad (8)$$

where $|F(nf_0)|$ is known as the magnitude spectrum of $f(X)$, and $ang[F(nf_0)]$ is known as the phase spectrum of $f(X)$.

In Figure 10.3, a one-dimensional square wave is shown with a 50% duty cycle. For this function, the real and imaginary frequency components are given by

$$F_r(nf_0) = 0 \qquad \text{for n not equal to 0} \qquad (9a)$$

$$F_r(nf_0) = \frac{A}{2} \qquad \text{for n = 0} \qquad (9b)$$

and

$$F_i(nf_0) = 0 \qquad \text{for n even} \qquad (10c)$$

$$F_i(nf_0) = \frac{A}{\pi n} \qquad \text{for n odd and n > 0} \qquad (10d)$$

$$F_i(nf_0) = \frac{-A}{\pi n} \qquad \text{for n odd and n < 0} \qquad (10d)$$

For n = zero the value of F(0) equals A/2 ,which is the average value of the square wave. In general, n equal to zero yields the average value for $f(X)$. F(0) is also sometimes referred to as the dc frequency component.

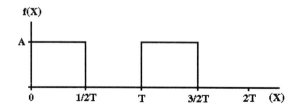

Figure 10.3 *A 50% duty cycle square wave.*

A plot of the magnitude spectrum for $f(X)$ equal to the square wave shown in Figure 10.3 is given in Figure 10.4. Two interesting points to note are that (1) the magnitude spectrum only contains odd harmonics of the fundamental frequency, and (2) that the spectrum contains periodic side lobes (n = −7, −5, −3, 3, 5, 7).

Now using Equation 3, the square wave in terms of its sine and cosine components can be written as

$$f(X) = \frac{A}{2} + \frac{2A}{\pi} \sin(\frac{2\pi X}{T}) + \frac{2A}{3\pi} \sin(\frac{2\pi 3X}{T}) + \frac{2A}{5\pi} \sin(\frac{2\pi 5X}{T}) + \frac{2A}{7\pi} \sin(\frac{2\pi 7X}{T}) \cdots \qquad (11)$$

Not shown in Equation 11 are the terms for N less than zero since these sine terms have been combined with the sine terms for when N is greater than zero, resulting in an additional factor of 2 for each coefficient. The effect of adding more and more terms to f(X) is to better approximate the discontinuity that exists in f(X). Whenever f(X) contains an infinite discontinuity as the case of a square wave, the number of frequency components contained within f(X) will be infinite.

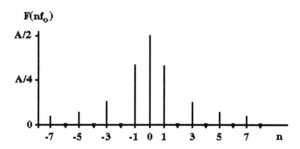

Figure 10.4 *The magnitude spectrum for a square wave.*

Figure 10.5 illustrates the effect of adding more terms to the series for f(X). The plot shown in Figure 10.5a is the result of the first seven terms for N = 0, +/−1, +/−3, while the plot shown in Figure 10.5b is the result of the first fifteen terms N=0, +/−1, +/−3, +/−5, +/−7, +/−9, +/−11, +/−13. As more high-frequency terms are added to f(X) the slope of the step or edge increases. This indicates that the sharpness of the edge is defined by its high-frequency components. If some high-frequency terms are eliminated, the slope of the step will be smaller, effectively smoothing the edge.

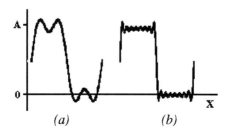

(a)   (b)

Figure 10.5 *Reconstruction of a square wave from a finite number of frequency components.*

10.2 Discrete Fourier Transforms

In Section 10.1 the Fourier series was presented for a continuous periodic function f(X). In Equation 4 an integral had to be evaluated to determine the frequency components of f(X). If the continuous periodic function f(X) is replaced by a sampled periodic function, the integral in Equation 4 is replaced by a summation, allowing for easy computer computation. Figure 10.6 illustrates a typical function f(X) sampled over N points. The interval between samples has been normalized to a value of 1.

Since the function f(X) used in the Fourier series is assumed to be a continuous periodic function as described by Equations 3 and 4, and since $f_S(X)$ as illustrated in Figure 10.6 is not periodic over the N sample points it must be converted to a periodic function.

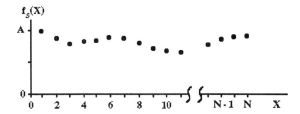

Figure 10.6 *A typical sampled function.*

To accomplish this, $f_S(X)$ is simply made periodic over the N sampled points [$f_S(X) = f_S(X + N)$]. This approach of making $f_S(X)$ periodic doesn't gain or lose any information contained in the sampled function $f_S(X)$. The main reason for this is that all of the information contained in $f_S(X)$ is contained within one of the periods of $f_S(X)$. For all practical purposes only the first period will be consider (N=0). An example of a sampled periodic function is given in Figure 10.7. With the period of $f_S(X)$ now set to T = N the fundamental frequency is now given as $f_0 = 1/N$. Replacing the integral in Equation 4 with a series of sine and cosine terms that varies over X and $f_0 = 1/N$ the discrete Fourier transform (DFT) in one dimension is defined to be,

$$F(n) = \frac{1}{N} \sum_{X=0}^{N-1} f(X) \, [\cos(2\pi nX/N) + j \sin(2\pi nX/N)] \qquad (12)$$

and the inverse discrete Fourier transform (IDFT) is,

$$f(X) = \sum_{n=0}^{N-1} F(n) \, [\cos(2\pi n X) - j \sin(2\pi n X)] \qquad (13)$$

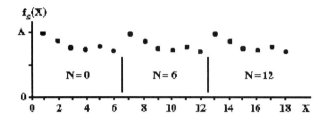

Figure 10.7 *An example of a sampled periodic function.*

There are several fundamental differences between the Fourier series as described by Equations 3 and 4 and the discrete Fourier transform and its inverse given in Equations 12 and 13. Besides the fact that f(X) is now sampled and assumed to be periodic over the N sampled points, the maximum positive frequency that is obtainable occurs at n = N/2. This results in a normalized frequency of f = n/N or 1/2. A normalized frequency of 1/2 is a direct consequence of the Nyquist Theorem, which states that the maximum allowable frequency is one-half the sampling frequency.

Since the sample rate was normalized to 1, that is X = 0, 1, 2, ... N − 1, the sample frequency that equals the reciprocal of the sample rate is also 1. Using the Nyquist theorem the maximum allowable frequency is 1/2, which is in agreement with Equation 12. Stated another way, the positive frequencies are defined from n = 0 to N/2 − 1, and the negative frequency components defined are for n = N/2 to N − 1. The negative frequency components are normally obtained from Equation 3 for n less than 0. An example of this effect is shown in Figure 10.8 for the spectrum of a sampled square wave.

To implement the one-dimensional discrete Fourier transform, four arrays of size N are needed. The first two are used to store the real and imaginary components of the sampled function $f_s(X)$. Since f(X) is usually a real function which also yields a real function for $f_s(X)$, the imaginary array for $f_s(X)$ is usually set to zero. The other two arrays are used to store the real and imaginary parts of the frequency components of F(n). Figure 10.9 shows the interaction between the real and imaginary parts of the original function f(X) and its Fourier spectrum F(n). An example of the partial code to implement the discrete Fourier transform and its inverse is given in Figure 10.10. Arrays fri[] and fqi[] are the real and imaginary arrays for the components of f(X) computed by the discrete Fourier transform algorithm. The input f(X) is stored in the arrays fr[] and fi[] upon entering the discrete Fourier transform. Typically, fi[] is set to 0 since f(X) is usually real.

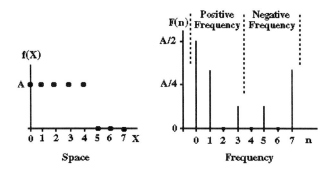

Figure 10.8 *The discrete Fourier transform of a sampled square wave.*

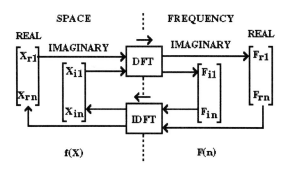

Figure 10.9 *Data storage requirements for the DFT.*

There are many cases when the sample interval for $f_s(X)$ is not normalized to 1 as was presented previously. In the derivation of the discrete Fourier transform, the sample interval was normalized to 1 so that the index increment in the implementation of the DFT was an integer and corresponded to the array index increment. Given that the increment for X is some distance ΔX, then the actual spatial frequency in cycles/distance is given by

$$f = \frac{n}{N \, \Delta X} \tag{14}$$

The development of the discrete Fourier transform in one dimension allows for easy understanding of its development and concept. Since the goal of this chapter is to use frequency techniques to modify an image, the one-dimensional equations for the Fourier transform must be modified. Assuming an image of size X = N by Y = M pixels the two-dimensional and its inverse become

$$F(n, m) = \frac{1}{NM} \sum_{Y=0}^{N-1} \sum_{X=0}^{N-1} f(X, Y) \cdot [\cos(2\pi nX/N) + j \sin(2\pi nX/N)]$$

$$\cdot [\cos(2\pi mY/M) + j \sin(2\pi mY/M)] \tag{15}$$

$$f(X, Y) = \sum_{n=0}^{N-1} \sum_{m=0}^{N-1} F(n, m) \cdot [\cos(2\pi nX/N) - j \sin(2\pi nX/N)]$$

$$\cdot [\cos(2\pi mY/M) - j \sin(2\pi mY/M)] \tag{16}$$

```
ForwardFourier( float fr[], float fi[], float fqr[], float
fqi[] )
        {p = 3.141592654;
        for (n=0; n<N; n++)
            for(x=0, x<N; x++){    /*FORWARD*/
                fqr[n] = fr[x]*cos(2pnx/N) -
                fi[x]*sin(2pnx/N)/N;
                fqi[n]  = fr[x]*sin(2pnx/N) +
                fi[x]*cos(2pnx/N)/N;
            }
        }

    InverseFourier( float fr[], float fi[], float fqr[], float
fqi[] )
        {p=3.141592654;
        for (x=0; x<N; x++)
            for(n=0; n<N; n++){   /*INVERSE*/
                fr[x] = (fqr[n]*cos(2pnx/N) +
                fqi[n]*sin(2pnx/N));
                fi[x] = (fqr[n]*sin(2pnx/N) -
                fqi[n]*cos(2pnx/N));           }
        }
```

Figure 10.10 *Partial C code for the discrete Fourier transform.*

Figure 10.11 shows an image of a two-dimensional square wave and its corresponding two-dimensional magnitude spectrum. In Figure 10.11b, the dc frequency term (n, m = 0) is located in the center of the image. The negative frequency components for the X direction (n less than 0) are located to the left of center, while negative frequency components for the Y direction (m less than 0) are located above the center of the image. Note the main frequency lobe in the center of the spectrum and the addition of side lobes surrounding the main lobe.

In Figure 10.12 is a three-dimensional plot of the magnitude spectrum. In the center of the graph is the main lobe, and to each side of the main lobe are the surrounding side lobes. The three-dimensional plot has been normalized so that the maximum value that occurs at n, m = 0 is 255.

10.3 Properties of Discrete Fourier Transforms

Several important properties of Fourier transforms permit manipulation of the frequency components of an image. The first is separability. Separability allows for the separation of the two-dimensional discrete Fourier transform into two sets of one-dimensional discrete Fourier transforms in the X and Y direction.

Equations 15 and 16, which are the two-dimensional discrete Fourier transform and its inverse, can be rewritten as follows

$$F(n, m) = \frac{1}{M} \sum_{Y=0}^{N-1} [\cos(2\pi m Y/M) + j\sin(2\pi m Y/M)]$$

$$\frac{1}{N} \sum_{X=0}^{N-1} f(X, Y) [\cos(2\pi n X/N) + j\sin(2\pi n X/N)] \tag{17}$$

$$f(X, Y) = \sum_{m=0}^{N-1} [\cos(2\pi m Y/M) - j\sin(2\pi m Y/M)]$$

$$\sum_{n=0}^{N-1} F(n, m) [\cos(2\pi n X/N) - j\sin(2\pi n X/N)] \tag{18}$$

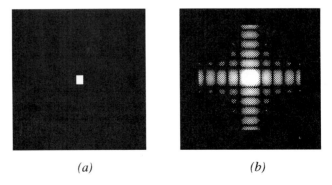

(a)   *(b)*

Figure 10.11 *The two-dimensional DFT of a square.*

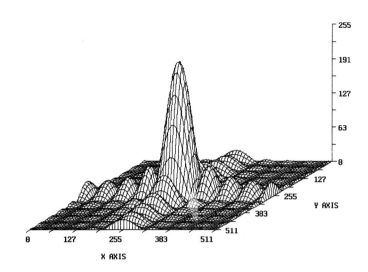

Figure 10.12 *Fourier magnitude three-dimensional plot of the magnitude spectrum in Figure 10.11.*

Immediately on viewing Equation 17 it is noticed that the first series is the one-dimensional discrete Fourier transform in the X direction. The second summation over Y is the one-dimensional discrete Fourier transform in the Y direction of the results of the first transform. Defining the discrete Fourier transform over X as F(n, Y),

$$F(n, Y) \ = \ \frac{1}{N} \sum_{X=0}^{N-1} f\,(X, Y)\,[\cos(2\pi nX/N) \ + j\,\sin(2\pi nX/N)] \tag{19}$$

the second transform over Y becomes

$$F(n, m) \ = \ \frac{1}{M} \sum_{Y=0}^{N-1} F(n, Y)\,[\cos(2\pi mY/M) \ + j\,\sin(2\pi mY/M)]\ . \tag{20}$$

Figure 10.13 illustrates how the property of separability converts a two-dimensional discrete Fourier transform into a combination of one-dimensional discrete Fourier transforms. First, the one-dimensional discrete Fourier transform is performed N times in the X direction. Each individual row is Fourier transformed separately to generate a new two-dimensional complex image F(n, Y). Next, the one-dimensional discrete Fourier transform is applied in the Y direction on F(n, Y). Again each column is Fourier transformed separately. The total number of one-dimensional discrete Fourier transforms needed is N + M.

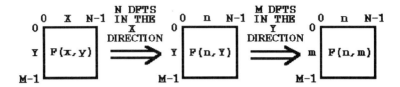

Figure 10.13 *Separability property of the discrete Fourier transform.*

Table 10.1 gives several additional Fourier transform properties for the case of a square image (N = M). Of these, two important ones are the Fourier transform of an image containing a two-dimensional cosine and the Fourier transform of a constant. The Fourier transform of the image (cos 2πaX · cos $2\pi$by) yields four points in the Fourier domain located at the frequencies (a, b),(−a, b),(a, −b), and (−a, −b). This is to be expected since the Fourier transform is a decomposition of an image into a set of cosines and sines. The frequencies a and b and their negatives correspond to the frequencies of the cosine image in the X and Y directions.

For the case of an image that is constant, the two-dimensional Fourier transform yields a point in the Fourier domain located at the frequency n = m = 0. For n = m = 0, this is known as the dc or average value of the image. Since the image is a constant, no spatial frequencies are associated with this image. Having the Fourier transform yield a component located at n = m = 0 is not surprising since no other spatial frequencies are present in this image.

Figure 10.8 illustrates how negative and positive frequencies are stored after a one-dimensional discrete Fourier transform. The positive frequency components are stored first, followed by the negative frequency components. Figure 10.14 shows an image of the magnitude of a Fourier transform of a white box similar to Figure 10.11b, except that the frequencies are shown in reverse order. In the n direction the positive frequencies are to the left of the negative frequencies, while in the m direction the negative frequencies are above the positive frequencies.

Typically, when viewing the magnitude spectrum of an image, it is desired to have the center of this image be the zero frequency. To the left of the center of the image are the negative frequency terms in the n direction, and to the right of center are the positive frequency terms. In the Y direction above the center are the negative frequencies, while below the center are the positive frequencies. The centering of the two-dimensional discrete Fourier transform is easily accomplished by multiplying the original image f(X, Y) by −1 to the X + Y power,

$$f(X, Y) \text{ is replaced by } f(X, Y)(-1)^{X + Y} \qquad (21)$$

prior to taking the Fourier transform of the image f(X, Y). This is how the centered magnitude discrete Fourier transform was generated in Figure 10.11b.

Table 10.1 *Several discrete Fourier transform properties.*

f(X, Y) IMAGE	F(n, m) MAGNITUDE
A cos 2πaX · cos 2πbY	A/4 at (a, b) A/4 at (−a, b) A/4 at (a, −b) A/4 at (−a, −b)
A	A at n = 0, m = 0
A at X = 0, Y = 0 0 elsewhere	$\dfrac{A}{N\,M}$
f(X, Y)(−1)$^{(X + Y)}$	F(n, m) centered
f(aX, bY)	1/|a b| F(n / a, m / b)
f(X, Y) + G(X, Y)	F(n, m) + G(n, m)
exp[−π(X^2 + Y^2)]	exp[−π(n^2 + m^2)/N]
F(n, m)	f(−X,− Y)
f(X, Y) rotated by an angle θ	F(n, m) rotated by an angle θ

Figure 10.14. *Uncentered magnitude Fourier spectrum of the box image given in Figure 10.11.*

Two additional properties of the two-dimensional Fourier transform are the rotational invariant property and the symmetrical property. If an image f(X, Y) has a Fourier spectrum given by F(n, m) and if this image is now rotated by some angle θ, the Fourier spectrum will also be rotated by this same angle θ. The symmetric property of the Fourier transform states that the magnitude of the Fourier spectrum is symmetric about the dc frequency (n = m = 0) as seen in Figure 10.11b. Stated another way,

$$|F(n, m)| = |F(-n, -m)|, \qquad (22)$$

where |F(n, m) | means the magnitude of F(n, m).

The magnitude of the Fourier spectrum yields a spatial frequency spectrum that is the same for both positive and negative frequencies. This can be easily seen in the spectrum shown in Figure 10.11b, where the dc frequency component (n = m = 0) is located in the center of the image. Several examples of the two-dimensional Fourier spectrum along with its corresponding original image are given in Figure 10.15. Figures 10.15a, c, and e are the original images and Figures 10.15b, d, and f are their respective magnitude spectrums.

10.4 Fast Fourier Transforms

The fast Fourier transform (FFT) was developed by J. W. Cooley and J. W. Tukey in 1965 as a fast algorithm for the discrete Fourier transform. The number of complex multiplications and additions required to compute the discrete Fourier transform is on the order of $N \times N$. The FFT algorithm reduces this number of calculations to $N \log_2 N$. For example a 512 one-dimensional discrete Fourier transform is about 57 times slower than a 512-point FFT. More to the point, an 8192-point FFT is 630 times faster than implementing the discrete Fourier transform directly.

The FFT algorithm decomposes the discrete Fourier transform in such a way as to take advantage of the periodicity of the sine and cosine functions, hence reducing the number of calculations necessary. Initially, the FFT divides the N-point input function f(X) into N/2 points and then computes 2 - N/2 point discrete Fourier transforms. The output from this operation is then divided into a set of N/4 points and 4 - N/4 point transforms are computed. This process repeats itself until N − 2 point transforms are computed. Since the FFT algorithm works by dividing the input array by 2 repeatedly, the size of the input array must be a power of 2.

Typical input sampled function sizes are 2, 4, 16, 32, 64, 128, and 256. For image-processing applications, the typical image sizes of interest are 256×256, 512×512, and 1024×1024. When one of the dimensions of the image is not a power of 2 the size of the image should be increased to the closest power of 2. All the new pixels are given the value of 0. This process is called *padding* the image with zeros. This process does not modify the spectral response of the original image. Information is neither lost nor gained. For example a 320×200 image would be expanded to a 512×256 image. To reduce the complexity of the two-dimensional FFT, a better image dimension would be 512×512, making the dimension of the padded image the same in both the X and Y directions.

Figure 10.16 gives the partial code for the one-dimensional FFT. The program expects the input function f(X) to be stored in the array data[] upon its call. Since the discrete Fourier transform expects complex numbers, the real and imaginary parts of the input are stored in adjacent locations in array data[]. The first element of array data is the real part of the first sample of f(X) or f(0). The next element in the array data[] is the imaginary part of the first sample f(X). This sequence repeats until all the samples of f(X) are stored in array data[]. Since array data[] stores both the real and imaginary parts of f(X), and since the total number of sampled points for f(X) is equal to N, the size of array data[] is $2 \cdot N$.

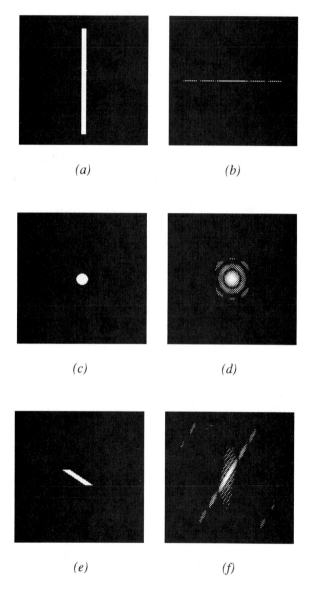

(a)   *(b)*

(c)   *(d)*

(e)   *(f)*

Figure 10.15 *Several two-dimensional FFT examples.*

Typically f(X) is a real-valued function containing no imaginary terms. For this case, every other element in array data[] is set to 0; that is, this sets the imaginary part of f(X) to 0. Upon returning from the FFT subroutine, the real and imaginary parts of F(n) are stored in the adjacent cells of array data[x]. The first element is the real part of the first frequency term

F(0), while the next element is the imaginary part of the first frequency term F(0). The first N terms of array data[] give the real and imaginary parts of the positive frequencies of F(n). The last N terms of array data[] give the real and imaginary terms of the negative frequencies of F(n). To center the resulting Fourier spectrum in array data[] just simply multiply the sampled function f(X) by −1 to the X prior to taking the FFT.

In calling the FFT subroutine the variable num is the size of the FFT desired, and the variable dir is used to set the FFT algorithm to either the forward or inverse FFT. To perform a 512-point FFT, num would be set to 512. For dir equal to −1 the FFT algorithm in Figure 10.16 becomes the inverse FFT, while setting the variable dir to +1 gives the forward FFT.

```
fft(float data[],int num, float dir)
    {
    int array_size, bits, ind, j, j1, i, i1, u;
    int step, inc;
    float wcos, wsin, tr, ti;
    bits=log(num)/log(2)+.5;
    for (i=0;i<513;i++){
    sine[i]=dir*sin(3.141592654*i/512);
    cose[i]=cos(3.141592654*i/512);}
    array_size=num<<1;
    for(i=0;i<num;i++){
    ind=0;
    for(j=0;j<bits;j++){
        u=1<<j;ind=(ind<<1)+((u&i)>>j);}
    ind=ind<<1;j=i<<1;
    if(j<ind){
        exchange(data[j],data[ind]);
        exchange(data[j+1],data[ind+1]);}}
    for(inc=2;inc<array_size;inc=step){
        step=inc<<1;
        for (u=0;u<inc;u+=2){
        ind=((long)u<<9)/inc;
        wcos=cose[ind];wsin=sine[ind];
        for (i=u;i<array_size;i+=step){
            j=i+inc;j1=j+1;i1=i+1;
            tr=wcos*data[j]-wsin*data[j1];
            ti=wcos*data[j1]+wsin*data[j];
            data[j]=data[i]-tr;data[i]
        =data[i]+tr;
            data[j1]=data[i1]-ti;data[i1]
        =data[i1]+ti;}}}
    }
```

Figure 10.16 *The one-dimensional FFT algorithm.*

The results of the FFT algorithm given in Figure 10.16 are equivalent to the discrete Fourier transform as defined in Equation 12, except for the factor of 1/N. To use the algorithm for both the forward and inverse Fourier transforms, this factor must be included in the code.

This is not a major issue in image-processing since for most applications the viewing of the magnitude spectrum is of interest and this image is usually autoscaled to fit the graylevel range of the image processing system. If the 1/N factor is required the resulting spectrum stored in array data[] can simply be divided by N when taking the forward Fourier transform.

In special cases when the size of the FFT desired is fixed, a speed improvement for the FFT algorithm given in Figure 10.16 can be made. Under these circumstances, the two sine[] and cose[] arrays should be made global and their trigometric values computed only once.

The two-dimensional fast Fourier transform is easily computed using the one-dimensional FFT algorithm given in Figure 10.16. Assuming a square image of size N × N, an input image array IMAGE[x, y], and an output Fourier array FOUR[n, m], to compute the two-dimensional Fourier transform, the one-dimensional FFT algorithm is first used in the x direction row by row on the input array IMAGE[x, y] to compute FOUR[n, y]. Next the one-dimensional FFT algorithm is applied to the array FOUR[n, y] in the y direction column by column to compute the two-dimensional Fourier transform FOUR[n, m]. This method of computing the two-dimensional Fourier transform is the same procedure used in Figure 10.13.

10.5 Other Transforms

In its derivation it was stated that the Fourier transform was the decomposition of an image into a set of sines and cosines. A different transform can easily be derived for different types of decompositions. Another common transform is to decompose an image into a set of square waves. This transform is known as the Walsh transform. Equation 23 defines the one-dimensional Walsh transform (WT) as

$$F(n) = \frac{1}{N} \sum_{X=0}^{N-1} f(X) \prod_{i=0}^{q-1} (-1)^{b_i(X)b_{q-1-i}(n)} \tag{23}$$

and the inverse discrete Walsh transform (IWFT) as

$$f(X) = \sum_{n=0}^{N-1} F(n) \prod_{i=0}^{q-1} (-1)^{b_i(X)b_{q-1-i}(n)} , \tag{24}$$

where $b_i(X)$ is a binary bit representation and

$$\prod_{i=0}^{N-1} (-1)^i = (-1)(-1)(-1) \cdots (-1) , \tag{25}$$

which are N products of (-1). For example if the total number of bits (q) equals 4 (hence N = 16) and X equals 7 (0111) then $b_0(7) = 1$, $b_1(7) = 1$, $b_2(7) = 1$, and $b_3(7) = 0$. Since -1 raised to an integer power can only take on the values of 1 for even powers and –1 for odd powers, the cosine and sine functions given in the Fourier transform are replaced by a square wave of ±1.

The Walsh transform is easily expanded into two dimensions as

$$F(n, m) = \frac{1}{NM} \sum_{Y=0}^{N-1} \sum_{X=0}^{M-1} f(X, Y) \cdot \prod_{i=0}^{q-1} (-1)^{b_i(X)b_{q-1-i}(n) + b_i(Y)b_{q-1-i}(m)} \qquad (26)$$

and its inverse

$$f(X, Y) = \sum_{m=0}^{N-1} \sum_{m=0}^{M-1} F(n, m) \cdot \prod_{i=0}^{q-1} (-1)^{b_i(X)b_{q-1-i}(n) + b_i(Y)b_{q-1-i}(m)} . \qquad (27)$$

A close cousin to the Walsh transform is the Hadamard transform. Instead of using a product of –1 the product term is replaced by a summation. The two-dimensional Hadamard transform is defined as

$$F(n, m) = \frac{1}{NM} \sum_{Y=0}^{N-1} \sum_{X=0}^{M-1} f(X, Y) \cdot (-1)^{\sum_{i=0}^{q-1} b_i(X)b_i(n) + b_i(Y)b_i(m)} . \qquad (28a)$$

and its inverse

$$f(X, Y) = \sum_{n=0}^{N-1} \sum_{m=0}^{M-1} F(n, m) \cdot (-1)^{\sum_{i=0}^{q-1} b_i(X)b_i(n) + b_i(Y)b_i(m)} . \qquad (28b)$$

The Hadamard transform also decomposes an image into a set of ±1 square waves. Because of the similarities between the Walsh and the Hadamard transforms, they are sometimes referred in the literature as the Walsh-Hadamard transform.

The attractive advantage of the Walsh and Hadamard transforms over the Fourier transform is that these transforms do not require the computation of sines and cosines. Thus they are computationally much faster than the Fourier transform. The disadvantage of these transforms is the physical interpretation of the frequency space that is generated. The Fourier transform allows for easy interpretation of its frequency space.

The Walsh and Hadamard transforms find use in image coding and compression. Here, an image is decomposed into a set of square waves and only the nonzero coefficients of $F(n, m)$ are saved. For most images, many of the coefficients of $F(n, m)$ are zero. This results in storage compression of an image since only the nonzero coefficients need to be saved.

Another transform of interest is the discrete cosine transform. This transform is very similar to the real part of the Fourier Transform. The discrete cosine transform defined in two dimensions is given by

$$C(n, m) = k(n) \, k(m) \sum_{Y=0}^{N-1} \sum_{X=0}^{N-1} f(X, Y) \cdot \cos\left[\pi n \frac{2X + 1}{N}\right] \cdot \cos\left[\pi m \frac{2Y + 1}{N}\right] \qquad (29)$$

where n and m are defined from 1 to $N - 1$, and

$$k(n) = \begin{cases} \sqrt{\dfrac{1}{N}} & \text{for } n = 0 \\[2ex] \sqrt{\dfrac{2}{N}} & \text{otherwise} \end{cases} \qquad (30)$$

The inverse discrete cosine transform is given by

$$f(X,Y) = \sum_{n=0}^{N-1} \sum_{m=0}^{N-1} k(n) \cdot k(m) \cdot F(n, m) \cdot \cos\left[\pi n \frac{2X + 1}{N}\right] \cdot \cos\left[\pi m \frac{2Y + 1}{N}\right] \qquad (31)$$

One nice feature of the discrete cosine transform is that it can be easily computed in the same manner as the two-dimensional Fourier transform. In fact, the one-dimensional FFT algorithm can be used to compute the discrete cosine transform.

The discrete cosine transform is typically used in image enhancement and restoration. This transform decomposes an image in such a way that the modification of the discrete cosine coefficients allows for easy image enhancement. The discrete cosine transform has also found some use in image coding and compression.

10.6 Spatial Frequency Filtering

The concept of spatial filtering is to manipulate the frequency components of an image so as to enhance the image. The type of enhancement depends on the type of filter implemented. For example, if the high-frequency components of an image are attenuated, the resulting image tends to be softened or blurred. On the other hand, if the high frequencies of an image are enhanced, the result of this filter operation is to sharpen the image. In addition to sharpening an image, amplifying the high frequencies also enhances the edges in an image.

Figure 10.17 shows the four types of one-dimensional ideal filters. The most common of these is the lowpass filter shown in Figure 10.17a. This filter passes all frequency components unmodified from zero frequency to some frequency cutoff n_c. Above this point, all frequency components are set to zero. The opposite of the ideal lowpass filter is the ideal highpass filter shown in Figure 10.17b. This filter eliminates all frequency components from zero frequency to some cutoff frequency n_c.

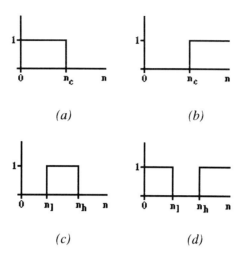

(a)   *(b)*

(c)   *(d)*

Figure 10.17 *Four types of ideal filters: (a) lowpass; (b) highpass; (c) bandpass; (d) notch.*

Figure 10.17c is the bandpass filter. This filter passes all frequency components unmodified between n_l and n_h, and sets all other frequency terms to zero. The last ideal filter shown in Figure 10.17d is the ideal notch filter. This filter removes all frequency components between n_l and n_h and leaves all other frequency components unmodified. The four equations used to describe these four filters are

$$F(n) = \begin{cases} 1 & \text{for } n \leq n_c \\ 0 & \text{for } n > n_c \end{cases} \qquad \text{lowpass filter} \tag{32}$$

$$F(n) = \begin{cases} 0 & \text{for } n \leq n_c \\ 1 & \text{for } n > n_c \end{cases} \qquad \text{highpass filter} \tag{33}$$

$$F(n) = \begin{cases} 1 & \text{for } n_l \leq n \leq n_h \\ 0 & \text{elsewhere} \end{cases} \qquad \text{bandpass filter} \tag{34}$$

$$F(n) = \begin{cases} 0 & \text{for } n_l \leq n \leq n_h \\ 1 & \text{elsewhere} \end{cases} \qquad \text{notch filter} \tag{35}$$

From these four equations it is easily seen that the lowpass and the highpass filters are complements of each other. In other words, the addition of an ideal lowpass filtered image with a highpass filtered image yields the original unfiltered image. Likewise an ideal bandpass filter is the complement filter of an ideal notch filter.

Figure 10.17 gives the ideal filters in one dimension. To expand these ideas to two dimensions two approaches can be taken. The first is simply to apply the desired one-dimensional ideal filter in the n frequency direction, followed by applying the desired one-dimensional filter to the m frequency components. This approach applies a single-dimensional filter separately to both frequency directions. Equation 36 describes how to convert a one-dimensional filter $H_1(n)$ into a two-dimensional filter $H_2(n, m)$ using this approach.

$$H_2(n, m) = H_1(n) \cdot H_1(m) \tag{36}$$

or, in general,

$$H_2(n, m) = H_1(n) \cdot G_1(m) \tag{37}$$

where $H_1(n)$ is one type of filter applied to the frequency components (n) in the X direction, and $G_1(m)$ is a different filter applied to the frequency components (m) in the y direction. In Equation 37 the one-dimensional filters in each of the frequency directions can be the same or different depending on the application.

The second approach is to use only a single one-dimensional filter and to apply this filter radially to all frequencies in the image. First, a radial distance from the zero frequency term is computed, and all frequencies that are located the same radial distance from the zero frequency term are filtered the same. In other words, all frequency components that lie on a circle with a given radial frequency are filtered the same. Defining the radial frequency as

$$R = \sqrt{n^2 + m^2} \tag{38}$$

the two-dimensional radial filter becomes

$$H_2(n, m) = H_1(R) \tag{39}$$

The radial filter given by $H_2(n, m)$ is generated from a one-dimensional filter $H_1(R)$. This type of filter is referred to as a *circularly symmetric filter*. Figure 10.18 shows the effect of converting the one-dimensional ideal lowpass and highpass filters to two dimensions using the radial filtering approach.

For the lowpass filter, when R is less than the radial cutoff frequency R_c, all frequency components are passed unmodified. For R greater than the radial cutoff frequency R_c, these frequency components are set to zero. Hence only low frequencies are allowed to pass through this filter. The circularly symmetric highpass filter is just the opposite of the circularly symmetric lowpass filter.

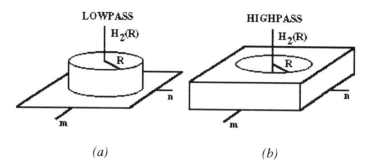

Figure 10.18 Ideal (a) lowpass and (b) highpass circularly symmetric filters.

Equations 40 through 43 give the four ideal circularly symmetric filters in terms of the radial frequency R.

$$F(R) = \begin{cases} 1 & \text{for } R \le R_c \\ 0 & \text{for } R > R_c \end{cases} \qquad \text{lowpass filter} \qquad (40)$$

$$F(R) = \begin{cases} 0 & \text{for } R \le R_c \\ 1 & \text{for } R > R_c \end{cases} \qquad \text{highpass filter} \qquad (41)$$

$$F(R) = \begin{cases} 1 & \text{for } R_l \le R \le R_h \\ 0 & \text{elsewhere} \end{cases} \qquad \text{bandpass filter} \qquad (42)$$

$$F(R) = \begin{cases} 0 & \text{for } R_l \le R \le R_h \\ 1 & \text{elsewhere} \end{cases} \qquad \text{notch filter} \qquad (43)$$

A maximally flat non-ideal lowpass filter that is easily implemented as a circularly symmetric filter is given Equation 44. Some may recognize this filter as the lowpass Butterworth filter. Equation 45 gives the equation for a highpass circularly symmetric non-ideal filter.

$$H_2(R) = \frac{1}{1 + 0.414 \left[\dfrac{R}{R_c} \right]^{2n}} \qquad R > 0 \qquad (44)$$

$$H_2(R) = \frac{1}{1 + 0.414\left[\dfrac{R_C}{R}\right]^{2n}} \qquad R > 0 \qquad (45)$$

The term n adjusts the order of the filter. This term determines how fast the transition from passing frequency components to attenuating various frequency components should be.

For the ideal filter this transition region is zero. Figures 10.19 and 10.20 give the plots of the lowpass and highpass circularly symmetric non-ideal filters for various values of n. In generating these figures, the frequency axis was normalized in reference to the cutoff frequency R_C. Note that as n becomes extremely large both the lowpass and the highpass non-ideal filters approach the ideal lowpass and highpass filters.

The value of R_C, the cutoff frequency, determines where the filter transitions from passing frequency components to attenuating frequency components. For the lowpass filter, as R_C becomes smaller fewer high-frequency components are passed unmodified. The cutoff frequency R_C is also sometimes referred to as the 3-decibel (dB) cutoff frequency, because at the cutoff frequency the filter response is attenuated by 3 dB compared to the frequency components that pass unmodified.

Figure 10.21a is the original picture of three geometrical shapes showing sharp edges. Figure 10.21b is the result of lowpass filtering Figure 10.21a with a first-order (n = 1) circularly symmetric non-ideal lowpass filter with a cutoff frequency of $R_C = 0.589$. In this picture the sharpness of the edges is no longer present. This is to be expected since the high-frequency terms in the original image shown in Figure 10.21a have been reduced. Figure 10.21c shows even further the blurring effect of a lowpass filter caused by removing even more high-frequency terms by reducing the cutoff frequency to $R_C = 0.195$. Figure 10.21d shows the removal of most of the high frequencies with the cutoff frequency set to 0.0195.

Figure 10.22a is an original picture of a young girl. A circularly symmetric highpass non-ideal filter of order 1 and cutoff frequency of 0.0195 was applied to this image to sharpen the edges within the image. The result of this filtering process is shown in Figure 10.22b. Note the enhancement of the edges within the picture, while contrast in the large regions (low-frequency content) was reduced.

The filtering process used in generating the images in Figures 10.21 and 10.22 first begins by taking the two-dimensional fast Fourier transform of the original image. Next, either the circularly symmetric highpass or lowpass non-ideal filter is applied to the Fourier spectrum of the original image to modify its respective frequency components. Finally, the inverse fast Fourier transform is taken of the filtered spectrum, yielding the filtered image.

10.7 Wiener Filtering

Another common filter used in image processing is the Wiener filter. This filter does an excellent job of restoring images in the presence of noise. Figure 10.23 is a block diagram describing an image that has been degraded by a fixed degradation process h(x, y). Typically, the degradation process is known and can be modeled as a linear filter. Noise is then added to the output of the filtered and degraded image. The addition of noise at this point makes it difficult to completely restore the noise-degraded image even if the degradation model is accurately known.

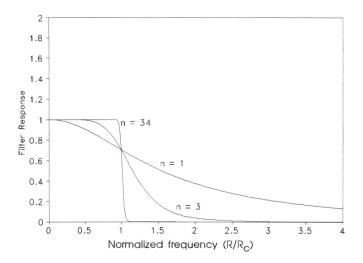

Figure 10.19 *Radial plot of the lowpass circularly symmetric non-ideal filter for various n.*

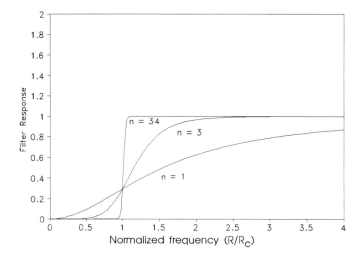

Figure 10.20 *Radial plot of the highpass circularly symmetric non-ideal filter for various n.*

(a)

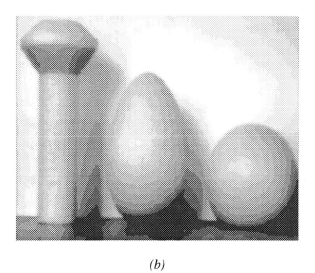

(b)

Figure 10.21 *Examples of lowpass circularly symmetric non-ideal filtered images.*

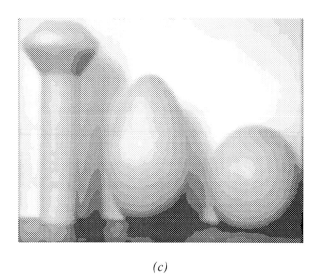

(c)

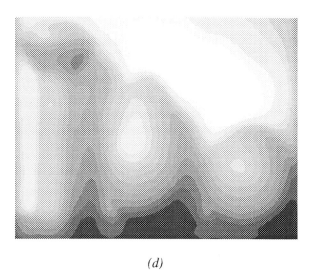

(d)

Figure 10.21 *continued*

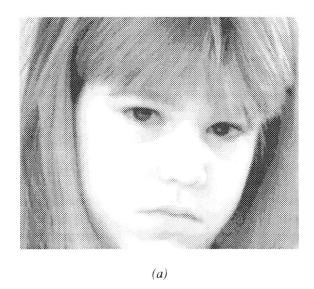

(a)

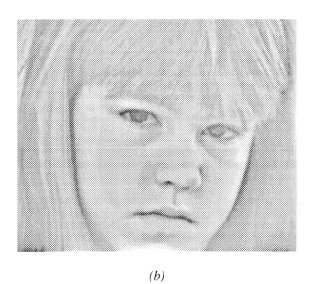

(b)

Figure 10.22 *Example of a highpass circularly symmetric non-ideal filtered image.*

The noise is added at this point in the model because it represents the appropriate location at which camera noise should be added to the process. Equation 46 describes the output spectrum G(n, m) for the noise degradation model given in Figure 10.23.

$$G(n, m) = F(n, m) \cdot H(n, m) + N(n, m) \quad, \tag{46}$$

where F(n, m) is the frequency spectrum of the original image, H(n, m) is the frequency spectrum of the degradation, and N(n, m) is the frequency spectrum of the noise. The desire is to recover the original spectrum F(n, m) from the degraded spectrum G(n, m).

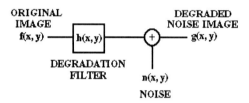

Figure 10.23 *A model for a degraded image with additive noise.*

There are many applications in image processing where the degradation filter is accurately known. Under these circumstances, the Wiener filter can estimate the original spectrum F(n, m) in the presence of noise. With the Wiener filter, an estimate of the original image frequency spectrum can be obtained given knowledge of the degradation process. The Wiener filter is defined as

$$F(n, m) = \left[\frac{|H(n, m)|^2}{|H(n, m)|^2 + S_n(n, m)/S_f(n, m)} \right] \frac{G(n, m)}{H(n, m)} \quad, \tag{47}$$

where $|H(n, m)|^2$ is the squared magnitude of the frequency spectrum of the degradation model, and $S_n(n, m)$ and $S_f(n, m)$ are the averaged squared magnitude frequency spectrums of the noise and original image, respectively.

The difficulty with Equation 47 is that it requires knowledge of the square magnitude frequency spectrums of both the noise and original image. Unfortunately, this is not the usual situation. If either the noise or original frequency spectrums are not known, Equation 47 is approximated by

$$F(n, m) = \left[\frac{|H(n, m)|^2}{|H(n, m)|^2 + K} \right] \frac{G(n, m)}{H(n, m)} \tag{48}$$

Under this situation the constant K is varied until the best restored image is obtained. For the special case when K is zero, Equation 48 reduces to

$$F(n, m) = \frac{G(n, m)}{H(n, m)} \qquad (49)$$

Application of Equation 49 is known as inverse filter restoration.

To apply the Wiener filter to a degraded image, the fast Fourier transform spectrums of the degraded image $g(x, y)$ and the degradation function $h(x, y)$ are obtained. Next, Equation 48, with an estimated value for the constant K, is used to generate the restored spectrum $F(n, m)$. The inverse fast Fourier transform is finally used to generate the restored image $f(x, y)$. This process is repeated for different values of K until the best restored image is obtained. A more advanced technique for picking the value of K is to use a constrained least-squares approach. This approach is beyond the scope of this book. The reader is referred to any one of the more advanced image processing books given in the annotated bibliography.

Chapter 11

Adaptive Filters

11.1 Introduction

In previous chapters in this book various types of image filters have been discussed. Each of these filters operated either locally or globally on an image with their filtering characteristics remaining constant. In many instances, the best type of filter required varies throughout the image. Depending on the type of noise that is present within an image, the type of filter that is chosen to remove the noise can radically affect the important details that must remain unchanged in an image. For example, if the noise within an image has a uniform distribution, then this noise is best filtered using a mean filter, but at the expense of losing some image details. On the other hand, if the noise is impulsive-type noise, this noise is best removed from an image using a median filter.

The disadvantage of a mean filter over a median filter is that a mean filter removes fine spatial details and tends to blur the edges within an image. An ideal filter to use on an image is a filter that adaptively changes its filtering characteristics depending on the image content within a local window. For example, if the image content within a local window contains only edges then a median filter would be used to preserve the edge details. If, within a local window, a uniform background is detected, then the filter will change its characteristics to perform a mean filter within this local window.

Adaptive filters can be separated into two areas. The first is the decision process that is used to determine the type of filter required. This can be as simple as a Sobel or gradient edge detector or as elaborate as determining statistical parameters about the noise within an image. Once the decision process has been determined, the other area for adaptive filters is to determine which is the best filter to use. As mentioned previously, if an edge is detected, a median filter does a better job preserving edge details as compared to a mean filter. The final goal of any adaptive filter is to change its characteristics to best preserve the desired image contents, but at the same time reduce the noise within the image.

This chapter first introduces the reader to some fundamentals of noise analysis that are required to understand the various types of adaptive filters discussed later in the chapter. Statistical parameters such as the mean, variance and median and how each of these affects the image's histogram are discussed.

11.2 Statistical Background

The presence of noise within an image requires the use of statistical techniques to characterize the noise. Statistical techniques can determine the types of noises that are present within an image by comparing the noise histogram obtained from the image to known theoretical histograms. The amount of noise that is present can be compared against the desired information within an image to determine a number quantifying the amount of noise degradation an image has undergone.

Before a discussion of statistical techniques can be given, a definition of noise must be stated. By definition, *noise* is considered to be any type of unwanted information that obstructs the acquiring and processing of desired information. This definition is very general and applies to more than noise contained within images. For example, when one is listening on a phone and people are talking next to the phone, making it difficult to hear, the sounds that these individuals are making are considered noise. Another example of noise is the unwanted popping sound coming from a stereo playing caused by a scratch on the record. Noise is very common in radio and television broadcasts. Many times, these broadcasts are corrupted by noise, making it difficult to understand the information within the broadcast.

Sometimes the noise degrades the information to the point that the viewer quits listening or viewing the broadcast. Many years ago during one of the Super Bowl games, one national television network had its video portion of the football game corrupted by electromagnetic interference, making the viewing of the game difficult at best. After calls nationally from viewers, it was revealed that the source of the noise was out of the control of the engineers running the program and was due to sunspot activity on the sun. This is an example of how noise affected many people and how the loss of the desired information resulted in huge losses in revenues for companies advertising during the game.

To really see the effects of noise, consider the following characters within this sentence that have been corrupted by positional noise, pisgegm eaoirscn. At first glance, these characters look as if they are unreadable, but with a little character and word recognition, they can be reordered to produce the correct words, image processing. In this example, the noise destroyed the meaning of the characters by changing their position.

In images, noise degrades the overall appearance of the image, reducing if not eliminating the visual information contained within the image. There are several types of noise that are present in images; they are determined by the shape of the histogram of the noise. A common type of noise that appears in images is uniformly distributed noise. This type of noise has a uniform histogram as discussed in chapter 5. Figure 11.1 shows a plot of a uniform histogram for a noise image that contains 256 possible graylevels. Along the horizontal axis are all of the 256 possible graylevels within the image, and along the vertical axis is the probability of a noise value having a particular graylevel value. From Figure 11.1, the probability of a noise value having graylevels between a and b is $1/(b - a)$ and outside this range it is 0. Equation 1 defines the histogram for uniformly distributed noise for each element of the histogram h_i as a function of the noise image's graylevel value G_i. The peak deviation of uniform-type noise is simply $(b - a)$.

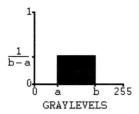

Figure 11.1 *A histogram of uniform noise.*

For example, if b = 200 and a = 100 then the uniform noise will be in the range of 100 to 200, with each graylevel value having a probability of 0.01 or 1%.

$$h_i = \begin{cases} \dfrac{1}{b-a} & \text{for } a \le G_i \le b \\ 0 & \text{elsewhere} \end{cases} \tag{1}$$

Another very common type of noise is Gaussian distributed noise. This noise is often used to model unknown noises because of an important property called the Central Limit Theorem. The *Central Limit Theorem* states that the sum of a large number of random noise terms yields a final noise that is Gaussian distributed and independent of the types of noises that are added together. In many situations in nature the noise corrupting the desired information can be modeled as a sum of many types of noise. Then, with the use of the Central Limit Theorem, this noise can be treated as Gaussian-type noise. Gaussian noise is very common in images due to the electronic noise that is present in video cameras. Figure 11.2 shows a plot of a histogram for Gaussian-type noise as a function of the input graylevel values G_i. The Gaussian histogram is symmetric about the central peak m. Unlike the uniform distribution, in which each graylevel value for the noise is equally likely to occur within the range of a to b, the probability of a noise value taking on a particular graylevel decreases as the graylevel values move farther away from the graylevel value of the central peak m.

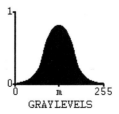

Figure 11.2 *A histogram of Gaussian noise.*

The equation describing a Gaussian histogram in terms of its two parameters m and σ is given in Equation 2. The variable m determines the location of the central peak, and the variable σ determines the width of the histogram.   The larger σ is, the wider the central peak becomes. The variables m and σ have two important meanings. The variable m is known as the *mean*, and the variable σ is called the *standard deviation*.

$$h_i = \frac{\exp^{-(G_i - m)^2/\sigma^2}}{\sigma\sqrt{2\pi}} \qquad \text{for } -\infty < G_i < \infty \tag{2}$$

Gaussian-type noise only approximates the noise that is present in digitized images. Because the noise within a digitized image can only take on a finite number of graylevels values (256 for an 8-bit image), Equation 2 is only an approximation to the actual noise. Equation 2 is defined over the graylevel range of $-\infty$ to ∞, but a digitized image is only defined over a finite range of graylevels. This usually distorts the first and last bins of an image's histogram. All noise values exceeding the graylevel range of the imaging system will cause it to saturate, resulting in a higher number of pixels at the minimum and maximum graylevels than would be predicted by Equation 2.   In comparing an image histogram to Equation 2, care must be taken when comparing the end histogram values.

Another common noise seen in images that are illuminated by a laser is known as *negative exponentially distributed noise*.   This noise comes about because the surfaces illuminated by a laser are usually very rough as compared to the wavelength of the laser. For example, for an object illuminated by a helium-neon laser to be considered smooth, the roughness of the surface must be less than 0.6328 μm, which is the wavelength of the laser. A plot of a histogram for negative exponentially distributed noise is shown in Figure 11.3. The peak of this histogram is located at graylevel 0 and decreases toward zero as the graylevel values are increased.

The negative exponential distribution is defined in Equation 3 as

$$h_i = \frac{\exp^{-(G_i/a)}}{a} \qquad \text{for } 0 \leq G_i < \infty , \tag{3}$$

where the variable a determines how fast the histogram decays to zero. Again, care must be taken when using Equation 3 to model negative exponential noise.   Typically, there will be more pixels within the image at graylevel value 255 than predicted by Equation 3.

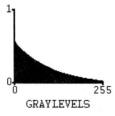

Figure 11.3 *A histogram of negative exponential noise.*

The last type of noise to be discussed is salt and pepper impulsive noise. This noise usually occurs in images due to defects in the imaging system. For example, dead pixels within a camera will cause either salt or pepper noise to appear in the digitized image. Figure 11.4 shows a histogram plot of salt and pepper noise. The histogram shows that salt and pepper noise contains two graylevels located at graylevels a and b with probability of occurrence equal to p. The total probability of salt and pepper noise is the sum of the probabilities for both salt and pepper noises and is given as 2p. The white noise pixels are called salt while the black noise pixels are called pepper. When viewing an image containing salt and pepper noise, the image looks as if it is covered with salt and pepper. Equation 4 defines the histogram for salt and pepper noise as

$$h_i = \begin{cases} \text{pepper noise with probability p} & \text{for } G_i = a \\ \text{salt noise with probability p} & \text{for } G_i = b \\ 0 & \text{elsewhere} \end{cases} \qquad (4)$$

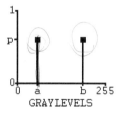

Figure 11.4 *A histogram of salt and pepper noise.*

Figure 11.5 shows uniform, Gaussian, negative exponential, and salt and pepper noise images. The uniform noise image was created with variables a = 79 and b = 177, while the Gaussian noise image was created with $\sigma = 14.1$ and m = 128. The negative exponential noise image was generated with a = 500. It is much darker than the uniform and Gaussian noise images. This is what should be expected since, from the negative exponential noise histogram, most of the pixels take on a dark graylevel. The salt and pepper noise shown in Figure 11.5d was created with a background having a graylevel value of 128 and 5% salt and 5% pepper noise.

In Figure 11.6, two examples of an image of a girl's face corrupted with uniform and salt and pepper noise are shown. The uniform noise was created with the variables a = +77 and the variable b = +128. Salt and pepper noise was added to the image with a probability of 5% for each noise with graylevel values of 0 and 255. As stated earlier, the salt and pepper corrupted image appears to have salt and pepper contained within the image.

There are two ways to corrupt an image by noise. The first, is *additive noise*, which is simply noise added to a noise-free image. Equation 5 describes a noise-corrupted image g(x, y) as the addition of a noise-free image f(x, y) and a noise term n(x, y). The uniform noise corrupted image in Figure 11.6a was created by using uniform noise for n(x ,y) and adding an additional criterion to handle image saturation. If g(x, y) < 0 then set g(x,y) to 0 and if g(x, y) > 255 then set g(x,y) to 255 were added to limit the range of possible graylevel values between 0 and 255. This was required since the imaging software (UCFImage) used has only 256 graylevels, with graylevel values ranging from 0 to 255.

$$g(x, y) = f(x, y) + n(x, y) \tag{5}$$

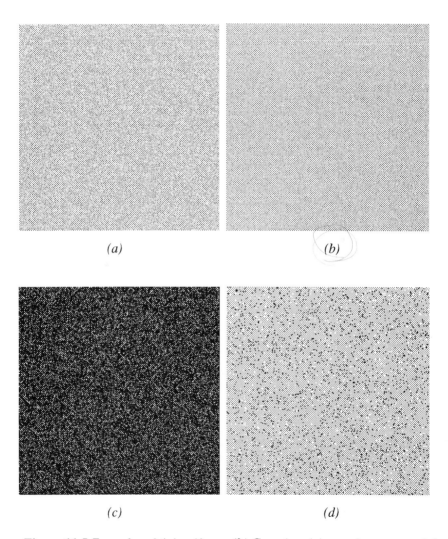

(a)   *(b)*

(c)   *(d)*

Figure 11.5 *Examples of (a) uniform, (b) Gaussian, (c) negative exponential, and (d) salt and pepper noise images.*

The second way that noise can corrupt an image, *multiplicative noise*, is to multiply each pixel within an image by a random noise term. Equation 6 defines a multiplicative noise-corrupted image, $g(x, y)$, in terms of a noise-free image, $f(x, y)$, and a noise term, $n(x, y)$.

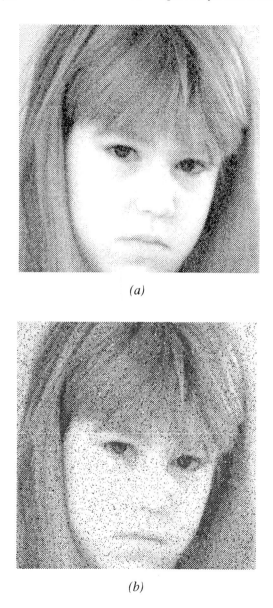

(a)

(b)

Figure 11.6 *Examples of an image corrupted by uniform and salt and pepper noise.*

$$g(x, y) = f(x, y) \cdot n(x, y) \tag{6}$$

To generate the salt and pepper corrupted noise in Figure 11.6, a modification to Equation 6 was made. For the pepper noise, Equation 6 was used directly since $n(x, y) = 0$ yields $g(x, y) = 0$. To generate the salt noise, the criterion if $n(x, y) = 255$ replace $g(x, y)$ by 255 was used. The four types of noises described are the most common that appear in digitized images, but there are many more noise types. For a more detailed discussion on noise and its effects on physical systems, the reader is referred to the many books on electrical communication theory and signal processing.

The goal of determining the type of noise that is present within an image allows for the determination of the best type of filter to use in reducing the noise within the image. The way to compare measured noise data with theoretical predictions is to compute the histogram of the image in which only noise is present and to compare the actual image's histogram to the theoretical histograms for various types of noise. Determining regions within an image where only noise is present can be a major challenge in some images. If images contain large regions of uniform background areas that are mixed with noise, these regions can be used to measure the noise statistics. In a uniform background region that contains noise, the fluctuations in each of the pixel graylevel values will be the result of the noise.

To determine the noise that is present within an image, the various parameters used to describe the histogram must be determined. The best way to determine the noise parameters is to compute the moments of the noise. There are two ways to compute the first n moments from an image. Using Equation 7, the first way is to scan the image pixel by pixel and sum each pixel's graylevel value raised to the nth power. This sum is then divided by the total number of pixels summed.

$$< f(x, y)^n > = \frac{1}{NM} \sum_{Y=0}^{N-1} \sum_{X=0}^{N-1} f(X, Y)^n \tag{7}$$

In Equation 7, N and M are the number of pixels in the X and Y directions, and the brackets $<$ $>$ are used to denote averaging. Another method of computing the first n moments is to first compute the histogram and then to use Equation 8 to sum over all the elements of the histogram.

$$< f(x, y)^n > = \sum_{i=0}^{M-1} i^n \cdot h_i \quad . \tag{8}$$

Two important moments are for $n = 1$, the mean, and $n = 2$, the second moment and are given in Equations 9, 10, 11 and 12.

$$< f(x, y) > = \frac{1}{NM} \sum_{Y=0}^{N-1} \sum_{X=0}^{N-1} f(X, Y) \qquad (9)$$

$$< f(x, y)^2 > = \left(\frac{1}{NM}\right) \sum_{Y=0}^{N-1} \sum_{X=0}^{N-1} f(X, Y)^2 \qquad (10)$$

$$<f(x, y)> = \sum_{i=0}^{M-1} i \cdot h_i , \qquad (11)$$

$$< f(x, y)^2 > = \sum_{i=0}^{M-1} i^2 \cdot h_i \qquad (12)$$

The variance σ^2 is related to the first and second moments by the difference between the second moment and the square of the mean or first moment.

$$\sigma^2 = < f(x, y)^2 > - < f(x, y) >^2 \qquad (13)$$

mean value

The standard deviation σ is simply the square root of the variance σ^2. The standard deviation determines the peak-to-peak deviation of the noise. For the Gaussian distribution, 99.7% of the time the peak-to-peak deviation will be within $\pm 3\sigma$. For uniform distributed noise, the standard deviation in terms of the peak-to-peak deviation $(b - a)$ is

$$\sigma = \frac{(b - a)}{\sqrt{12}} . \qquad (14)$$

Consider the following $25 \times 25 \times 256$ graylevel image given in Figure 11.7. Assume that this image is a sample from a larger image taken from a background region within the image. Thus, the variations in the pixels graylevel values must be due to the noise present in the image. Using Equation 9, with $N = M = 25$, the mean is found to be 121.48, and using Equation 10, the second moment is computed to be 14,784. Finally, using Equation 13, the variance is found to be 26.61. Alternatively, the histogram for this image could have been determined first. The histogram for the image in Figure 11.7 is given in Table 11.1. Using Equations 11 and 12 for the mean and variance, yields the same results as using Equations 9 and 10. The histogram of this noise image shows that the noise is approximately uniformly distributed between graylevel values of 113 to 131. Using Equation 14 and then solving for $(b - a)$ with a variance σ^2 of

26.61, the peak-to-peak deviation is found to be 17.87. The peak-to-peak deviation computed from the image directly is 18.

120	126	118	114	131
122	127	124	117	116
114	121	130	122	119
125	127	113	127	118
116	123	120	118	129

Figure 11.7 *A sample image with noise.*

As seen from the previous example, the mean gives the average value and the variance gives the peak deviation of the noise. The first question that should be raised is "What is the variance of a constant background or image?" Under this condition the histogram would have only one element not equal to zero. For this histogram, combining Equations 11, 12, and 13, the variance would simply be zero. The average for a constant background image is just equal to its graylevel value. The next question that should be asked is, "Can statistical techniques be used to measure any graylevel variations within an image independently of whether these variations were caused by desired features or noise within the image?" The best way to answer this question is to look at the $3 \times 3 \times 256$ graylevel image of a noise-free vertical edge given in Figure 11.8. Computing the histogram for this image yields only 2 elements out of the 256 elements in the histogram that are nonzero $h_0 = 0.667$ and $h_{200} = 0.333$. The mean and variance are computed as 66.67 and 8,888 respectively. Hence, statistical techniques can be used to measure the variations in the graylevel values of an image independently of what caused the variations.

Table 11.2 gives a summary of the first two moments and how these moments relate to the parameters of the histograms for the uniform, Gaussian, and negative exponential noise distributions. Once the type of noise has been determined by comparing the shape of the actual noise histogram to the various theoretical histograms, Table 11.2 can then be used to determine the theoretical parameters of the histogram. For example, the Gaussian histogram parameter m is equal to the first moment, and the variance parameter σ^2 is equal to the difference of the second moment and the square of the first moment.

Care must be taken in using this method of matching theoretical histogram parameters to the actual data taken from an image. If the end elements of the actual histogram show a high number of pixels at these graylevel values due to graylevel saturation because of the finite dynamic range of the image, then this method cannot be used. A better method then is to use a least-squares algorithm to match the theoretical histogram to the actual histogram. Saturation is not normally a major problem in image processing, because usually an image's intensity is adjusted so that its intensity values lie within the dynamic range of the image-processing system.

As an example, a uniform noise histogram can be used to model the noise in the image shown in Figure 11.7. From Table 11.1, the histogram shows that the noise is approximately uniformly distributed with a first moment of 121.48 and a second moment of 14,784. The parameters a and b given in Table 11.2 can then be solved in terms of the first and second moments

$$a = < f(x, y) > + \sqrt{3} \sqrt{< f(x, y)^2 > - < f(x, y) >^2} = 112.54 \tag{15}$$

$$b = < f(x, y) > - \sqrt{3} \sqrt{< f(x, y)^2 > - < f(x, y) >^2} = 130.41 , \tag{16}$$

where $< f(x, y) >$ is equal to the first moment and $< f(x ,y)^2 >$ is equal to the second moment. Equations 15 and 16 are found by first solving for the parameter a and then solving for the parameter b in Table 11.2.

Table 11.1 *The histogram of the image given in Figure 11.7.*

GRAYLEVEL	n_i	h_i
113	1	1/25
114	2	2/25
115	0	0
116	2	2/25
117	1	1/25
118	3	3/25
119	1	1/25
120	2	2/25
121	1	1/25
122	2	2/25
123	1	1/25
124	1	1/25
125	1	1/25
126	1	1/25
127	3	3/25
128	0	0
129	1	1/25
130	1	1/25
131	1	1/25
n_t	25	

0	0	200
0	0	200
0	0	200

Figure 11.8 *An example of a noise-free vertical edge.*

Table 11.2 *Theoretical histogram parameters as a function of their moments.*

Histogram	First Moment	Second Moment
$h_i = \begin{cases} \dfrac{1}{b-a} & \text{for } a \le G_i \le b \\ 0 & \text{elsewhere} \end{cases}$	$\dfrac{(a+b)}{2}$	$\dfrac{(a-b)^2}{12} + \dfrac{(a+b)^2}{4}$
$h_i = \dfrac{\exp^{-(G_i-m)^2/\sigma^2}}{\sigma\sqrt{2\pi}} \quad \text{for } -\infty < G_i < \infty$	m	$\sigma^2 + m^2$
$h_i = \dfrac{\exp^{-(G_i/a)}}{a} \quad \text{for } 0 \le G_i < \infty$	a	$2a^2$

11.3 Order Statistics

Another means of obtaining information about the statistics of an image is to use order statistics. Order statistics is a method in which all the image pixels are ordered from a minimum graylevel value to a maximum graylevel value. Several estimators are easily obtained from this ordered set of data such as the minimum and maximum graylevel values, the median, the range, the midpoint, and the extreme deviate. Even the first and second moments can still be computed from this ordered set of data since ordering the pixels in terms of their graylevel values does not change the final results computed in Equations 9 and 10.

Given N pixels, each having graylevel values P_1, P_2, P_3, ..., P_N, these pixels can then be arranged in ascending order in terms of their graylevel values. Equation 17 defines this newly ordered set of pixels.

$$P_{(1)} \le P_{(2)} \le P_{(3)} \le \cdots \le P_{(N)} \tag{17}$$

The median is computed as the center element of the ordered set if N is odd or as the center two elements if N is even,

$$h_i = \begin{cases} P_{(N/2+1/2)} & \text{for N odd} \\ [P_{(N/2)} + P_{(N/2+1)}]/2 & \text{for N even} \end{cases} \tag{18}$$

The *median* is the value at which 50% of the pixels have graylevel values below the median and 50% have graylevel values which are above the median. One of the most important features of the median is that for symmetric histograms like the uniform and the Gaussian noise histograms, the median equals the first moment. Hence, the median can be used as an estimator of the first moment.

The *range* is defined as the difference between the maximum graylevel value and the minimum graylevel value. The minimum graylevel value is the first value in the ordered data set $P_{(1)}$, and the maximum graylevel value is the last value $P_{(N)}$. The range is then defined as

$$R(P_i) = P_{(N)} - P_{(1)} . \tag{19}$$

The range is directly related to the variance of the fluctuations in the graylevel values within an image. As the variance of the graylevel variations increases so does the range.

Another order statistic is the midpoint. The *midpoint* is the average of the minimum and maximum graylevel values

$$MID(P_i) = \frac{P_{(N)} + P_{(1)}}{2} . \tag{20}$$

The last order statistic of interest to the reader is the *extreme deviate* from the mean, which is defined as the difference between the maximum graylevel value $P_{(N)}$ and the first moment or mean value

$$ED(P_i) = P_{(N)} - \text{mean} . \tag{21}$$

For example, consider the $3 \times 3 \times 256$ graylevel image given in Figure 11.9. The order set for this image is

$$43, 43, 44, 44, 45, 45, 45, 46, 46$$

The median for this image is $P(5) = 45$, the range is 3, and the midpoint is 44.5. Plotting the histogram for this image yields a symmetric histogram. Hence the median should be equal to the mean. In this case the mean is 44.56, which is very close to the expected median value of 45. The reason why the median is not exactly equal to the mean is due to the very small sample set from which the mean and median were computed. Finally, the extreme deviate is computed to be 1.44.

45	43	46
44	45	43
46	44	45

Figure 11.9 *A $3 \times 3 \times 256$ graylevel image.*

The main interest in using order statistics is to estimate the first and second moments of the noise within an image. The problem in using Equations 9 and 10 to estimate the first and second moments is that if any of the pixels used in Equations 9 and 10 have graylevel values that deviate radically from typical values, these pixels can drastically influence the estimates of the first and second moments. Pixels that deviate from the normal graylevel values are referred to as *outliers*. Usually, when outliers are detected within an image, it is desirable to remove them from the image. Salt and pepper noise is a good example of noise that produces outliers. Figure 11.10 is an image containing uniform noise with one outlier with a probability of 6%. The outlier pixel is located at the lower-right corner of the image and has a graylevel value of 196. Using Equations 9 and 10 on the whole image, the first and second moments are found to be 31.94 and 2,816.3, respectively. Using Equation 13, the variance is calculated to be 1,796.3. These numbers do not truly represent the statistics of the uniform noise. Manually removing the outlier and then recomputing the first and second moments using Equations 9 and 10, the new values become 21 and 443. The variance is now computed to be 2, which is much closer to the actual uniform noise graylevel variations within the image. On the other hand, if the median were used as the estimator of the mean, from the order data

$$19, 19, 19, 20, 20, 20, 21, 21, 21, 22, 22, 22, 23, 23, 23, 196,$$

a better estimate of the first moment could be obtained. Since there are 16 pixels within the image, the median is given as

$$MED(P_i) = \frac{P_{(9)} + P_{(8)}}{2} = 21 \quad , \tag{22}$$

which is identical to the mean or first moment computed by removing the outlier from these calculations. The advantage of using the median as an estimator of the first moment is that up to 50% of the pixels can be outliers and the median will still yield the correct estimate of the first moment.

22	23	22	21
20	19	23	19
21	20	22	21
23	20	19	196

Figure 11.10 *A 4 × 4 uniform noise image with one outlier.*

A better estimator for the variance of a symmetric noise histogram in the presence of outliers is the $MAD(P_i)$ estimator, which is defined as

$$\sigma^2 = \{(1.483 \ MED[\ |\ P_i - MED(P_i)\ |\ ]\}^2 \quad , \tag{23}$$

where $|X|$ means the absolute value of the variable X. To use Equation 23, the median of the order data is first computed. Next, the absolute difference between all the order data is computed, and then the median of this value is computed. Finally, the last median is multiplied by 1.483 and this result is squared. The following steps illustrate how to use Equation 23 to estimate the variance for the uniform noise in Figure 11.10. First, the median of the image is computed as previously shown: $MED(P_i) = 21$. Next, the absolute difference is computed for each pixel within the image and then arranged in ascending order by the magnitude of the absolute difference between each pixel and the median value.

$$0, 0, 0, 1, 1, 1, 1, 1, 1, 2, 2, 2, 2, 2, 2, 175$$

The last step is to compute the median value of this new ordered set

$$MED(\text{absolute difference}) = \frac{X(8) + X(9)}{2} = 1 \tag{24}$$

and then multiply this number by 1.483 and square the result. Performing these operations yields a variance equal to 2.2. This value is very similar to the variance of 2 that was computed after eliminating the outlier pixel from the image.

From the previous results, it looks as if the median filter would do a better job filtering impulsive noise as compared to the mean filter. Figure 11.11 shows a $3 \times 3 \times 256$ graylevel constant background image containing one outlier due to salt and pepper noise. A 3×3 median filter, as discussed in Chapter 8, yields an output for the center pixel of 120, while a 3×3 mean filter yields a graylevel value of 130.8. Clearly, the median filter has done a better job removing the outlier from the image compared to the mean filter. The general rule is that a mean filter does a better job filtering uniform and Gaussian-type noise, while a median filter does a better job filtering negative exponential and salt and pepper noise. The other consideration in comparing a median filter to a mean filter is that a median filter does a better job preserving edges within an image compared to a mean filter. A mean filter tends to blur the edges of an image.

120	120	120
120	217	120
120	120	120

Figure 11.11 *A constant background image with one outlier pixel.*

Understanding how noise affects the various statistical measures such as the mean and the variance is important in the understanding of adaptive filters. As stated earlier in this chapter, outliers are usually the result of salt and pepper noise in a noise image. But in an image that contains both edges and noise outliers, a large variance can be the result of noise outliers or edges within an image. If a local variance is computed in a background portion of the image, the variance will be solely due to the noise. On the other hand, if a local variance is computed on part of an image that contains both noise and edges, this variance will be larger than the variance computed from a background area. It looks as if the variance within a local region can be used as a measure of noise and edge information within an image. This measure can then be used to determine the best filter to apply to a local region. This is the concept behind the minimum mean-square error filter.

11.4 Minimum Mean-Square Error Filter

The Minimum Mean-Square Error filter (MMSE) makes use of knowledge of the local variance to determine if a mean filter is to be applied to the local region. This filter works best if the noise is additive-type noise. Equation 25 shows an additive noise image $g(x, y)$ which is the addition of a noise-free image $f(x, y)$ and a noise term $n(x, y)$.

$$g(x, y) = f(x, y) + n(x, y) \tag{25}$$

The MMSE filter does the best job of filtering the noise when the noise term $n(x, y)$ is either uniform or Gaussian-type noise. The MMSE filter uses the variance of the noise along with a local variance to make its filter decision and is defined as

$$r(x, y) = (1 - \frac{\sigma_n^2}{\sigma_l^2}) \cdot g(x, y) + \frac{\sigma_n^2}{\sigma_l^2} \cdot K, \tag{26}$$

where $r(x, y)$ is the MMSE filter image, $g(x, y)$ is the noise corrupted image, σ_n^2 is the variance of the noise, σ_l^2 is the local variance about the pixel located at x, y, and K is the output from a local mean filter.

In the background region of an image, the only variations in the pixel values are due to the noise alone. Computing the local variance in this region will yield a value that is approximately equal to the noise variance. Under this condition, the ratio of the noise variance to the local variance is approximately 1,

$$\frac{\sigma_n^2}{\sigma_l^2} \approx 1 \tag{27}$$

The filtered image output then reduces to the output of the local mean filter

$$r(x, y) = K . \tag{28}$$

This is what is desired, since in a background region of the image, a mean filter will be able to filter the noise without blurring any edges because no edges are present in the background region of the image. As the local region moves into an area within an image that contains edges, the local variance will become much larger than the noise variance due to the edge

$$\sigma_l^2 >> \sigma_n^2 . \tag{29}$$

The output from the MMSE filter given in Equation 26 reduces to

$$r(x, y) = g(x, y) , \tag{30}$$

which is simply the original unfiltered image. Hence, in regions that contain edges, the filter simply performs no filtering, preserving the original image's edges. These two examples are the two extremes of the MMSE filter. In between these two cases, a proportional amount of the original image and the local mean filter output are added together to produce the MMSE filter output. The amount of the original image added to the mean filter output is proportional to how sharp the edges are within a local region of the original image. Slowing changing graylevels within a local region will be filtered much more than strong distinct edges.

Figure 11.12a shows a noise-free image of a girl's face and Figure 11.12b shows the same image corrupted with Gaussian noise with a variance of 200. Figure 10.12c shows the output from a 5×5 local MMSE filtered image. The noise variance that was used to corrupt the noise-free image was also used as the noise variance in the MMSE filter. If the noise variance is not known, the noise variance for this image could have also been determined by locating a region within the image that contained no edges, and computing the variance within this region; and then using this result as an estimate of the noise variance. The image was scanned pixel by pixel, and the local neighborhood variance was computed for each pixel and applied to Equation 26 to produce the MMSE filter output. Notice the reduction in the noise and how well the edges are preserved in the MMSE filtered image. Even though the MMSE filter did not remove all the noise, it did a good job of reducing a good portion of the noise without blurring the image.

The partial code to implement a 3×3 MMSE filter is given in Figure 11.13. The program assumes that the input noise-corrupted image of size 512×512 pixels is passed to the routine in the two-dimensional array IMAGE[X][Y], and the filtered output image is stored in the two-dimensional array FILTER[X][Y]. It is also assumed that the noise variance has already been determined either manually or from a preselected region within the image and that this value is passed to the program in the variable NVAR. The program scans the image pixel by pixel and computes the first and second moments using Equations 9 and 10 (with $M = N = 3$) in a 3×3 local region. The variance for this local region is then computed using Equation 13. Finally, Equation 26 is used to determine the MMSE filter output. Since an eight-pixel neighborhood around the pixel of interest is used to estimate the local mean and variance, the border rows and columns of the image that do not have eight neighbors are not filtered. The program effectively reduces the size of the filtered image to a 510×510 pixel image.

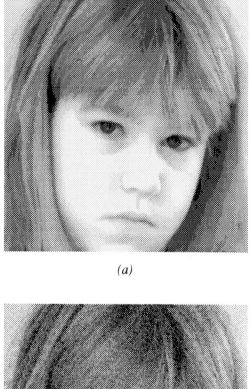

(a)

(b)

Figure 11.12 *An example of using a 5 × 5 MMSE filter.*

(c)

Figure 11.12 *continued.*

```
MMSE_filter(unsigned char IMAGE[][],unsigned char
  FILTER[][], float NVAR)
      {
      int X,Y,x1,y1;
      long int total, sum, sum1;
      float FSECOND, FVAR, FMEAN;
      for(Y= 1; Y<=510; Y++)
          for(X=1;  X<=510; X++){
              sum=0; sum1=0; total =0;
              for(y1=-1; y1<=1; y1){
                for(x1=-1; x1<=1; x1){
                  sum=sum+IMAGE[X+x1][Y+y1];
                  sum1=sum1 + IMAGE[X+x1][Y+y1]*
                          IMAGE[X+x1][Y+y1];
                  total = total +1;}
              if(FVAR !=0.0){
                  FSECOND=(float)sum1/(float) total;
                  FMEAN = (float)sum/(float)total;
                  FVAR=FSECOND - FMEAN*FMEAN;
                  FILTER[X}[Y] = (int)((1- NVAR/FVAR)
                  *IMAGE[X][Y] + NVAR/FVAR*FMEAN+.5);}
              else {FILTER[X][Y] = IMAGE[X][Y];}
              }
          }
      }
```

Figure 11.13 *The partial C code to implement the MMSE filter.*

The difficulty with the MMSE filter is that it does not do any filtering if the local variance is much larger than the noise variance. For an image containing only uniform or Gaussian-type noise, the local variance will be much greater than the noise variance only in regions where edges appear. There are two reasons why the local variance can be much larger than the noise variance, the first is if an edge is encountered within the image, and the second is if a noise outlier is present. For the first case, the presence of an edge causes no problems for the MMSE filter. But if a noise outlier is present within the local region, the local variance will be much larger than the noise variance, and no filtering will occur in the local vicinity of the noise outlier. Hence, the noise outlier will not be removed from the image. The MMSE filter does a poor job of filtering images containing impulsive-type noise such as salt and pepper noise.

11.5 Double Window-Modified Trimmed Mean Filter

The adaptive double window modified trimmed mean (DW-MTM) filter overcomes the difficulties of using the MMSE filter in the presence of impulsive noise by using the median estimator to estimate the local mean. Then a new local mean is computed only using pixels within a small graylevel range about the median. This effectively removes the outliers in the calculation of the mean estimate. Hence, this filter works equally well with both uniform and Gaussian-type noise, as well as with impulsive-type noise like salt and pepper noise.

The adaptive DW-MTM filter algorithm is described as follows. Given a pixel located at x, y within the image, a median filter (MED[$g(x, y)$]) is computed within an $n \times n$ local region surrounding the location x, y. The median value computed from this filter is used to estimate the mean value of the $n \times n$ local area. Next, a larger-sized window surrounding the pixel at location x, y of size $q \times q$ is used to calculate the mean value. In computing the mean value in the $q \times q$ window, only pixels within the graylevel range of

$$\text{MED}[g(x, y)] - c \text{ to } \text{MED}[g(x, y)] + c \tag{31}$$

are used, eliminating any outliers from the calculations. The output of the DW-MTM filter is this $q \times q$ mean filter. The value of c is chosen as a function of the noise standard deviation

$$c = K \cdot \sigma_n . \tag{32}$$

Typical values of K range from 1.5 to 2.5. This range for K is based on the assumption that for Gaussian noise statistics the peak-to-peak graylevel variations will be in the range of $\pm 2\sigma_n$ for 95% of the time and any values outside this range are more than likely outliers. For $K = 0$, the DW-MTM filter reduces to an $n \times n$ median filter, and for K very large, the DW-MTM reduces to a $q \times q$ mean filter. Hence, as K decreases, the filter does a better job of filtering impulsive noise, but does a poor job of filtering uniform and Gaussian-type noise.

The 5 × 5 uniform noise image shown in Figure 11.14 with a standard deviation σ_n equal to 1.62 contains two noise outlier pixels with graylevel values of 10 and 114. Assuming n = 3, q = 5 and K = 1.5, the DW-MTM filter is computed for the center pixel as follows. First, the 3 × 3 median is computed from the ordered set

$$57, 58, 59, 60, 60, 61, 62, 62, 114$$

to be $P_{(5)}$ = 60. Next the 5 × 5 mean filter is computed only on pixels in the range of 60 − 1.62 · 1.5 to 60 + 1.62 · 1.5 or from 57.57 to 62.43. In Figure 11.14, this leaves pixels with graylevels 10, 57, and 114 out of the mean calculations. The mean value is computed to be 60.15, and the center pixel with a graylevel value of 114 is replaced by 60, removing the noise impulse from the image.

60	61	58	62	59
58	57	61	60	62
59	62	114	59	61
57	62	60	58	61
61	60	59	57	10

Figure 11.14 *A 5 × 5 uniform noise image with two outlier pixels.*

(a)

Figure 11.15 *An example of using the DW-MTM filter on a noise-corrupted image.*

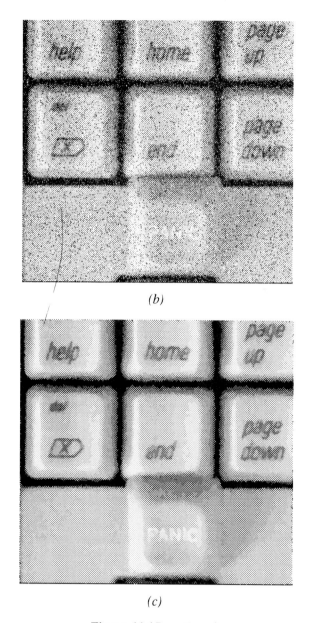

(b)

(c)

Figure 11.15 *continued.*

Figure 11.15a shows a noise-free image of a computer keyboard. In Figure 11.15b, the keyboard image has been corrupted with both Gaussian and salt and pepper noise. The variance of the Gaussian noise is 200, and the probability of the salt and pepper noise is 10% (5% salt and 5% pepper). For n = 3, q = 5, and K = 1.5, the output of the DW-MTM filter is shown in Figure 11.15c. The noise standard deviation was computed from the uniform background region to the left of the panic key within the image and was found to be 41.2. As can be seen from Figure 11.15c, both the Gaussian and salt and pepper types noise have been almost completely eliminated without the blurring effect associated with a mean filter.

The partial code to implement an n = 3, q = 5 DW-MTM filter on a 512 × 512 × 256 graylevel image is given in Figure 11.16. The input image is passed to the program in the two-dimensional array IMAGE[X][Y], and the output filtered image is stored in the array FILTER[X][Y]. Also passed to the program is the noise variance in variable NVAR and the constant K in variable K.

```
DWMTM_filter(unsigned char IMAGE[][],unsigned char
FILTER[][],float NVAR,float K)
    {
    int X, Y, x1, y1, med[9], median;
    int gray, i, j, temp;
    long int total, sum;
    for(Y= 2; Y<=509; Y++)
        for(X=2; X<=509; X++){
            total=0;
            for(y1=-1; y1<=1; y1++)
              for(x1=-1; x1<=1; x1++){
                  med[total]=IMAGE[X+x1][Y+y1];
                  total=total+1;
                  }
            for(j=1; j<=8; j++){
                temp=med[j];
                for(i=(j-1); i>=0; i--){
                    if(med[i]<=temp)
                        go to LABEL lp;
                        med[i+1]=med[i];
                    }
                i=i-1;
        lp:     med[i+1]=temp;
                }
            median=med[4]; sum=0; total=0;
            for(y1=-2; y1<=2; y1++){
                for(x1=-2; x1<=2; x1++){
                    gray= IMAGE[X][Y];
                    if(gray>(median-K*NVAR))
                    if(gray<(median+K*NVAR)){
                    sum=sum+IMAGE[X+x1][Y+y1];
                    total = total +1;}
                    }
                }
            FILTER[X][Y]=(int)((float)sum/(float)total);
            }
    }
```

Figure 11.16 *The partial C code to implement the DW-MTM filter.*

The first thing the program does is the center pixel located at the coordinates X, Y and its surrounding eight neighbors are stored in the array med[I]. Next, this array is sorted in ascending order by graylevel value, and the fifth element is selected as the median value. After the median is found, a 5×5 pixel region surrounding the center pixel is scanned, and all pixels with graylevel values between the median minus K times the noise standard deviation to the median plus K times the noise standard deviation are summed together. This result is then divided by the total number of pixels summed to yield the modified mean. The modified mean value is then stored in the output image array FILTER[X][Y].

11.6 Adaptive Window-Edge Detection Filter

The goal of an adaptive filter is to reduce noise at the same time as preserving edges within an image. As the size of the local window (3×3 or 7×7, and so on) is increased, the ability of a filter to reduce the noise within an image increases. But as the size of the window increases, the filtered output image becomes increasingly blurry. The adaptive window-edge detection (AWED) filter overcomes these problems by changing the size of its local filter window. When an edge is present, the size of the window is reduced to a 3×3 window, and when a background region is detected the size of the window is increased to a 7×7 window. The AWED filter gives the best of both situations by reducing the size of the filter window to preserve edges and at the same time increasing the size of the window when edges are not present to get the most filtering.

A block diagram for this filter is given in Figure 11.17. For a given input pixel located at the coordinates x, y the initial window size is set to 7×7 pixels. Next, the histogram is computed and used to determine if any noise outliers are present within the window. If so, these pixels are flagged as outlier pixels. An edge detector such as a Soble edge detector, is applied to the remaining pixels to determine if an edge is present within the window. If an edge is not present a 7×7 mean filter is applied to the non-outlier pixels and used as the output for the filter. If an edge is detected, the filter size is decreased to a 5×5 window, and the process repeats itself again for this window. The histogram is computed again and new outlier pixels are flagged. The edge detector then determines if any edges are present and, if present, the window size is again reduced to a 3×3 window and the algorithm is repeated one more time. On the other hand, if no edges are detected a 5×5 mean filter becomes the output of the AWED filter. If the last iteration is needed and if an edge is still detected, a 3×3 median filter is used as the filter output. Otherwise a 3×3 mean filter is used as the filter output. The AWED filter uses a median filter to preserve edges within the image.

The implementation of the AWED discussed changes its filter window size from a 7×7 to a 3×3. The use of a 3×3 median filter when an edge is present guarantees the preservation of edges within the filtered image. When the filter is located within a background region of an image, the AWED filter tries to use the largest filter that is possible without overlaying an edge within the filter window.

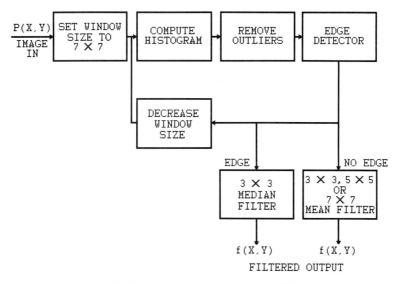

Figure 11.17 *A block diagram of the AWED filter.*

The partial code to implement the AWED filter on a $512 \times 512 \times 256$ graylevel image is given in Figure 11.18. The program expects the input image to be stored in the array IMAGE[X][Y] and outputs the filter image in the array FILTER[X][Y]. The first thing the program does is set the window size to 7×7 (winsize=7) and call the subroutine that computes the histogram on the window. The histogram subroutine stores the computed histogram in array hist[winsize]. Next, the program calls the subroutine remove_outlier to flag which pixels are outlier pixels and stores this information in array flag[winsize]. The edge-detector subroutine is now called and returns a true if an edge is detected. If an edge is detected, the variable winsize is reduced by 2 and the program repeats itself again. If no edge is detected, a mean filter subroutine is called with a window size given by the variable winsize. In addition, the mean filter subroutine uses the information about the outlier pixels to remove these pixels from the calculation of the mean value. The output of the mean filter is then used as the output of the AWED filter for this pixel. If the program continues until winsize=3 and an edge is still detected, a 3×3 median filter subroutine is called with the output of this median filter being the output of the AWED filter.

11.7 Signal Adaptive Median Filter

The signal adaptive median filter (SAM) uses the fact that a uniform background region within an image contains very little high-frequency information and that most high-frequency information is contained within edges and impulses. Given an image g(x, y), it can be separated as the sum of a low-frequency component and a high-frequency component

```
AWED_filter(unsigned char IMAGE[][],unsigned char
    FILTER[][],float NVAR, float K)
    {
    int X, Y, edge, winsize=7;
    int flag[49], hist[49];
    for(Y= 3; Y<=508; Y++){
        for(X=3; X<=508; X++){
lp:    Compute_histogram(X,Y,winsize,hist);
        remove_outlier(X,Y,hist, flag);
        edge=edge_detector(X,Y,flag);
            if(edge==true){
                if(winsize==3)
                    FILTER[X][Y]=median_filter(X,Y,3);
                    go to LABEL finished;
                }
                else
                {
                    winsize=winsize-2;
                    go to LABEL lp;
                }
            else
                FILTER[X][Y]=
        mean_filter(X,Y,flag,winsize);
        finished:
        }
    }
}
```

Figure 11.18 *The partial C code to implement the AWED filter.*

$$g(x, y) = g_{lf}(x, y) + g_{hf}(x, y) .\qquad(33)$$

Figure 11.19 is a block diagram of a filter that separates an image into its low- and high-frequency components. Once separated, only the low-frequency components will be used as the output of the filter if the filter is located within a background region of the image. In regions containing edges, both the low- and high-frequency components will be used as the output for this filter. The value of K determines how much of the high-frequency components appears in the output of the filter. As K increases from zero, the filtered image changes from a lowpassed filtered image to a high-frequency enhanced image.

There are many ways of filtering an image to obtain its low- and high-frequency components. One of the two most popular ways of obtaining the low-frequency components of an image is to use either a mean or median filter. Equation 33 can then be rewritten so that the high-frequency component of the image is found using the original unfiltered image and a lowpass filtered image.

$$g_{hf}(x, y) = g(x, y) - g_{lf}(x, y)\qquad(34)$$

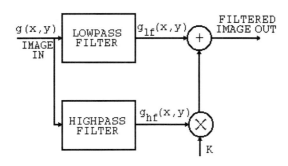

Figure 11.19 *A two frequency component image filter.*

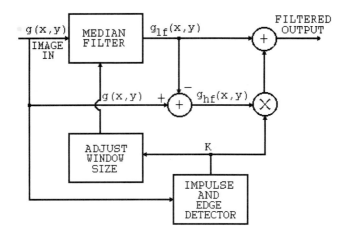

Figure 11.20 *A block diagram of a signal adaptive filter.*

The block diagram for a signal adaptive median filter is shown in Figure 11.20. The median filter is used to perform the lowpass filtering, and Equation 34 is implemented to obtain the high-frequency components. An edge and impulse detector is used to set the window size and determine the value of K. The filter starts with a 7×7 window size, if an edge is detected, the window size is decreased to a 5×5 window. Again, the presence of an edge is checked. If an edge is still present, the window size is reduced to a 3×3 window. If no edges are detected within the filter window, the window size remains unchanged. Once the window size has been determined, the value of K is chosen based on the local variance computed within the window and an estimate of the noise variance. Equation 35 gives the decision process in determining the constant K. If the local variance is smaller, the product of a constant c times the noise variance, then the output of the median filter becomes the output of the SAM filter. If the local variance is larger than c times the noise variance, then a linear amount of the high-frequency components are added back into the SAM filter output. This is what should be expected if the local variance is larger than the noise variance, since this usually indicates the presence of an edge.

$$
K = \begin{cases} 0 & \text{for } c\sigma_n^2 \geq \sigma_l^2 \\[2em] \left(1 - c \cdot \dfrac{\sigma_n^2}{\sigma_l^2}\right) & \text{elsewhere} \end{cases} \tag{35}
$$

where σ_n^2 is the noise variance, and σ_l^2 is the local variance.

The constant c is used to adjust the sensitivity of the filter to edges. As the constant c is increased from zero, the filter changes from a mean filter and becomes more sensitive to edges, adjusting the amount of high-frequency components added back to the lowpass filtered image. There are many more types of adaptive filters than those mentioned in this chapter. Usually, most adaptive filters are based on a decision as to whether an edge or an outlier is present within a local region to define the appropriate filter for this region. Some adaptive filters use heuristics of the image to enhance the filter's decision process. For further information on adaptive filters, the reader is referred to *Nonlinear Digital Filters Principles and Applications* by I. Pitas and A. N. Venetsanopoulos which is listed in the annotated bibliography.

Chapter 12

UCFImage© Software

12.1 Introduction

UCFImage is a digital image-processing package designed for MS-DOS compatible personal computers (PCs). This program can edit, display, enhance, analyze, print and identify images. Multiple image file formats are supported, including GIF, TIFF, PCX,and BMP files. Standard image-processing functions available include zoom, pan, threshold, histogram equalization, profile, smoothing and sharpening filters, edge detection, and noise reduction. Pseudocoloring, spatial convolutions with user defined masks up to 7×7, morphological, adaptive, circularly symmetric, and two-dimensional FFT filtering are supported. UCFImage is also able to generate five different types of noise distributions.

UCFImage is a menu-based system separated into the following categories: file manipulations, algebraic and logical operations, geometric transformations, grayscale profile and measurements, object identification, histogram equalization, spatial and frequency filters, dynamic color palette, and noise generation.

Three region definitions are assumed in UCFImage. An understanding of these regions, the buffer region, the ROI, and the display region, is necessary for accurate system orientation by the user.

> **1.** Buffer region: The buffer region is the area in computer memory containing the complete image upon which all image operations are performed. This region is restricted to 512×512 8-bit pixels.

> **2.** Region of interest (ROI): The ROI is a subset of the buffer area selected by the user. This is the area of the buffer in which the desired operation is performed. The ROI may be equal to the size of the entire buffer, 512×512 pixels.

> **3.** Display Region: The display region is the actual image shown on the screen. This image is a *subsample* of the complete image stored in the buffer. The 512×512 pixel image is compressed to 256×200 pixels in the region of display. This is done so that the operations menu and the entire image may be viewed at one time. To view a portion of the image at full resolution, the PAN function

195

must be selected. This is especially necessary after calling certain filtering operations so that the changes that have occurred can be viewed in detail.

When UCFImage is activated, memory is allocated for the main image buffer and the temporary buffers required for operation. Whatever is left up to 16K is allocated for the undo buffer. Operations on the ROI can be canceled using the *undo* function as long as the pixel area does not exceed the size allocated to it. Therefore, if the user does not like the output of an operation, the buffer can be restored with its previous contents. Some systems cannot allocate the full 16K memory; however, in any case, UCFImage produces a warning before performing any irreversible operation.

All of the routines in UCFImage operate on the ROI. This rectangular subregion is user defined by either *Cursor* or the *1st point* and *2nd point* functions. These ROI selection functions may be selected from several menus and are accessible via PowerKeys (defined below). The default ROI established upon initial start-up is a 16,384-pixel square, 128 pixels per side, centered at image coordinates (256,256) (Figure 12.1). If 16,384 bytes of memory are not available, UCFImage scales the ROI accordingly. If the ROI is smaller than 128 × 128, then the available memory is less than that required.

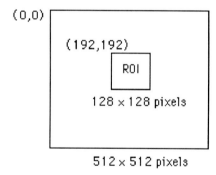

Figure 12.1 *Default Region of Interest (ROI).*

12.1.1 System Requirements. For complete operation, UCFImage requires either a 80286 or 80386 MSDOS™ computer with 520K bytes of available memory. Also required is a standard VGA display and card and DOS version 3.3 or better. An 80387 math coprocessor is recommended for filtering large (256 × 256 or larger) regions of interest. A Hewlett-Packard Laserjet, Deskjet, or Epson printer (or compatibles) is required for printing images. For quick menu selection, an MS-DOS compatible mouse may be used.

12.1.2 Menu System. All functions in UCFImage are accessed by the first letter or symbol of each command listed in the menu to the left of the display region. The top item in the menu indicates which command set is currently being accessed and is in all uppercase. Uppercase and lowercase keys have different meanings in UCFImage and thus they are used for the selection of different options. The program ignores the entry of unspecified characters. The area to the right of the menu is the display region and results of operations are displayed here. The *ESC* (escape) key is used to travel up the menu tree and also to quit or exit various functions. A question mark, (?),entered from any menu calls up the help system screen.

In this chapter, section and subsection headings refer to menu commands available in UCFImage and their descriptions. The Contents entries provide a convenient menu hierarchy of the system. The menu labels are shown in parentheses after the section heading, and the function is accessed by entering the first letter of this label. If the menu item may be accessed using a PowerKey (described at the end of this section), then a set of brackets is also given showing the *ALT* key required for immediate access.

UCFImage supports all mice that are MS-DOS compatible. Only two buttons are supported. If a three-button mouse is used, the middle button is inactive. When mouse hardware is detected by UCFImage, a bright green cursor will appear on the screen and be responsive to mouse movement. The left mouse button is used for selection, and the right button is used in place of the *ESC* key to exit menus. If a single-button mouse is used, only the select function will be active.

If a mouse is available, then any option may also be selected by placing the small green cursor over the name of the desired routine and clicking the left mouse button. In most menus, to return to a previous menu simply click the right mouse button. In routines that prompt the user to *Hit any key to continue*, the left mouse button will continue the operation, while the right mouse button will abort the procedure. The mouse can also be used to replace the use of arrow keys for either image or cursor movements.

Figure 12.2 lists the functions in the main, or startup, menu. Figure 12.3 shows the actual start-up menu screen, with the main menu shown on the left of the screen and the display region with an image to the left. The sections in this chapter follow the elements of this main menu (with the exception of the *credits* and *DOS* functions) and their submenus. To access a menu function, the user simply enters the first letter of the menu function desired or places the mouse cursor over the function name and left-click. Note that the *file* function has a lowercase *f* , while the *Filter* function uses the uppercase (as with *credits* and *Cfile*). Many functions reveal other menus, and these are dicussed in later sections of this chapter.

12.1.3 PowerKeys. PowerKeys (sometimes called "hotkeys" in other programs) allow you to jump immediately to often used UCFImage functions without having to go through the menu system. A PowerKey is accessed by holding down the *ALT* key and pressing the desired function key as listed in Figure 12.4. For example, to immediately enter *PAN* mode, press *ALT-p*.

```
credits    -- Primary authors of UCFImage, version being used.
file       -- Load, save, print images.
Cfile      -- Load and save images using compressed formats:
              GIF, TIFF, PCX, and BMP;
algebra    -- Arithmetic and logical operations on images;
geometry   -- Rotation, zooming, masking, thresholding;
histogram  -- Image statistics, equalization, specification;
measure    -- Pixel values, profiling, object identification,
              three-dimensional mesh plots;
Filter     -- Spatial, adaptive, circular, symmetric, and
              morphological filters,  two-dimensional FFT;
palette    -- Dynamic modification of color palette,
              pseudocoloring;
noise      -- Generation of noise distributions.
warping    -- pixel location transformation.
DOS        -- DOS shell.
```

Figure 12.2 *Startup (main) menu functions.*

Figure 12.3 *UCFImage main menu screen.*

12.1.4 Graphic Help Facility. When a question mark (?) is entered, a list of help screens is displayed with help topics labeled with alphabetic letters. Selection of a topic displays a graphic screen giving on-line information about the selected topic.

ALT-p	Pan
ALT-s	Scale
ALT-t	Threshold
ALT-1	1st Pt
ALT-2	2nd Pt
ALT-x	Exit
SHIFT-?	Help

Figure 12.4 *UCFImage PowerKeys*

12.2 File Menu

The file menu (Figure 12.5) allows for access to images stored under DOS in UCFImage and raw data formats. The default format for UCFImage is 513 rows of 512 pixel columns. This allows for an extra row, the first row, to act as an information header describing the content and format of the image contained in the file. See Figure 12.6 for a graphic that illustrates this format.

12.2.1 Dos Directory (dos dir). This command, *dos dir*, displays the contents of a directory when a DOS directory pathname is entered. If the escape key *ESC* or enter key is hit instead of a pathname, then the contents of the current directory are displayed. A backslash must be placed at the end of the pathname entered. If the backslash is inadvertently omitted, then a message of "file not found" or "pathname dir" will be displayed.

Correct usage example:

```
C:\DOS\    =>     CURRENT DIRECTORY WILL BE DISPLAYED
```

Incorrect usage examples:

```
C:         =>      file not found    C:\DOS  => DOS DIR
```

Up to 18 lines are displayed at a time. If more files are found, then pressing any key will display the next screen. The escape *ESC* key may be entered at any time during the displaying of the directory contents to return to the file menu.

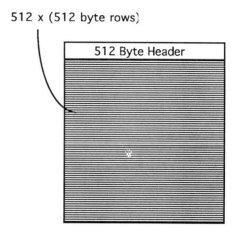

Figure 12.5 *File menu screen.*   **Figure 12.6** *File with 512 byte header.*

12.2.2 Open (open). The **open** command is used to load and display images with a 512 pixel header. The user is prompted for a filename:

```
Enter filename including the path:
```

If the escape key, *ESC*, is hit prior to completely entering the filename, then the Open procedure is aborted and control is returned to the file menu. If a nonexistent filename is entered, or the correct path is not specified, then the following message results:

```
ERROR File Not Found
Hit any key to continue.
```

Once a correct filename and path are entered, the image is loaded into the buffer region and the display region. As with the **new** call, the previous contents of the buffer are destroyed, and a call to **save** must be made prior to **open**, if the previous buffer contents are needed for future use. Loading images from a diskette is very time consuming, therefore, for quicker results, copy needed images to the hard drive prior to running UCFImage. Loading and saving images using the hard drive will reduce the wait time substantially.

12.2.3 Load & Process submenu (loadP). The **loadP** function, load and process, combines a file specified by user with the current contents of the buffer in the indicated way. The allowed operations driving the combinations are multiplication, division, addition, subtraction, logical or, logical and, and logical exclusive or. The load and process menu is illustrated in Figure 12.7.

```
┌─────────────────┐
│LOAD &           │
│PROCESS          │
│                 │
│ mult            │
│ div             │
│   buf/fil       │
│ Div             │
│   fil/buf       │
│ add             │
│ sub             │
│   buf-fil       │
│ Sub             │
│   fil-buf       │
│ Or              │
│ And             │
│ Exor            │
│                 │
│ ESC-Exit        │
└─────────────────┘
```

Figure 12.7 *Load and process menu.*

Upon selection of an operation, the user is prompted for the filename and path. If the escape key, *ESC*, is hit prior to completely entering the filename, the procedure is aborted and control is returned to the load and process menu. If a nonexistent filename is entered or the correct path is not specified, the following message results:

```
ERROR File Not Found
Hit any key to continue.
```

Once a correct filename and path are entered, the image in the file is combined with the image in the buffer in the selected manner. As with the NEW and OPEN call, the previous contents of the buffer are destroyed, and a call to SAVE must be made prior to using the load and process options if the previous buffer contents are needed for future use. The file specified must be of size 513 × 512. Combinations involving alternate file sizes produce unpredictable results. However, to convert an image from other formats and sizes, the *save* command within the *Special* command located in the *File* menu should be used after loading.

Multiply (mult). Multiply corresponding pixel values of buffer and selected file. Results are placed in the buffer. Products exceeding 255 are set to 255.

Divide File by Buffer (div). Each pixel value of the buffer is divided by the buf/fil corresponding file pixel value. If the value of the pixel in the file is 0 then the result placed in the buffer is set to 0.

Divide Buffer by File (Div). Each pixel of the selected file is divided by the matching pixel's value in the buffer. Division by 0 is handled the same as above (quotient = 0).

Add (Add). Add corresponding pixel values of the buffer and the specified file. Sum is placed in the buffer. If the final sum is greater than 255, then the final result is set to 255.

Subtract File from Buffer (sub). The pixel values of the file are subtracted from buf-fil corresponding pixels in the buffer. If the difference is less than 0, it is set to 0.

Subtract Buffer from File (Sub). Buffer contents are subtracted from the file pixel fil-buf values. Differences less than 0 become 0.

Or (Or). Or is a logical (Boolean) operation. The binary equivalent of the pixel value is compared to the binary equivalent of the corresponding file pixel value. The resultant is determined according to:

```
           Logical OR
  1st | 2nd | 1st OR 2nd
  ----|-----|-------------
   0  |  0  |     0
   0  |  1  |     1
   1  |  0  |     1
   1  |  1  |     1
```

Example: Pixel value 250 is ORed with entered value 200:

```
      250 => 11111010
      200 => 11001000
           --------
           11111010 => 250 (result)
```

And(And). And is a logical (Boolean) operation. The binary equivalent of the pixel value is compared to the binary equivalent of the corresponding file pixel value. The resultant is determined according to:

```
          Logical AND
  1st | 2nd | 1st AND 2nd
  ----|-----|------------
   0  |  0  |     0
   0  |  1  |     0
   1  |  0  |     0
   1  |  1  |     1
```

Example: Pixel value 250 is ANDed with entered value 200:

```
250 => 11111010
200 => 11001000
    --------
    11001000 => 200 (result)
```

Exor (Exor). EXOR (logical exclusive or) is similar to the logical Or in that the result of 1 is produced if one or the other is 1; however, the results of the exclusive or when both values are 1 is equal to 0. The resultant is determined according to:

```
             Logical EXOR
1st | 2nd | 1st EXOR 2nd
----|-----|-------------
 -
  0 |  0  |      0
  0 |  1  |      1
  1 |  0  |      1
  1 |  1  |      0
```

Example: pixel value 250 is EXOR-ed with entered value 200:

```
250 => 11111010
200 => 11001000
    --------
    00110010 => 50 (result)
```

12.2.4 Save (save). Save contents of the buffer with a 512 header placed at the beginning to the filename specified by the user. If no path is given, the file is saved to the current drive and path. If the escape key, *ESC*, is hit while entering the filename or the return key is hit prior to entering the filename, then the *save* procedure is aborted and control is returned to the file menu. The contents of the buffer and display region are not affected by this function.

12.2.5 Special submenu (Special). This submenu enables the user to load and save files of raw image data of different sizes, with or without a header. Image X and Y dimension and header length are entered manually. The menu is shown in Figure 12.8. The open and save commands in this menu are similar to the same commands located in the file menu; however, in this case the files are loaded and saved according to the size indicated and options selected.

Files are loaded and saved according to the dimensions indicated; therefore, the correct horizontal (x) width and vertical (y) height of the image must be set before a call to open or save.

```
┌─────────────┐
│  SPECIAL    │
│             │
│  open       │
│  save       │
│             │
│  header     │
│    (0)      │
│             │
│  x size     │
│   512       │
│             │
│  y size     │
│   512       │
│             │
│  ESC-Exit   │
└─────────────┘
```

Figure 12.8 *Special menu.*

Open (open). See Section 12.2.2.

Save (save). See Section 12.2.4.

Header (header). Upon selection of this option (default: 0), the user is prompted for the size of the header. This value must be an integer value of 0 or greater. The default is 0, corresponding to no header. UCFImage will read **header** bytes from the file and discard them; then **x** column bytes will be read **y** times. (See **x size** and **y size** below.)

X Size (x size). The user is prompted for the number of rows in the image file or buffer. Valid entries are between 1 and 512. Invalid entries are ignored, and the user is continuously prompted for the width until a valid size is finally entered. If the escape key, ESC, is hit prior to completely entering the value, then this procedure is aborted and control is returned to the calling menu.

Y Size (y size). Number of columns contained in the raw image file is set by this call. Same conditions as in *x size* above.

12.2.6 Print (print). The contents of the buffer region are sent to the local printer. The user must only make this selection if one of the following printers (or compatibles) is available:

Hewlett-Packard Laserjet™ with one meg of memory
Hewlett-Packard Deskjet™
Epson™ MX-80

The user is asked to enter an offset level desired. This may range from values greater than -20 to values less than +20. If an image is dark and the user desires a lighter print, a positive offset should be entered. If a darker print is desired, then choose a negative offset. If a zero offset is selected, there is no change in the data values from those of the buffer to what are printed; however, images will appear brighter on the screen than they will on paper. If the escape key, *ESC*, is pressed prior to entering a valid offset, the **Print** procedure is aborted and control is returned to the file menu. However, if an offset is entered and the required type of printer is not available, the user must reset the computer system to abort the function, thus losing all buffer contents if not saved.

12.2.7 New (new). The display window is reinitialized and filled with the current background color. The image buffer region is cleared without saving the previous buffer contents; therefore, if the contents of the current buffer are needed for future use, the user must select **Save** prior to making a call to **NEW**. Once selected this command cannot be aborted with *ESC*.

12.2.8 Reset (reset). This option reinitializes the program variables to the system start-up values. The user is prompted to continue or abort this operation.

12.2.9 Pan (Pan) [ALT-p]. A portion of the image is viewed at full resolution. The full image is viewed in using the entire display and no menu is visible. There is a one-to-one correspondence between the pixels shown on the display and the pixels in the buffer, instead of the usual subsampled picture. This procedure is especially necessary for viewing images after morphological filtering has been applied or when the user wishes to view fine detail in the image.

The cursor keys are used to pan the display window over the full-resolution image. The panning window is 300 × 200 pixels in area and is composed of up to 256 graylevels or colors. The number of positions moved for each key press is designated by the step size. Step sizes of one, two, four and eight pixels may be set by hitting the corresponding number key. For quicker movement throughout the image, choose step size 8. To zero in on a specific region, choose the smallest step size, 1.

This process cannot be aborted prior to displaying the full image; however, since the buffer is not altered by this expansion, the previous contents are not lost. The subsampled image is again displayed upon exiting this routine. To return to the subsampled image after viewing the full image, simply press the *ESC* key and control will be transferred back to the menu system.

If a mouse is available, the left mouse button advances the screen to the pan mode. The window will pan across the image in response to mouse movement. To restore the screen when finished with the pan mode, click the right mouse button.

12.3 Compressed File Menu

The *Cfile*, or compressed file, function in the main menu allows access to load and save functions that use compressed formats. UCFImage supports GIF, TIFF, PCX, and BMP file types. Selecting *Cfile* from the start-up menu displays a submenu with selections for the various file types supported. Each of these, in turn, displays a submenu for *open* and *save* operations using the selected file format.

12.3.1 GIF submenu (gif). This function allows loading and saving of Graphics Interchange Format™ (GIF) images, developed by Compuserve™. GIF format allows for high-quality, high-resolution graphics to be displayed on a variety of graphics hardware. GIF images have a coded header containing image information, such as the picture size and color palette. UCFImage allows for the opening of GIF image files up to the size of 1024×1024 pixels; however, only 512×512 pixels are read into the buffer. UCFImage allows the user to specify a start point in the image to begin loading. The actual image data in a GIF file are compressed using the Lempel-Ziv-Welch algorithm; therefore, GIF images tend to be very small and, because of this, it is a good idea to save images as GIF files. GIF typically yields a compression factor of 50%.

Open GIF (open). User is prompted for a GIF filename. If the file to be opened is not a GIF file, the following message is displayed to the screen:

```
Invalid GIF dataset...screen description
Hit any key to continue.
```

If the GIF image is greater than 512x512, the user is requested to enter the upper-left corner starting point where the image is to be extracted. If the GIF file contains a color image, it is recommended that the image be converted to a black and white image using the Grayconv command located in the Palette menu (Section 12.9) prior to performing image-processing functions other than Palette manipulations.

Save GIF (save) User is prompted for a filename. The contents of the buffer are saved in a pecified filename in the GIF format. If the escape key, *ESC*, is hit while entering the filename, or the return key is hit prior to entering a filename, the *save* procedure is aborted and control is returned to the GIF menu, and the contents of the buffer and display regions are not altered. The image is saved as a 512×512 GIF format image.

12.3.2 TIFF submenu. This function allows loading and saving of Tagged Image File Format (TIFF) images. The operations and size restrictions for this format are identical to those of the GIF file format submenus as are the submenu selections *open* and *save*.

12.3.3 PCX submenu. This function allows loading and saving of PC Paintbrush format images. The operations and size restrictions for this format are identical to those of the GIF file format submenus as are the submenu selections *open* and *save*.

12.3.4 BMP submenu. This function allows loading and saving of Microsoft Windows compatible Bit Map Picture format images. The operations and size restrictions for this format are identical to those of the GIF file format submenus, as are the submenu selections *open* and *save*.

12.4 Algebra Menu

The algebra menu (*algebra*) allows arithmetic and Boolean operations to be performed between a *scalar* value entered by the user and the image buffer. The arithmetic operations are multiply, divide, add, and subtract, and the boolean operations are Or, And, Exor, and Not. The user selects the desired function by choosing the first letter of the option listed in the menu. If the escape key, *ESC*, or return key is hit prior to completely entering the requested value, then the selected operation is aborted, control is returned to the algebra menu, and the buffer contents and display region are left unaffected by this call.

Other menu options include an autoscale routine, undo command, cursor call, and 1st point and 2nd point specifications. See Figure 12.9 for the Algebra Menu.

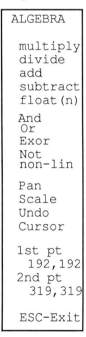

Figure 12.9 *Algebra menu.*

12.4.1 Multiply by Scalar (multiply). The ROI is multiplied by a positive value specified by user. Products greater than 255 are reduced to 255 and products less than 0 are set to 0. Multiplying the buffer by 0 will produce a completely black image; multiplication by any other acceptable value produces a brighter image.

12.4.2 Divide by Scalar (divide). The ROI is divided by the user-specified positive value. A darker image is usually produced.

12.4.3 Add Scalar (add). The entered value is added to each pixel in the ROI. Positive and negative values are accepted. Sums less than 0 become 0, and sums greater than 255 become 255.

12.4.4 Subtract Scalar (subtract). The entered value is subtracted from each pixel in the ROI. Positive and negative values are accepted. Differences less than 0 become 0, and differences greater than 255 become 255.

12.4.5 Set Float Mode (float). Selecting causes a toggle action between (n)o and (y)es. When toggled yes, the entered value for scalar operations may be a floating-point number.

12.4.6 Or Scalar (Or). The entered value is logically ORed with each pixel in the ROI. Only values of zero or greater are accepted. An entered value of 0 has no effect on the image.

12.4.7 And Scalar (And). The entered value is logically ANDed with each pixel in the ROI. Only values of 0 or greater are accepted. An entered value of 255 has no effect on the image.

12.4.8 Exclusive-or Scalar (Exor). The binary equivalent of entered value is Exclusive Ored with each pixel in the ROI. Only values of 0 or greater are accepted.

12.4.9 Not (Not). This produces a reversed image. What is previously light becomes dark and dark becomes light. Thus it produces the photographic negative of the image. The user may abort this call by pressing the escape key *ESC*, or continue with the procedure by pressing any other key.

The binary representation of each pixel value is inverted according to:

```
        Logical NOT
       1st | NOT 1st
        0  |    1
        1  |    0
```

Example: Pixel value 250 is inverted :

```
250 => 11111010  becomes   00000101 => 5
```

12.4.10 Non-linear Pixel Mapping (non-lin). Activates non-linear mapping submenu. This operation allows the user to specify a piece-wise non-linear mapping function using a graph. This submenu has the following six menu choices.

Define Map (define). Enters the graph specification mode and allows definition or redefinition of a pixel value mapping. Arrow keys or mouse allow positioning of the cursor, the enter key or right mouse button set the point. The graph x-axis represents the buffer pixel value and the y-axis the mapped value. Use the Esc key to exit or click the mouse on the Exit label in the upper left corner of the screen.

Save Map (Save). User is prompted for a filename in which to store the current mapping function.

Load Map (load). User is prompted for a mapping function filename that was stored earlier using the Save function.

New Map (new). The current map is cleared and the graph specification mode is entered.

Compute Map (compute). The current mapping function, either defined or loaded from a file, is applied to the pixels in the image buffer.

Graph Mode (grphmode). Toggles between *line* (default) and *bar* mode for the graph specification function. In line mode, the mapping function is represented as vertical lines from the x-axis. In bar mode, the graph is shown as a piecewise linear function.

12.4.11 Pan (Pan) [ALT-p]. See Section 12.2.9.

12.4.12 Scale (Scale) [ALT-s]. Performs an autoscaling routine on the ROI and updates the display. The ROI is searched for the maximum and minimum pixel values, then each pixel is multiplied by the scale factor created through the use of the found maximum and minimum. The scale factor is calculated by the following equation:

$$\text{Scale} = \frac{255}{(\text{maximum} - \text{minimum})}$$

If the difference between the maximum and minimum is zero then the scale factor is set to 1, and the buffer is left unchanged. The maximum and minimum values found, along with the calculated scale factor, are reported after the scaling is complete and the display area is updated. This procedure is aborted and control is returned to the calling menu if the *ESC* key is the first key entered after the initial selection.

12.4.13 Undo (Undo). The user is able to restore the ROI with the image data present prior to the last operation performed on the buffer. The last operation performed is canceled if the ROI does not exceed an area determined by the amount of free RAM available at program start-up. The maximum size that the *undo* buffer will achieve is 16K, or a rectangular ROI of 128×128 pixels. Prior to beginning a specified operation, if the current ROI exceeds the size of this buffer, the user is warned and given an opportunity to abort the operation.

12.4.14 Cursor submenu (Cursor) [ALT-c]. This selection calls up an arrow key or mouse-controlled cursor to define the corner points of the ROI. The ROI can be set to the entire image size (512×512, or 256,652 pixels); however, the *undo* operation will not work. Therefore, if the previous buffer contents are needed for later use, a call to save should be made prior to any operation on the whole image. The arrow keys located at the right of the keyboard are used to move the cursor throughout the screen. Upon selection of the cursor, a horizontal line and a vertical line are displayed on top of the image with a corresponding *cursor* submenu (see Figure 12.10). The information in the lower half of the cursor menu pertains to the point of intersection of the two lines. As this point is moved about the image, its intensity and x-y coordinates are tracked.

The speed of the cursor motion can be modified using the step selections (1, 2, 4, 8) described in the PAN entry of the file menu. To select the corner point simply move the point of intersection to the desired point in the image and press the return key. In this routine, two corner points must be entered. The mouse may be used to move the cursor to the desired location. Pressing the left mouse button selects the point of interest. The right mouse button returns control back to the calling menu. The order of the selection, that is, top left to bottom right, or bottom left to top right, is irrelevant due to the fact that the needed top-left corner and bottom-right corner of the rectangular region interest can be found given any two diagonally opposite corners via a swapping routine embedded in the program.

The menu item entitled *Value* displays the current intensity value of the pixel at the current cursor position and the numbers displayed under the X and Y labels designate the pixel coordinates. The *R*, *G*, and *B* symbols represent the red, green, and blue content of the pixel of interest.

12.4.15 1st Point (1st Point) [ALT-1]. Allows for the manual (by keyboard) setting of the ROI starting coordinates from numerical input values. Note that the coordinates of the current ROI are displayed in parentheses in the calling menu. Upon selection, the user is prompted to enter an x coordinate between 0 and 511 and then a y coordinate in the same range. If the enter key is hit instead of a number, the corresponding coordinate will be reset to 0. If the escape *ESC* key is hit in place of a number, the present coordinate will remain unchanged and control is returned to the calling menu. The same swapping routine discussed in the previous *cursor* section is applied here; therefore, orientation of the first and second points is irrelevant.

12.4.16 2nd Point (2nd Point) [ALT-2]. Allows selection of the 2nd coordinate pair for the ROI. See *1st Point* above.

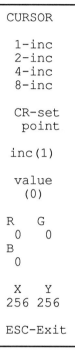

```
CURSOR

1-inc
2-inc
4-inc
8-inc

CR-set
 point

inc(1)

value
 (0)

R    G
 0    0
B
 0

X    Y
256  256

ESC-Exit
```

Figure 12.10 *Cursor submenu.*

12.5 Geometry Menu

The *geometry* menu contains routines that operate on the spatial positions of the image pixels. The available spatial operations unique to the geometry menu are zoom, squeeze, expand, rotate, threshold, fill, and text. The illustration of this menu screen is shown in Figure 12.11.

12.5.1 Zoom submenu (zoom). The user is able to increase the size of the displayed image. Zooming may be viewed as a stretching routine. This menu allows the user to stretch the display image horizontally, vertically, or in both directions simultaneously. Due to the subsampling process used to display the image, changes to the buffer after filtering may be hard to notice. As in the *Pan* procedure, this operation allows the user to see changes more clearly. The contents of the buffer remains unchanged in this routine; only the display region is altered (Figure 12.12).

If zoom X&Y, xzoom, or yzoom is selected, then the menu shown in Figure 12.13 is displayed. This is the zoom factor menu. If a positive zoom factor is chosen, the display is expanded by the number of pixels indicated in the specified direction. By selecting a zoom factor of 1, the display magnification is setback to one in the chosen direction. Selection of a negative zoom factor causes the display to flip about the axis perpendicular to the indicated direction. For example, if the horizontal direction is specified with a zoom factor of -1 and a mirror is placed along the vertical axis of the screen, then the mirror image will be seen in the normal orientation.

```
GEOMETRY

zoom
squeeze
expand
Pan
Move
rotate

mask
threshld
Text
fill

Scale
Undo
Cursor

1st pt
 192,192
2nd pt
 319,319

ESC-Exit
```

```
ZOOM

zoom X&Y

x zoom
 (1)

y zoom
 (1)

X center
 (256)

Y center
 (256)

Cursor
Update

ESC-Exit
```

Figure 12.11 *Geometry menu.*   **Figure 12.12** *Zoom submenu.*

Zoom X&Y (zoom X&Y). The display undergoes a vertical and horizontal magnification by the selected factor. A call to this routine only sets the zoom factor; the display is not alter at this point. To view the display with this selected zoom factor, the user must select the *update* option (described later) from the menu.

X Zoom (x zoom). The display undergoes horizontal magnification by the selected factor. Selection of a negative factor produces a mirror image about the y axis (vertical).

Y Zoom (y zoom). The display undergoes vertical magnification by the selected factor. Selection of a negative factor produces a mirror image about the x axis (horizontal).

X Center (X center). Allows the user to change the x coordinate of the center position of the display image. To move the display image to this new center point, *update* must be selected by the user.

Y Center (Y center). Allows user to change the y coordinate of the center position of the display image. To move the display image to this new center point, the user must call *update* .

```
A    1
B    2
C    4
D    8
E   -1
F   -2
G   -4
H   -8

ESC-Exit
```

Figure 12.13 *Zoom Factor submenu.*

Cursor submenu (Cursor) [ALT-c]. See Section 12.4.14.

Update (Update). This routine refreshes the screen. The screen is updated with the current zoom x and y factors and the x-y center that may have been recently altered. Once the display screen has been changed, it retains the *zoom x* and *zoom y* factors and x y center until *Update* or the *Cursor* of this menu is recalled.

Pan (Pan) [ALT-p]. See Section 12.2.9.

12.5.2 Squeeze buffer (squeeze). The user is able to compress the image in the buffer. This routine operates on the buffer region and updates the display. This is a simple compression routine based on subsampling of the pixels. The user selects the increment to use for the subsampling algorithm that achieves the desired compression. The 512×512 pixel image is compressed to (512/selected factor) pixels squared.

The increments, or scale factors, available to the user are 2 and 4. If the user selects 2, every other pixel is saved and the image is compressed to an observed size of 256×256. This routine places the compressed image in the buffer starting at the upper-left corner (0, 0). The rest of the buffer is filled with black (0). Therefore, the image displayed appears to be of a smaller size, however, due to the filling in of the rest of the buffer, the image is still 512×512.

Once selected, this routine may be aborted by pressing the escape key (ESC), or executed by selecting any other key. This function operates on the complete buffer; therefore, the *undo* command is unavailable. If the contents of the buffer is needed for future use, then a call to *save* must be done prior to calling *squeeze*.

12.5.3 Pan (Pan) [ALT-p]. See Section 12.2.9.

12.5.4 Move ROI submenu (move). This routine enables the user to copy the ROI to another location in the buffer. The ROI and the move location can be entered manually with *1st point*, *2nd point*, and *Move to,* or this information can be set using the arrow key or mouse controlled cursor.

Copy (copy). Once the three needed points have been set, this menu item is selected to execute the move that alters the buffer and updates the display. The user is prompted with the message:

```
Hit any key to continue;
ESC-Exit.
```

Hence, the user is given the opportunity to abort this call, before carrying out the copy. If the ROI exceeds the UNDO buffer boundary or the buffer region boundary, a warning message is sent to the user. At this point the user has the choice of continuing or aborting the call.

Cursor (cursor). This cursor routine is similar to the main cursor entry routine with only one modification. Like the other cursor entry, once called, the user is to input two diagonal corner points to define the ROI. After selecting the corner points the user may then select the point in the buffer at which to move the ROI. This move point is the point to which the upper-left corner of the ROI is to be copied.

Move To (move to). Allows for the manual keyboard setting of the point to which the ROI is to be copied, starting with the upper left hand corner. The coordinates of the current move point are displayed in parentheses in the calling menu. Upon selection of M, the user is prompted to enter in an x coordinate between 0 and 511 and then a y value in the same range. If the enter key is hit instead of a number then the corresponding coordinate will be reset to 0. If the escape key, *ESC*, is hit in place of a number then the present coordinate will remain unchanged and control is returned to the calling menu. If the selected ROI exceeds the buffer region at part of a boundary, then only the region within the boundary will be copied. The user, in this case, is given a warning to this effect and an opportunity to abort the call prior to the actual copy.

12.5.5 Rotate (rotate). The entire buffer is rotated a positive or negative 90°. Once selected the user is prompted with a short menu containing two selections, +90 and -90. By selecting -90, the image is rotated to the right, clockwise, and selecting +90 rotates the image to the left or counterclockwise. See Figure 12.14 .

12.5.6 Mask (mask). The pixels of the buffer *outside* the ROI are filled with a value specified by the user. The user is prompted for a value between 0 and 255. Once the value is entered, to continue with the operation the user may hit any key other than the escape key. To abort this operation, the user must hit the escape key. If the enter key is pressed prior to entering a value, then the region outside the specified area will be filled with the value 0. This operation alters the buffer and then displays the results. The full 512×512 buffer is used in this routine; therefore, the *undo* command (Section 12.10) is not available. If the previous buffer contents are needed for later use, a call to save must be done prior to this call.

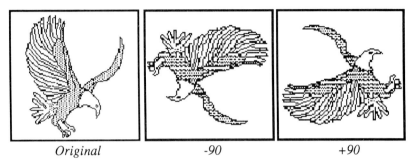

Original   *-90*   *+90*
Figure 12.14 *Rotate example.*

12.5.7 Threshold submenu (threshld) [ALT-t]. The *threshold* function is needed for operations requiring binary images (morpho and identify). When *threshold* is selected, a palette appears below the display and the threshold is arbitrarily set to 128. All pixels above the threshold appear red in the image and all pixels below 128 appear their normal gray level or color. When the arrow keys are pressed, the cursor will move and the threshold will change accordingly. If a mouse is available, to change the threshold, simply move the mouse cursor to the desired location in the palette window and click the left mouse button. The image will also change, corresponding to the change in the threshold value.

The increment used for moving the cursor may be chosen by selecting 1, 2, 4, or 8 steps from the menu. For more information regarding the step increments see *pan* (Section 12.2.9) or *cursor* (Section 12.4.14). When the desired threshold has been determined, that is, all desired objects are highlighted in red, *binarize* should be selected. This will cause all pixels at and above the threshold to be set to 255 (white) and all below to be set to 0 (black). See Figure 12.15 for the menu screen.

Manual Threshold Set (set). The user is prompted for a threshold value between 0 and 255. If the return is pressed prior to entering a value, the threshold is set to 0. If the escape key is hit while entering a value, the procedure is aborted and the threshold is not changed.

Binarize(binarize). This command executes the thresholding of the image. Thresholding causes all pixels at and above the desired threshold value to be set to 255 (white) and all the pixels falling below to be set to 0 (black). Once selected, the current threshold value is displayed and the user is given the opportunity to abort this procedure. *Cursor, 1st point*, and *2nd point*, found within this menu, are used to set the ROI upon which the binarization operation is to be performed

12.5.8 Fill Buffer with Value (fill). This routine is the exact opposite of the *mask* operation. The user is able to *fill* the ROI with a specified value. The pixels of the buffer inside the ROI are assigned the designated value. The user is prompted for a value between 0 and 255. Once the value is entered, to continue with the operation, the user may hit any key other than the escape key. To abort this operation, the user must hit the escape key. If the enter key is pressed prior to entering a value, the region outside the specified area will be filled with the value 0.

12.5.9 Expand Buffer (expand). The size of the object in the ROI is increased by a factor of 2 or 4. This operation, unlike zoom, changes the contents of the buffer; therefore, this is a permanent change. To complete this operation there must be at least 262K of disk space available.

```
    SET
 THRESHLD
 set
  val=128

 Binarize

 a-1 step
 b-2 step
 c-4 step
 step(1)

 Undo
 Cursor

 1st pt
  192,192

 2nd pt
  319,319

 ESC-Exit
```

Figure 12.15 *Threshold submenu.*

12.5.10 Annotate Buffer with Text submenu (text). The user is able to enter text characters into the display region. The size and gray level are selected, along with the position in the display area to which the text is to be placed. After desired options have been set, a call to text will place the entered text into the display region. See Figure 12.16.

```
┌─────────────┐
│    TEXT     │
│             │
│  size       │
│   (2)       │
│  text       │
│ graylevl    │
│   (200)     │
│             │
│  center     │
│  left       │
│  right      │
│   (left)    │
│             │
│  Pan        │
│  Undo       │
│  Cursor     │
│             │
│  begin      │
│   point     │
│  256,256    │
│             │
│  ESC-Exit   │
└─────────────┘
```

Figure 12.16 *Text submenu.*

Size (size). The size of the text (1, 2, 4, 8)may be specified.

Text (text). The user is prompted for the text to be placed in the display region. Once the enter key is hit, the text is placed in the display region at the previously specified begin point.

Graylevel (graylvl). The graylevel intensity of the text may be specified. It ranges from zero (black) to 255 (white).

Justification (center, left, right). *Center*, *left*, and *right* justification is available. This selection determines to which side of the selected beginning point the entered text will be placed. *Center* justification balances the entered text about the begin point. *Left* justification places the start of the entered text at the begin point, and *right* justification places the end of the entered text at the begin point.

```
Examples:    Left Justify:              .HELLO
             Center Justify:            HELLO
             Right Justify:          HELLO.
```

To select the type of justification, enter the first letter of the desired justification, or if a mouse is in use, click on the appropriate choice. The current justification choice is placed in parentheses in the TEXT menu.

Pan(Pan). See Section 12.2.9.

Undo(Undo). See Section 12.4.13.

Cursor(Cursor). See Section 12.4.14.

Begin Point (begin point). The coordinate in the display region to which the text is placed may be set manually by this call or automatically by a call to cursor. Only one point is specified.

12.6 Histogram Menu

Histogram allows computation, display, and manipulation of the histogram of the ROI. See Figure 12.17 below. A histogram of an image is described as the frequency distribution of its grayscale values. In UCFImage, the histogram is simply a plot of the number of pixels at a particular graylevel from 0 to 255. The abscissa of the histogram is labeled in grayscale values, and the ordinate is the total number of pixels at that grayscale. Note the shapes of the histograms for the various images shown below in Figure 12.18.

The mean and standard deviation of the most recently computed histogram is displayed at the bottom of the histogram menu.

12.6.1 Compute Histogram (compute). The histogram of the ROI is computed. The user is able to abort this procedure by hitting the escape key or continue with the operation by hitting any other key.

12.6.2 Display Histogram (display). A graph or plot of the histogram of the ROI is displayed with the pixel intensity value place along the x axis and the number of pixels at that intensity value along the y axis. An arrow key-controlled cursor line is provided that slides back and forth along the graph with the aid of the left and right arrow keys. The step increments of this cursor range from 1 to 8, and they may be selected by hitting the corresponding number key.

If a mouse is used, then the bar indicating the graylevel values and number of occurrences can be moved by placing the green cursor in the desired new location and clicking the left mouse button. The intensity level and number of pixels at that level corresponding to the position of the cursor are displayed at the bottom of the screen. The total number of data points in the region of interest is also displayed at the bottom of the screen.

12.6.3 Save Data (Sav data). The histogram data are saved to the file given by the user. The information saved in this file is the gray-level value followed by the number of pixels occurring in the ROI with that graylevel. The total number of points involved in the histogram is also saved at the end of this file. See SAVE entry (Section 1.4) in the File Menu for more help.

12.6.4 Equalize Histogram (equalize). This technique is used to obtain a uniform histogram distribution. This procedure can take a dark image histogram and convert it to an equalized histogram image (Figure 12.18). By equalizing, an image can be recovered from one that is on the dark side and almost completely invisible. For more information regarding the histogram equalization algorithm, consult <u>Digital Image Processing</u>, Gonzalez and Wintz, in the Annotated Bibliography.

12.6.5 Specify Histogram submenu (specify). The user is able to specify interactively particular histograms capable of highlighting certain gray-level ranges in an image. This process is done by:

1. Equalizing the levels of the original image.
2. Specifying the desired density function and obtaining the appropriate transformation function.
3. Applying the inverse transformation function to the levels obtained in step 1.

This process yields a new image, where the new gray levels are characterized by the user-specified histogram. As the number of graylevels decreases, the error between the specified and resulting histograms increases. Therefore, the exact specified histogram may not always be obtained. A workspace is set up for the user to create or edit their own histograms. Two types of graphs, bar and line, are available. The bar graph shows only those points selected by the user. The line graph interpolates the levels between the selected gray levels. Either histogram may be applied to the image.

New Histogram (new). The workspace is cleared and the user may create a new density (histogram) function. This operation is irreversible; therefore, the old editor contents are lost. The horizontal axis contains the graylevel, and the vertical axis of the workspace represents the number of image pixels with the corresponding gray level.

Upon entering the workspace, vertical and horizontal cursor bars are located at the center of the workspace. These bars are moved to the desired graylevel/pixel number by use of the arrow keys or by first moving the green mouse cursor to the desired location and then pressing the left mouse button. The graylevel and corresponding number of pixels are located at the crossing of the two bars. To select a specific graylevel and pixel number, simply press the enter key or hit the right mouse button. To exit the workspace, the user must hit the ESC key. If a mouse is being used, place the mouse over the word *EXIT* in the top-left corner of the workspace and then press either the left or right mouse button to exit.

Edit Histogram (edit). The user is able to edit a previously created histogram. See the previous section for more information. If the *SPECIFY* menu is exited, all contents of the workspace is lost. Therefore, to save the workspace contents, select Savdata prior to exiting this menu.

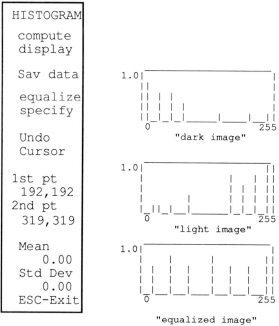

Figure 12.17 *Histogram menu.*   **Figure 12.18** *Histogram shapes.*

Set Specification Graphmode (mode). Successive graph-mode selections switch this option from line to bar. As stated earlier, the bar graph shows only those points selected by the user, and the line graph interpolates the levels between the selected gray levels. Either histogram may be applied to the image.

Load Histogram (load). A previously created histogram/density function may be loaded into the workspace. The data retrieved are the gray level value followed by the number of pixels at that level. The last entry of this retrieved file is the total number of pixels involved.

Save Histogram (save). The workspace may be saved to a data file. The results of the workspace are saved to a text file in pairs consisting of first the graylevel value and next the number of pixels corresponding to that level. The graylevel value is saved as an integer, and the number of occurrences of the graylevel is saved as a long integer. The last entry of this file is the value 256, followed by the total number of pixels involved in the workspace.

Compute Histogram (compute). The user-specified histogram is applied to the ROI. Upon selection of this option, the user is asked to abort by pressing the *ESC* or to continue by pressing any other key. See Section 12.6.1.

12.6.7 Undo (Undo). See Section 12.4.13.

12.6.8 Cursor (Cursor). See Section 12.4.14.

12.6.9 Set first coordinate (1st pt). See Section 12.4.15.

12.6.10 Cursor (Cursor). See Section 12.4.16.

12.7 Measure Menu

Measure allows the user to perform pattern analysis functions on an image. See Figure 12.19 for the Measure menu.

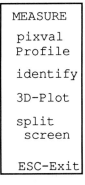

Figure 12.19 *Measure menu.*

12.7.1 Pixel Value submenu (pixval). Places a cursor over the displayed image and shows the pixel value at the cursor location as well as its red, green, blue (RGB) value. RGB values will be equal for monochrome images. The menu (Figure 12.20) is very similar to the *cursor* menu shown in Figure 12.10; however, in this menu the ROI points are not modified. For further explanation of this menu see *cursor* (Section 12.4.14). To return to the Measure Menu, press *ESC* or the enter key.

12.7.2 Profile Plot submenu (Profile). Allows for the selection of two points in the image using the cursor. Upon selection of the *show* option, an x-y plot of the pixel values along the line connecting the two selected points is displayed. Save data saves the data to a file in ASCII (text) format for further analysis. The Euclidean distance between the points is displayed on the menu screen. See Figure 12.21.

   Save Profile Data (Savedata). The profile data are saved to the file specified by the user. Each x-y value along the line connecting the two specified points is saved to this file, along with its corresponding graylevel value. See SAVE entry (Section 12.2.4) in the File Menu for more information.

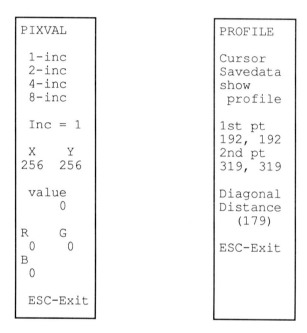

Figure 12.20 *Pixval submenu.*   **Figure 12.21** *Profile submenu.*

   Show Profile (show). A graph or plot of information pertaining to the line connecting the two user- specified points is displayed with the pixel intensity value along the y axis and the point number of the line, starting with 0 (for 1st point), along the x axis. An arrow key-controlled cursor line is provided that slides back and forth along the graph with the aid of the left and right arrow keys. The step increments of the cursor range from 1 to 8, and they may be selected by hitting the corresponding number key. The intensity level of the point corresponding to the position of the cursor is displayed at the bottom of the screen. The cursor line may also be moved via the mouse. To move left, click the left mouse button and to move right, click the right mouse button. The increment size of the steps to the left and right may be altered via the mouse by moving the small green cursor over the desired increment value and clicking the left button. This function cannot be aborted by pressing the right mouse key. To exit, move the green cursor to the word *EXIT* in the top-left corner and click the left mouse button.

12.7.3 Identify Pixel Clusters submenu (identify). Performs a simple nearest-neighbor clustering algorithm on the ROI. *Identify, colorize, threshold, pan, undo, cursor* and *1st point/2nd point* are options included in this menu.

Locate Clusters (identify). Initiates identification process. Upon initial selection of this option, the user is prompted for the size in pixels of the clusters and then those clusters are located. To abort this procedure, press *ESC*. Upon completion of this process, the user is notified of the number of objects found. Hitting the return key prior to entering a size causes unpredictable results. The size pertains to the radius of the objects to be located. This size may range from 0 to 511. The maximum number of objects that can be located is 200.

Colorize Clusters (colorize). When colorize is selected, the clusters are given different color values so that they can be rapidly located. To return to the Identify submenu, simply press *ESC*.

Threshold (threshld) [ALT-t]. See Section 12.5.7.

12.7.4 Plot Three-dimensional Mesh of Buffer submenu (3D-plot). A 3-dimensional plot of the display region is made. Two types of graphs, line and mesh, are available. The user is able to select the resolution level and whether or not to remove hidden lines. See Figure 12.22.

```
3D-Plot
view
lines
  (32)
hide
  (no)
type
  (line)

ESC-Exit
```

Figure 12.22 *Mesh plot submenu.*

Set Mesh Resolution (lines). The user is able to select the level of resolution of the graph which determines the degree of detail in the graph. The graph resolutions available are 2, 4, 8, 16, and 32 lines. The higher the number selected, the less detail the graph will shown. Therefore, if a detailed graph is desired, select a *lines* value of 4 or 2. If a value other than the default is desired, this option must be selected prior to a call to view.

Remove Hidden Lines (hide). This option allows the user to remove hidden lines from the graph. This is a toggle value between yes, remove the hidden lines and no, do not remove them.

Set Type of Mesh (type). The user may select the type of graph to plot. This also is a toggle value between line and mesh. If line is selected, cross sections perpendicular to the y axis are shown. Cross sections perpendicular to both axes are shown simultaneously if the mesh plot is selected. On higher-value resolutions (16 and 32), the differences between the mesh and line plots are more readily apparent.

View Mesh Plot (view) . When the user has finished selecting the graphing options, this selection is made to view the three-dimensional plot. If at any time the user wishes to discontinue the plotting procedure, then he may simply press any key to quit. Regions of the image that are hidden can be seen by using the rotate command under the Geometry Menu.

12.7.5 Split Screen View (split screen). Permits simultaneous viewing and comparison of two images. This function is useful for comapring the results of a filtering operation. When selected from the measure menu, the user is prompted for a filename containing the image to be compared with the image in the buffer. The image must be in UCFImage format (see Section 12.2.2 and Figure 12.6). The image is loaded from the filename and shown sideby side with the image in the buffer. Figure 12.23 shows the screen configuration after load. A vertical green cursor appears between the two images and may be moved with the arrow keys or mouse. Motion increments of 1, 2, 4, or 8 pixels are set by pressing the corresponding number key. Pressing *ALT-O* gives an information screen explaining the split screen options. The user may pan both sides (images), move the cursor to expose or hide the images with respect to each other, pan left or right sides independently, and remove the cursor for more accurate pixel comparisons.

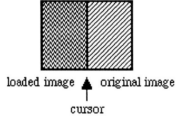

loaded image ⬆ original image

cursor

Figure 12.23 *Split screen display.*

12.8 Filter Menu

Filters are separated into three groups, spatial, adaptive, and morpho. The fast fourier transform is also available in this menu. In general, a filter is a mechanism or algorithm that removes or modifies something in the image. See Figure 12.24 for the menu display. This menu is the root of a large tree of submenus that span the entire range of filters that may be applied to images using the program. Special options appear in various combinations throughout the tree and the reader is referred to the sections given in the following list for discussions of their use as they are not included in the filter submenu discussion:

Pan (Pan) [ALT-p]. See Section 12.2.9.
Undo (Undo). See Section 12.5.13.
Cursor (Cursor) [ALT-c]. See Section 12.4.14.
Set first coordinate (1st pt). See Section 12.4.15.
Set second coordinate (2nd pt). See Section 12.4.16.
Scale (Scale) [ALT-s]. See Section 12.4.12.
Threshold (threshld) [ALT-t] . See Section 12.5.7.

```
FILTER

spatial
morpho
adaptive
FFT
circular
non-lin

Scale
Undo
Cursor

1st pt
 192,192
2nd pt
 319,319

ESC-Exit
```

Figure 12.24 *Filter menu.*

12.8.1 Spatial Filters submenu (spatial). These filters perform a discrete convolution on the image using a filter mask. Predefined standard masks are available to the user or the user may specify a custom mask with the user option. The Laplace, mean, highpass, median, and basic edge filters are provided. Masks up to 7×7 can be specified. Spatial filters operate in a small, local area of the image and are very fast in execution.

To perform spatial filtering of the ROI, simply select the desired filter and element size of the mask. The number of elements used in the mask can be changed by the user choosing the element option. Values of 3, 5, or 7 are accepted. See Figure 12.25 for the Spatial menu. After selecting a filter, the following message is displayed:

```
Hit any key to continue,
Esc-Exit.
```

At this point the user is able to continue with the selected mask or abort the entire procedure.

```
SPATIAL
FILTERS

Elements
 (3)
Laplace
Mean
highpass
median
edge
user

Pan
Scale
Undo
Cursor

1st pt
192,192
2nd pt
319,319

ESC-Exit
```

Figure 12.25 *Spatial Filters submenu.*

Element Count (Elements). The user is prompted for the mask size. The sizes available are 3×3, 5×5, and 7×8. The current element size is displayed in parentheses under the menu selection.

Laplacian Edge Detection (Laplace). The Laplacian is a second-order derivative operator that is useful for outlining edges in an image. The two-dimensional gradients are computed across the image. The user has the opportunity to abort this operation by pressing *ESC*. The Laplacian is typically unacceptably sensitive to noise, therefore, it is generally used in a secondary role for determining if a given pixel is on the dark or light side of an edge.

Mean Filter (Mean). The graylevel of each pixel is replaced by the average of the graylevel s of that pixel and its neighbors. This filter smooths the image (lowpass filter) and blurs the edges by preserving the low frequencies while attenuating the high frequencies present in the image. The user has the opportunity to abort this operation by pressing *ESC*.

Highpass Filter (highpass). Sharpens the image by preserving high frequencies while attenuating low frequencies present in the image. The highpass filter is generated by means of the lowpass filter (mean filter). The highpass filter value is simply 1 minus the lowpass filter value. The user is able to abort this operation by pressing *ESC*.

Median Filter (median). The graylevel of each pixel is replaced by the median of the graylevel s in the neighborhood of that pixel. This method is quite effective when noise patterns consisting of spikelike components is present. This filter smooths while preserving edges. The user is able to abort this operation by pressing *ESC*.

Figure 12.26 *Edge Filters submenu.*

Edge Enhancement/Detection submenu (edge). Enhances edges using a variety of techniques. An *edge* menu (see Figure 12.26) appears and allows the selection of the following high-pass filters:

```
Sobel Top       Sobel Bottom      Sobel Left      Sobel Right
-1 -2 -1           1   2   1        -1   0   1       1   0  -1
 0  0  0           0   0   0        -2   0   2       2   0  -2
 1  2  1          -1  -2  -1        -1   0   1       1   0  -1


        Line Vertical        Line Horizontal
          -1   2   -1           -1  -1  -1
          -1   2   -1            2   2   2
          -1   2   -1           -1  -1  -1


        Left Diagonal        Right Diagonal
```

```
-1  -1   2                    2  -1  -1
-1   2  -1                   -1   2  -1
 2  -1  -1                   -1  -1   2
```

To abort the selected operation, press *ESC*; to complete the indicated filter mask, press any other key.

User Mask submenu (user). Allows the user to specify the exact values of a mask, load a previously defined mask from a file, or save a mask to a file. A new user menu appears as shown in Figure 12.27.

Define User Mask submenu (def user). Allows user to define a mask to be implemented. Upon selection, a new menu appears along with an element sized grid with the current cell values. See Figure 12.28.

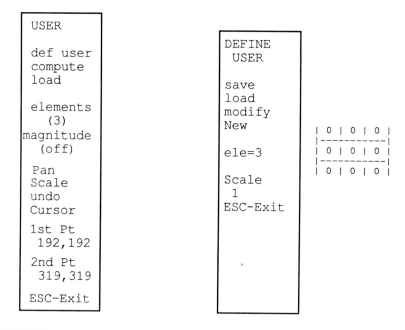

Figure 12.27 *User submenu.*   **Figure 12.28** *Def User submenu and mask edit form.*

Save User Mask (save). User is able to save contents of the mask to a text file. A special header is written to the beginning of the file upon saving. This header consists of the letter u followed by the element size of the mask and the associated scale factor. The user is prompted for a filename and path. If the escape key is hit at this point, the procedure is aborted.

Load User Mask (load). A previously created mask text file is loaded into the grid. Only mask files with the header information specified above are allowed. If you attempt to load a file without the appropriate header, the following message results:

```
File Type Mismatch
Hit Any Key to Continue.
```

Upon loading, the mask is placed into a grid of size element, where element is specified in the header. When creating a mask text file in another system, be sure to include the header at the beginning of the file.

Edit User Mask (modify). The user is allowed to change mask cell values. Upon selection, a green bar appears in the first cell of the grid. This bar may be moved from cell to cell by use of the arrow keys. When the bar is in the desired cell, the spacebar must be hit to select and edit the cell. Only values between -99 and +99 are valid. The enter key stores the new data in the cell.

When a mouse is available, use the left mouse button to move about the grid to the desired cell. Select the desired cell by clicking the right mouse button. The cell value may now be changed. To store the value, press the enter key. Two successive right clicks over a cell leave the cell unchanged. To exit the modify mode, place the mouse over the word EXIT in the top-left corner of the screen and click the left mouse button.

If the user attempts to input a value out of the designated range, the cell is reset to zero; if the escape key is hit after selection of a cell, the cell is left unchanged. To exit the modify mode, press the escape key or a capital *E*.

Clear User Mask (New). This routine resets all the cells of the user mask to zero. If the previous contents of the mask are needed for future use, a call to *save* must be done prior to a call to new.

Set User Mask Scale Factor (Scale). A normalizing factor may be specified by the user. After applying the desired filter to the specified ROI, this factor is divided into the ROI to scale the results. The user is prompted with the following message:

```
Enter Scale Factor For Mask between 1 and 999.
```

Only values between 1 and 999 are accepted. If the *ESC* key is pressed prior to entering the scale factor; the factor retains its previous value before this call.

Change User Mask Element Count (ele). The user is allowed to change the element size of the mask. For more information consult the earlier *elements* entry. Changing the element size does not clear the mask. When moving from a smaller to a larger mask, the new elements are set to zero. Changing from a larger to a smaller mask truncates the grid cells; however, the actual array elements are preserved. See Figure 12.29.

```
    5 × 5                   3 × 3                    7 × 7
                                              1  1  1  1  1  0  0
  1  1  1  1  1                               2  2  2  2  2  0  0
  2  2  2  2  2           1  1  1             3  3  3  3  3  0  0
  3  3  3  3  3   ==>     2  2  2    ==>       4  4  4  4  4  0  0
  4  4  4  4  4           3  3  3             5  5  5  5  5  0  0
  5  5  5  5  5                               6  6  6  6  6  0  0
                                              0  0  0  0  0  0  0
```

Figure 12.29 *Change of element example.*

Compute Filter with User Mask (compute). The most recently specified user mask along with the selected scale factor is applied to the ROI specified by the user. The user is able to abort this procedure with *ESC* or continue the filtering by pressing any other key.

Load User Mask. See the previous paragraph.

Change User Mask Element Count (elements). See the following paragraph.

Set Truncate/Absolute Value Mode (magnitude). While applying the user-specified mask to the ROI, if *mag* is on, then the absolute value of the filter mask is taken; if *mag* is off, the mask values greater than 255 are set to 255 and values less than 0 are truncated to 0. This value toggles on and off by successive m key presses.

12.8.2 Adaptive Filters submenu. Adaptive filters are general-purpose nonlinear filters that do not require the statistics of the noise or degradation to be known. UCFImage offers the double-window modified-trimmed-mean and the minimum mean square error filter. Upon selection of *adaptive* from the *filter* menu, the submenu shown in Figure 12.30a is displayed. Two choices are possible, *dw-mtm*, to select the double window-modified trimmed mean filter, and *MMSE* to select the minimum mean square error filter.

Double window modified trimmed mean (dw-dtm). When selected from the adaptive filter submenu, Figure 12.30a, the submenu shown in Figure 12.30b is displayed.

Minimum mean square error (MMSE). When selected from the adaptive filter submenu, Figure 12.30a, the submenu shown in Figure 12.30c is displayed.

Compute (compute). The selected adaptive filter is applied to the ROI. Filter applied is determined by which adaptive filter submenu is active.

Set C-Value (c-value). The user is asked to enter a value between 1.5 and 2.5. This value is needed for computing the allowable pixel range used in the DW-MTM filter. Lower c-values allow for more filtering. As the c-value increases, more noise is allowed to pass through the filter. Once this menu item is selected the user must enter a value in the valid range. The escape key (*ESC*) cannot be used to abort this option (not an option in the MMSE submenu, Figure 12.30c).

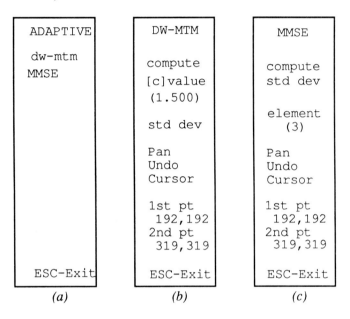

Figure 12.30 *Adaptive filter submenus.*

Set number of elements (elements). User may input the number of elements, 3, 5, or 7 to use in the computation grid of the MMSE filter (not an option in the dw-mtm submenu, Figure 12.29b).

Set Standard Deviation submenu (std dev). The standard deviation of the background noise is needed for this filter. The user is able to manually specify the standard deviation or have the computer calculate it automatically. See Figure 12.31 for a view of this menu. The user must specify the region in which the calculation is to be made, either manually or through the use of the CURSOR routine. The standard deviation is usually computed in a homogeneous background area near the ROI to be filtered.

Compute Standard Deviation (compute). The standard deviation of the specified ROI is calculated automatically. The region of the background noise in which this statistic is computed over may be specified by the Cursor (Section 12.4.14) routine or the 1st/2nd Point (Sections 12.4.15 and 12.4.16) routine found in this menu.

```
┌─────────────┐
│ Std Dev     │
│             │
│ compute     │
│ specify     │
│             │
│ Cursor      │
│             │
│ 1st pt      │
│   192,192   │
│ 2nd pt      │
│   319,319   │
│             │
│ ESC-Exit    │
└─────────────┘
```

Figure 12.31 *Standard Deviation submenu.*

Specify Standard Deviation (specify). Allows the user to manually enter the noise standard deviation. When *specify* is selected, the user is prompted for the value of the standard deviation of the background noise. Only positive values are accepted.

12.8.3 Morphological Filters submenu (morpho). This menu allows access to filters that operate on or define shapes. The morphological filters available in UCFImage include skeletonize, erosion, dilation, and outline. Opening and closing operations are also available as extensions of erosion and dilation. Morphological filters are particularly useful when analyzing images for objects in both classification and recognition tasks.

The morphological filters implemented in UCFImage require binary image files, therefore the threshold function (Section 12.5.7) is provided in this menu for convenience. See Figure 12.32 for the Morpho submenu.

Skeletonize (skeleton). Strips pixels away from the contour of the objects in the ROI until one single pixel is left, leaving the skeleton of the object. This filter is a member of a class of filters known as medial axis transforms. The user is given the opportunity to abort this operation by pressing the escape key or continuing on by pressing any other key.

Erosion (erosion). Removes a layer of pixels from the perimeter of the contour on each pass. The user is prompted for the number of passes he wishes to complete. Although as many passes as desired may be performed, it is recommended to perform only up to 20 passes in one call. If the escape key is hit at this point, the procedure is aborted and control reverts back to the Morpho submenu.

Dilation (dilation). Adds a layer of pixels to the perimeter of the contour on each pass. The user is prompted for the number of passes he wishes to complete. If the escape key is hit at this point, the procedure is aborted and control reverts back to the Morpho submenu.

```
┌──────────────┐
│   MORPHO     │
│              │
│  skeleton    │
│  erosion     │
│  dilation    │
│  outline     │
│  Opening     │
│  closing     │
│              │
│              │
│  item        │
│   value      │
│    (255)     │
│  Pan         │
│  Undo        │
│  Cursor      │
│  Scale       │
│  threshld    │
│              │
│  1st pt      │
│   192,192    │
│  2nd pt      │
│   319,319    │
│              │
│  ESC-Exit    │
└──────────────┘
```

Figure 12.32 *Morphological filter submenu.*

Outline (outline). Removes all pixels not on an object's perimeter contour, leaving the outline of the object. The user is able to abort this operation by pressing the escape key or continue on by pressing any other key.

Item Value (item value). The user is able to select the object color. A toggle is setup to alternate the object color from black (0) to white (255). The morphological filter algorithms use this color definition to determine objects. Thus, if the object is considered black, then erosion will erode the black regions of the image and dilate the white areas. Dilation will dilate the black regions and erode the white.

Opening (Opening). The morphological function of opening can be obtained by performing a set of erosions followed by an equal number of dilation passes. Opening causes fragmentation of lines after edge detection to increase and is useful in removing short line segments. The user is prompted for the number of passes. At this point the user may abort this operation with *ESC*.

Closing (closing). The closing function is the reverse of the opening process. Closing is used for sealing off contours or to reduce fragmentation. Again, the user is prompted for the number of passes to perform.

12.8.4 Fast Fourier Transform submenu (FFT). The FFT algorithm implemented here computes the real and imaginary parts of the Fourier transform, with these results being saved to an output file designated by the user. The user is able to display the magnitude images of the forward or reverse transforms with either a log or normal scaling option.

When the FFT computation is selected, the user is prompted for a filename in which the raw FFT data may be stored. When IFFT is selected, the user is prompted for the filename of the raw FFT data to be inverted.

The FFT routine can be performed on images of sizes 16×16, 32×32, 64×64, 128×128, 256×256, and 512×512 pixels in area. Both the forward and inverse transforms store the computed components in intermediate files. The FFT menu is shown in Figure 12.33.

Due to the large amount of temporary disk storage needed,UCFImage should be executed from the hard drive if this routine is used. For a 512×512 FFT, at least 4 meg of disk space should be available. The amount of time needed to complete a full FFT of size 512×512 is approximately 6 minutes with a 386 machine and an 80387 math coprocessor. With a 286 machine and no math co-processor, this processing time increases to approximately 25 minutes.

```
2D FFT

FFT
IFFT
display

begin pt
  0,0

size:512
center:n
phase: n
mag:   n

Pan
Cursor

ESC-Exit
```

Figure 12.33 *FFT Filter submenu.*

Compute FFT (FFT). This function computes the FFT of the specified size ROI at the specified beginning location. The FFT is computed on the data stored in the buffer. When the

FFT computation is selected, the user is prompted for a filename in which the raw FFT data may be stored (real term followed by the imaginary term). The FFT of the ROI is then computed, and the results are placed in the specified binary file. A header is placed at the beginning of this file, consisting of F followed by the size of the FFT. If *ESC* is hit at this point, the operation is aborted. If the magnitude option is selected, the user is next prompted for a filename for the scaled output. This file contains the magnitudes of the FFT data, scaled from 0 to 255, and it is used to display the magnitude of the FFT results. Finally, if the phase option is selected, the user is prompted for a filename for the phase output. At this point, the screen is frozen with the following information:

```
FFT results:   Filename w\path
Scaled image: Filename w\path  (if selected)
Phase image:  Filename w\path  (if selected)

Hit any Key to Continue.
```

Control reverts to the FFT menu upon hitting of any key or clicking the left mouse button at this time.

Compute Inverse FFT (IFFT). Compute the inverse FFT of a preselected size and beginning location. When the IFFT computation is selected, the user is prompted for a filename in which the raw FFT data may be found. This first line of this file must have either the letter I or the letter F followed by the size of the FFT. If the filename given is not a FFT data filename or the size does not match the currently selected size, then the operation is terminated. The IFFT of the ROI is then computed and the results are placed in the file named INVFFT.IMG, which has a header containing the letter T followed by the size of the IFFT. If the escape key is hit at this point, then the operation is aborted. The user is next prompted for a filename for the scaled output. When the scaled output is saved, the screen is frozen with the following information:

```
IFFT results:  Filename w\path
Scaled image: Filename w\path  (if selected)

Hit any Key to Continue.
```

Control reverts to the FFT menu upon hitting of any key at this time.

Display (display). Displays the magnitude of the FFT or IFFT calculation. If *ESC* is hit prior to completely entering the filename, then the operation is aborted and control is returned to the FFT menu. If a nonexistent filename is entered or the correct path is not specified, the following message results:

```
ERROR File Not Found
```

```
Hit Any Key to Continue.
```

Upon entering a correct filename, the image is loaded and control is returned to the FFT menu.

Set Begin Point for FFT/IFFT (begin point). Allows for the selection of the upper-left corner of the FFT ROI. The user is notified of the range of valid points determined by the previously selected size.

Example: If SIZE = 64, then

```
Begin Pt Range:  0 to 448.
Enter first X point (0)
```

is displayed followed by:

```
Enter first Y point (0)
```

The value in parentheses is the previously selected first point. If the escape key is hit prior to selecting the x and y points completely, the points are not altered.

Set Size of FFT/IFFT (size). Allows for the selection of the size of the FFT/IFFT ROI: 16, 32, 64, 128, 256, 512. The ROI for the FFT is assumed to be a square region. The value shown in parentheses in the FFT menu represents the current size selected.

Center Transform (center). This toggled value indicates whether to center the transform if it is turned on or leave the transform uncentered if it is off.

Select Scale Method (Scale). Allows user to select the scale method to be used in the creation of the magnitude files for display. This option is shown only if the magnitude option is turned on. The user may choose the normal scale or logarithmic (log 10) scale procedure. The current scale factor is displayed in parentheses in both the FFT menu and the Scale screen. If the log 10 scale is selected then the user is able to set a scale factor for use with the scaling routine. This factor is only displayed in the FFT Menu if the log 10 factor is selected. After selecting the log 10 scale factor, the user is prompted for a value. Only positive values are valid. The following equation is used for computation in the log scale process:

```
FFT = { log [ a * |FFT| ] } |scale  10| scaled 0-255
```

Compute Transform Magnitude (mag). This toggle value determines if a magnitude file is created upon taking an FFT of the ROI. This magnitude file is a graph of the Fourier spectrum displayed as an intensity function. When this option is selected, the current scale option is displayed in the FFT menu. The current scale factor may then be altered if need be.

Compute Transform Phase (phase). This toggle value determines if a phase angle file is created upon taking an FFT of the ROI. The components of the phase angle file are computed by taking the inverse tangent of the FFT imaginary component divided by the FFT real component. The results are then displayed as an intensity file with graylevel 0 representing an angle of 0°, and gray level 255 representing an angle of 360°.

12.8.5 Circular Symmetric Filtering submenu (circular). User is able perform a circular symmetric filter upon an image (Figure 12.34). Since the FFT raw data file is used for this filter, the forward FFT of the ROI, must first be performed before entering this menu. Prior to taking the FFT of the ROI the centering option must be turned on. After applying the desired circular filter, the user must take the IFFT of the ROI to complete the filtering process and view the results.

Define Filter (define). The user is able to edit a previously created filter. See the previous section for more information. If the Circular menu is exited, all contents of the workspace is lost. Therefore, to save the workspace contents, select SAVE prior to leaving this menu.

Save Filter Definition File (save). The workspace may be saved to a data file. The results of the workspace is saved to a text file in pairs consisting of first the radial frequency and next the amplitude corresponding to that level.

Load Filter Definition (load). A previously created filter may be loaded for editing or application to the ROI FFT source file. The data retrieved are the radial frequency followed by the filter amplitude at that frequency.

Clear Workspace (new). The workspace is initialized and the user may create a new filter function. This operation is irreversible; therefore, the old editor contents are lost unless a previous call to save has been completed. The x axis of the workspace represents the radial frequency. The amplitude of the filter, the filter gain, is plotted on the y axis. The maximum value of the amplitude is 10. However, due to the spatial resolution of the workspace, this value is scaled to 1,000. Therefore, a value of 500 represents an amplitude of 5; a value of 600 represents an amplitude of 6, and so on. Upon entering the workspace, vertical and horizontal cursors are located at the center of the workspace. This cursor is moved to the desired x y levels by the use of the arrow keys or by first moving the green mouse cursor to the desired location and then pressing the left mouse button. The x y level is located at the crossing of the two bars. To select a specific location simply press the enter key or hit the right mouse button. To exit the workspace, the user must hit the ESC-key. If a mouse is being used, place the mouse over the word EXIT in the top left hand corner of the workspace and then press either the left or right mouse button to exit.

```
CIRCULAR
  FILTERS

define

save
load
new
compute

grphmode
 (line)

ESC-Exit
```

Figure 12.34 *Circularly Symmetric Filter submenu.*

Compute Filter (compute). The user-specified filter is applied to the ROI FFT source file. Upon selection of this option, the user is prompted for the FFT source file corresponding to the ROI. If the enter key or *ESC* is pressed prior to entering a filename, or if the filename specified is not found, this operation is aborted. After entering a valid FFT source file, the user is next prompted for the output result filename. The IFFT of the results of this filter must next be taken to complete the filtering process. The final filtered image may then be viewed through the use of the Display command found in the FFT menu.

Set Graphics Editor Mode (grphmode). Successive graphmode selections switch this option from *line* to *bar*. The bar graph shows only those points selected by the user, and the line graph interpolates the levels between the selected radial frequency levels. Either filter may be applied to the FFT source file. Defining circular symmetric filters is similar to specifying histograms.

12.8.6 Non-linear Filtering submenu (non-lin). User is able perform a number of nonlinear filters upon an image (Figure 12.35).

Elements (ele). Allows selection of the number of horizontal and vertical elements of the computation grid, 3 (default), 5, or 7.

Set range (range). Allows entry of filter range value.

Maximum filter (Max). Maximum median filter.

Minimum filter (min). Minimum median filter.

```
NON-LIN
FILTERS

Ele (3)
range
Max
min
alph-trm
Lp mean
cp mean
geo-mean
harmonic
A-Mid-Pt

Pan
Scale
Undo
Cursor

1st pt
  192,192
2nd pt
  319,319

Esc-Exit
```

Figure 12.35 *Nonlinear Filter submenu.*

Alpha-Trim filter (alph-trm). Alpha-trimmed mean filter.

Order-statistic filter (Lp mean). Generalized order-statistic filter.

Time-varying order-statistic filter(cp mean). General time-varying order-statistic filter.

Geometric mean filter (geo-mean). Geometric mean (Log) filter.

Harmonic filter (harmonic). Harmonic mean (1/x) filter.

Filter (A-Mid-Pt). Midpoint trimmed-mean filter.

12.9 Palette Menu

Palette is used to modify the display system lookup table. The lookup table is nothing more than a mapping function. With gray-scale images, the palette maps one to one and all values of red green blue on the color screen are the same. This is the default palette mode for

UCFImage. If the display palette is set to display the inverse of each pixel in the image, then the negative of the image is displayed. Selecting palette shows the current palette graphically below the image display. For the screen menu see Figure 12.36.

In the following tables, the table on the left contains the actual pixel values of the image, 0 is black and 255 is white. The table on the right shows a modified display palette. With the modified palette, the black pixel in the image (0) will take a value of 99, or mid-gray. A white pixel will appear fairly black with only a display value of 4. Palette operations do not affect the image data, only what is viewed on the screen.

Figure 12.36 *Palette Menu.*

12.9.1 Select Positive Palette (Positive). Resets the color palette to the UCFImage 1-to-1 graylevel default.

12.9.2 Negative Palette (Negative). Inverts the palette. Negative is not the same as the NOT function found under the algebra menu. *Negative* inverts the palette, while *NOT* inverts the actual image pixel values. A grayscale image will look like a photographic negative.

12.9.3 Select Palette Color A (A Color). Built in pseudo-color palettes that illustrate the range of colors possible in UCFImage. The color range corresponds to the gray level value. For *A Color*, colors range from blue at the lower end to red at the upper end.

12.9.4 Select Palette Color B (B Color). Similar to A Color, except red is at the lower end of the scale and blue is at the high end. The A Color palette is reversed to form the palette of *B Color*.

12.9.5 Perform color corrections and grayscale conversion (Color). Allows entry into a submenu where grayscale conversion can be performed (*grayconv*), HSI color correction (*correct*), or gamma color correction (*Gamma*) may be performed.

Grayscale conversion computes graylevel values color pixels from the active color palette using an 8-bit color conversion formula. The process effectively converts a color image to monochrome for grayscale processing.

The HSI correction allows user to modify the hue and saturation components of the active color palette by moving cursors on two displayed bar garphs. Use the h key to select hue and the s key to select saturation. The active control is highlighted by an asterisk.

Gamma correction replaces the hue and saturation cursors with contrast (con) and brightness (brt) controls. Use the c key to select contrast and the b key to select brightness. The active control is highlighted by an asterisk.

12.9.6 Multiply Palette by Scalar (gain). Modify existing palette by multiplying it by a constant. Values should be greater than 0. Gains greater than 1 produce a higher contrast image, and gains less than one produce a lower contrast image. A gain of 1 does not change the image.

12.9.7 Set Palette Offset (offset). Existing palette is shifted by adding a constant value to it. Negative and positive values are accepted. An offset of 0 causes no change. Offsets greater than 0 produce a brighter image, and offsets less than 0 produce a darker image.

12.9.8 Cycle Palette Colors (cycles). The current palette is compressed and cycled across the full range of the palette by either 2, 4, or 8 cycles as specified by the user. For example, when cycles is set to 2, graylevels 0 to 127 correspond respectively to values 128 to 255. When cycles is 8, 0-31, 32-63, 64-95, 96-127, 128-159, 160-191, 192-223, and 224-255 overlap in gray level values; that is, 0, 32, 64, 96, 128, 160, 192, and 224 are considered the same graylevel.

12.9.9 Select User Defined Palette (1..4). Four user defined palettes are available in UCFImage. These are selected from the palette menu using keys 1,2,3 and 4. The user palette specified is the one selected upon entrance to the User Palette Menu from the Palette Menu. Before the implementation of one of these user palettes, the palette must be loaded or defined previously. The latest defined palette of the selected user is the one that is displayed upon selection.

12.9.10 Load User Defined Palette (Load). Recall a previously defined palette from a file. This palette is loaded into the user palette currently selected. If you attempt to be load a file without the appropriate header, then the following message results:

```
File Type Mismatch.
Hit Any Key to Continue.
```

When creating a user palette in another application , be sure to include the header at the beginning of the file.

12.9.11 Define User Palette submenu (Def User). The user is able to create a new palette or edit an old one. The palette to be manipulated is the most current one selected prior to this call. See Figure 12.37 for the screen menu.

Figure 12.37 *Defuser submenu.*

Set Red (red) Green (grn) Blue (blu) Values. By selecting *red*, *grn*, or *blu* the user determines which color to modify. Once a color has been selected, the color value may be changed by using the arrow keys. The up and the right arrow keys increase the color value, and the down and the left arrow keys decrease the color value.

Set Pixel Color Range (lo/hi). Lo and *hi* determine the range of pixel modification. This defines the upper and lower intensity positions of the desired color in the window. The range is specified using the arrow keys; up and right arrow keys increase the color value or the lo/hi position, and down and right keys decrease the lo/hi position. These selections establish a range of pixel values that should take on the chosen color attribute.

Note that color values 0, 7, and 1 cannot be changed. These values represent the text color, background color, and cursor color, respectively.

Slide Palette Window (slide). Slide allows the user to slide a specified palette window along the entire color palette. Although the window moves, the width of the window is preserved.

Set Palette Position (define). After establishing a palette window, the window is fixed by the selection of define. The newly created palette is now set on the palette bar and in the specified user storage space. Define must be called after editing to place the palette in the specified user storage space.

Set Step Increment (step). The *step* parameter determines how rapidly the arrow keys change a palette value. Step sizes of 1, 2, 4, and 8 may be selected.

Load User Palette (Load). See Section 12.9.10.

Save User Palette (Save). Save allows the user to save the selected palette to a text file. As in the user filter design, a special header is tacked onto the beginning of the file. This header consists of the letter P. The graylevel, followed by its red, grn, and blu components, is stored in this text file. If a mouse is used, to select an option, click the left mouse button. The most recent selected menu item is marked with an asterisk (*). Now move the mouse cursor to the palette display and click on the desired location. When *RGB* is selected the left mouse button increases the value, while the right button decreases the value. The created palette window is fixed within the currently selected user palette by placing the green cursor over define, and clicking the left mouse button. To exit the *DEF-User* palette, place the cursor over the word *EXIT* at the bottom of the menu and click the left mouse button to quit.

Palette Usage Example.

Once the *User Palette* option is entered, select (r) for red and move the up or right cursor key. A line will appear and change color as the red component is incremented. Set the red component to 63. A pink bar will result. Next select *b* for the blue component and move the up or right arrow keys again until the blue component is 63 and the bar becomes light purple. The width of the bar is now changed by selecting *lo* and *hi*. First select *lo* and use the left or down keys to lower the beginning position of the window to 80. Now select *hi* and use the same keys to lower the end position of the window to 100. By next selecting slide, the window moves along the palette window. Watch as the lo/hi values change as this window is repositioned on the palette strip. Select *define* at this time to fix the newly created window in the palette.

Now select *lo* again and raise this value to 70, and then select *hi* and lower this value to 75. Notice that nothing appears to change. Select (g) to lower the green component to zero. A darker violet purple appears within the first specified region. Lower the blue component to 32 by selecting *b* and using the left or down arrow keys. A smaller magenta region appears within the first defined purple area. Select slide again to move this smaller window until the lo value becomes 35. Hit *define* at this time to fix this window in the palette.

12.10 Noise Menu

UCFImage generates five common types of two dimensional noise. These include uniform, Rayleigh, Gaussian, negative exponential, and salt and pepper impulse distributions. The user may replace the image with the selected noise or overlay the noise on top of the image. The user must first specify the ROI before selecting a desired noise distribution. The *undo* command is available with the operations of this menu.

12.10.1 Uniformly Distributed Noise (uniform). The user is prompted for the variance and mean. Valid variances range from 0 to 40,000. The mean's range is from −255 to +255. The user may abort this operation by hitting ESC instead of entering the variance and mean.

12.10.2 Rayleigh Distributed Noise (Rayleigh). The user is prompted for the variance only. The valid variance range for this distribution is also 0 to 40,000.

12.10.3 Gaussian Distributed Noise (Gaussian). For the Gaussian distributed noise, the user is prompted for both the variance and the mean. The valid ranges of these statistics are 0 to 40,000 and −255 to +255, respectively.

12.10.4 Negative Exponential Noise (neg. exp.). Like the Rayleigh distribution, the negative exponential noise only requires the variance for generation. Again, 0 to 40,000 is the valid range for the variance.

12.10.5 Salt and Pepper Noise (salt&pep). For the salt and pepper impulse noise, the user is prompted for a probability of impulse occurrence. The valid range of this probability is 0 to 1.

12.10.6 Select Noise Mode (mode). The user is able to select how the noise is applied to the ROI. Successive calls to this option toggle the mode between create and add. The create mode replaces the ROI with the designated noise. This generates the noise only, and the previous image is completely removed. The additive mode adds the noise to the image in the ROI. Therefore the old image is now seen corrupted with the selected noise.

12.11 Warping Menu

The warping process allows the user to distort an image using an affine transformation. The transform is specified graphically by way of gridpoints. Figure 12.38a shows the warping submenu.

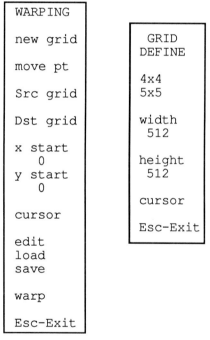

(a)   (b)

Figure 12.38 *Warping and Grid Define submenus.*

12.11.1 Select new grid (new grid). The grid define submenu, Figure 12.38b, is displayed. This menu allows selection of the number of points in the source and destination grids (4×4 or 5×5) and the width and height of the grids. The cursor option may be selected to set the grid size using the arrow keys or the mouse.

12.11.2 Move grid point (move pt). Allows grid points to be moved, either source or destination grid, depending on which is active (see Sections 12.11.3 and 12.11.4), using the arrow keys or mouse. A cursor displayed and moved to the desired point then selected using the right mouse button or return key. The cursor may then be moved to the new location. The point is set to the new location using the right mouse button or return key.

12.11.3 Select source grid (Src grid). Selects the source grid (displayed as green points) as the active grid. Note: grid must be specified using *new grid* (Section 12.11.1) or *load* (Section 12.11.9) before this item may be used.

12.11.4 Select destination grid (Dst grid). Selects the destination grid (displayed as yellow points) as the active grid. Note: grid must be specified using *new grid* (Section 12.11.1) or *load* (Section 12.11.9) before this item may be used.

12.11.5 Set x axis grid start point (x start). Sets the *x axis* start coordinate for the active grid.

12.11.6 Set y axis grid start point (y start). Sets the *y axis* start coordinate for the active grid.

12.11.7 Cursor (cursor). Invokes a cursor that permits the active grid to be moved by the user.

12.11.8 Edit grid points (edit). Displays an edit screen where the user can enter grid coordinates manually. Allows very accurate setting of grid coordinates.

12.11.9 Load grid points from file (load). Prompts for a filename to load previously stored warping coordinates. Allows a successful warping grid set to be applied to a different image.

12.11.10 Save grid points to file (save). Prompts for a filename to save warping grid coordinates to. Allows a successful warping grid set to be saved so that a different image may be loaded and warped.

12.11.11 Warp (warp). Warps the image buffer pixels so that the specified source and destination grid coordinates are aligned.

12.12 UCFImage File Formats

Data generated within UCFImage may be saved to ASCII or binary files for later retrieval or for use by other applications, specifically word processing, desktop publishing, spreadsheet and data visualization applications. Formats for these files are given next.

1. *User Defined Spatial Filters:*
Data from a user defined filter are saved in an ASCII (text) file. A lowercase *u* begins the file, followed by the element size of the mask and the scale factor specified. The elements of the mask are integer values.

```
u 3 1
1 1 1 2 2 2 3 3 3
```

2. *FFT/IFFT data files:*
Data generated by the FFT algorithm are saved in a binary file. In the FFT option, an uppercase F begins the file, and the IFFT datafile begins with an uppercase I. Next, the FFT/IFFT size (512, 256, 128, 64, 32, 16) is saved, followed by the FFT/IFFT data. This data is made up of 8 byte pairs of real-imaginary components, with the floating point number represented in the first 4 bytes denoting the real component and the next 4 byte floating number denoting the imaginary component.

```
F 512
11.9 122.8 21.4 32.3
. . .
```

3. *FFT/IFFT scaled image files:*
To view the results of the FFT/IFFT operation, a scaled image file is generated from the real-imaginary data file. This binary image file begins with a blank 512-byte header. The values are 1-byte unsigned characters representing the image gray-level intensities at the corresponding pixels.

```
------512 Byte Header------
---------------------------
1 2 8 24 128 255 32
. . . . . . .
```

4. *Histogram and circular symmetric results file:*
The results of the histogram computation are saved to an ASCII (text) file in pairs consisting of first the graylevel value and next the number of points in the image

with that graylevel. The graylevel value is saved as an integer and the number of occurrences of the graylevel is saved as a long integer.

0	10
1	15
2	8
. . .	
254	128
255	100

5. *User defined palette:*

Data from a user defined palette is saved in an ASCII (text) file. The file begins with an uppercase P, followed by the palette data. The palette data are integer values stored by the intensity value (0 to 255) with their corresponding red, green, and blue components.

0	10	30	42
1	15	9	28
2	8	63	63
. . .			
254	12	48	4
255	50	50	20

6. *Profile format:*

Data viewed in the Show Profile option of the Profile Menu may be saved to an ASCII (text) file with a call to SAVEDATA. This file contains the x y coordinates of the points along the line between the two user-specified points, followed by the graylevel value at that point.

0	1	0
1	1	9
2	1	163
. . .		
454	1	48
455	1	255

Appendix A

Image Processing Programming Strategies

Programming strategies for image processing involve the following three considerations, regardless of hardware or programming language used:

- Image input & storage
- Image representation
- Image output & display

After these elements are accommodated, then the programming of imaging algorithms may follow closely to the program segments given in the body of this book.

Image input and storage refers to the input of image data from an external source (camera, scanner, file, etc.) and the temporary storage of the image in a data structure. This becomes a major consideration if the hardware is limited, such as a personal computer, or if the source is complex, such as a hand scanner. After the image is input, then the *representation* of the image, what kind of data structure it is stored as, becomes important. It is the convenience of the data structure manipulation that determines whether the programming of the algorithms is straightforward or difficult. Finally, the *output* of the image to a display system so that it can be viewed and the *long term storage* methods selected to save image data, add to the complexity of the programming.

To illustrate the sequence of programming strategies, a program written in the C programming language to perform a *Laplacian* edge detection (See Section 8.3) using a 3×3 mask is given. Since the *Image_Size* define macro is 512, the program reads a raw, $512 \times 512 \times$ 8-bit image file, processes the image using the Laplacian mask, scales the data, then outputs the completed result to a file. The program, clearly, assumes rectangular images. The output may be viewed on an MS-DOS computer using the UCFImage© program (see Chapter 12) provided with the text. Multiple versions of program subroutines are given to show the various approaches to the programming. Two versions of **main** are given, the first with static allocation of the image array, Img, and the second using dynamic allocation. Both programs define the macro **Image(x,y)**. The macro is used by all of the subroutines given to access the image array so that all versions work regardless of the allocation scheme, or main routine, used.

The following main function assumes that a static array may be allocated of the necessary size, 512×512 (262,144 bytes). The array type is *unsigned character*, so that each element of

Img is treated as a single unsigned byte of data. The image data is accessed by the macro *Image*, which changes depending on the allocation scheme used.

```
/* Basic Image Processing Program for discrete convolution
   with static allocation of image array */

#include <stdio.h>
#define   Image_Size 512

#define LAPLACIAN   1     /* selects type of mask to load */

/* Image macro maps x,y indices directly to image array */
#define Image(x,y)  Img[x][y]

/* The actual array that stores the image data */
unsigned char Img[Image_Size][Image_Size];

main(){

  extern void Img_in(void),Img_convolve(int convolve_type),
              Img_out(void);

  Img_in();                  /* reads an image file */
  Img_convolve(LAPLACIAN);   /* Perform the Laplacian */
  Img_out();                 /* outputs the image */
}
```

The next version of *main* uses <u>dynamic</u> allocation of memory for the image array. Differences between this version and the static memory version are highlighted in bold. The pointer *Img* is dynamically assigned to the 262,144 byte data block returned by the *malloc* function. *Malloc* is a common memory allocation function available to C compilers. An include file that contains the function declaration is often required, this example uses *memory.h*. Note that the *Img* variable is a pointer to a contiguous block of memory. The macro, *Image*, must use a single index into this string of data. This is computed from the *x* (position in row) and *y* (row) index variables. Also note the liberal use of the C *casting* syntax[†] . Arithmetic on memory pointers must be performed using *long* data types to avoid errors, warnings and potential access problems.

```
/* Basic Image Processing Program
   with dynamic allocation of image array */

#include <stdio.h>
#include  <memory.h>

#define Image_Size 512
```

[†] Casting is used to force a data type in an expression, for example, *x* is cast as a *long* integer in the expression $*(Img + (long)x + (512L * y))$. The *y* variable is automatically cast to long because of its addition to the *long* 512 constant.

```
#define LAPLACIAN   1     /* selects type of mask to load */

/* Image macro maps x,y indices indirectly */
#define   Image(x,y*(Img+(long)x+(long)(Image_Size*y))

/* The actual array that stores the image data */
unsigned char *Img;

main(){
  extern void Img_in(void),Img_convolve(int convolve_type),
         Img_out(void);

  /* Allocate the memory for the image array */
  Img  =  (unsigned  char*)malloc(Image_Size*Image_Size);

  Img_in();                     /* Input an image file */
  Img_convolve(LAPLACIAN);  /* Perform the Laplacian */
  Img_out();                    /* Output the result */
}
```

The input of data involves the opening of files or the accessing of an image hardware device. Some image hardware is easily used and includes software to allow the user simple and transparent access. This factor has become an important consideration in the selection of imaging hardware. The following example of the *Img_in* function assumes the existence of a system subroutine called *Grab* that returns a 512 x 512 image from a camera and frame-grabber (See Section 2.8) when passed the image pointer, *Img*. The reader must be assured that systems this simple exist !

```
/* Input an image from hardware using a Grab routine*/

void Img_in(void){
  extern void Grab(char *image_pointer);

  Grab(Img);
}
```

There are many ways to load image data from a file, the following version of *Img_in* is possibly the simplest. It assumes that the image data is stored in a binary file called **MYIMAGE.PIC** in row-column order.

```
/* Input an image file indirectly*/

void Img_in(void){
  int ifile, i, j;
  char pixel;

  /* open the file for reading */
  ifile = open("MYIMAGE.PIC", 0);
```

```
    /* loop for all pixels, read 1 pixel at a time */
    for(i=0; i<Image_Size; ++i)
       for(j=0; j<Image_Size; ++j){
          read(ifile,&pixel,1);

          /* set image array value to pixel read */
          Image(i,j) = pixel;
       }
    close(ifile);
}
```

The previous routine, although simple, is very inefficient. The *Image(x,y)* macro was used to index into the memory array. Note that it was necessary to have an intermediate variable to read the pixel data into. If the image memory is accessed directly, then the routine can read data in more efficiently by accessing entire rows of the image file. The next function does this, but it will only work with the dynamic allocation approach used to establish the image array.

```
/* Input an image file directly*/

void Img_in(void){
  int ifile, i, j;

  /* open the file for reading */
  ifile = open("MYIMAGE.PIC", 0);

  /* read an entire Image_Size pixel row,
     Image_Size times, directly into the image array */

  for(i=0; i<Image_Size; ++i)
       read(ifile, Img + (Image_SizeL*i),Image_Size);

  close(ifile);
}
```

If the *read* statement from the previous routine is changed to the following, the function will work with the static allocation model:

```
            read(ifile, &Img[i][0],Image_Size);
```

Here the pointer to the buffer is provided by the address of the 1st (zeroth) pixel of the ith row in the *Img* array. Both examples show use of the low-level open/read functions, the routines may also be written using high-level fopen/fread functions as shown below. Note that the fread function takes four arguments. The first is a pointer to the buffer that is to receive the data, in this case the image array. The second argument is the number of bytes to be read. In this case, we want to read an entire row of pixels, or *Image_Size* of them. The third argument is the number of items. Here an item is one row of pixels. The last argument is the file pointer, *ifile*.

Also shown is the fread call for the static allocation version, where *Img* is loaded one row at a time.

```
/* Input an image file using fopen/fread functions*/

void Img_in(void){
  FILE *fopen(), *ifile;
  int i, j;

  /* open the file for reading */
  ifile = fopen("MYIMAGE.PIC", "r");

  /* read an entire Image_Size pixel row,
     Image_Size times, directly into the image array */

  for(i=0; i<Image_Size; ++i)
        fread(Img + (Image_Size*i),Image_Size,1,ifile);

        /* use for static allocation model
           fread(&Img[i][0],Image_Size,1,ifile);    */

  fclose(ifile);
}
```

It is also possible to load the entire image with one read, if the read statement on the compiler allows buffers large enough to accommodate the size of the image. Information as to whether or not this is possible will be found in the compiler users manual.

The image processing aspect of the program is performed by the *Img_convolve* function. This function replaces the original image with a discrete convolution using a selected mask, in this case, the Laplacian. This is just one of many masks that were discussed in Chapter 8, Spatial Filters. Simply put, the convolving function must be able to perform a shift and add process across all pixels in the image using the mask. To simplify our program, a fixed mask size of 3 x 3 elements will be used. More general routines can be written that allow the user masks of various sizes, yet the principles shown here are the same. The mapping of the Laplacian mask values to the indices of the image at a pixel located at coordinates **i, j** is shown below:

$$
\begin{array}{ccc}
0 & -1 & 0 \\
-1 & 4 & -1 \\
0 & -1 & 0
\end{array}
\longrightarrow
$$

i-1,j-1	i-1,j	i-1,j+1
i,j-1	i,j	i,j+1
i+1,j-1	i+1,j	i+1,j+1

The values of the mask array variable will be as follows,

```
[0][0] =   0    [0][1] = -1    [0][2] =   0
[1][0] = -1    [1][1] =   4    [1][2] = -1
[2][0] =   0    [2][1] = -1    [2][2] =   0
```

The strategy used is that the *mask* array is not indexed with variables in the convolution subroutine, but is assigned values based on the value of the *convolve_type* parameter passed as the argument to the Img_convolve routine. The value passed for this example was defined as 1 in the main calling program. The routine decides which values to use for the mask with a switch statement on *convolve_type* . Note that the routine given is also capable of processing a mean filter if the value of *convolve_type* is set to 2. In this case, each pixel is multiplied by 1/9 (0.1111) and the convolution result is just the average of all the pixels under the mask. Adding additional masks to the routine is a simple matter of adding additional case values. A static array, *conv_Img*, is declared to hold the intermediate result of the convolution. For this example, the array is one megabyte in size. Some compilers will not permit an array of this magnitude and the computation, in this case, must be performed in increments. It is relatively easy to write the program such that the convolution is calculated on three rows at a time, thus requiring a substantially smaller intermediate array. The *mask* array variable is also declared as **float** to allow for fractional values. If *convolve_type* does not switch to a predefined mask, the routine returns without altering the *conv_img* result array.

```
float conv_Img[Image_Size][Image_Size];

void Img_convolve(int convolve_type ){
  float mask[3][3], min=0.0,max=0.0;
  int    i, j;

  /* set the value of the convolution mask desired */
  switch(convolve_type ){

      case 1:                      /* set mask to be Laplacian */
          mask[0][0] =   0;
          mask[0][1] =  -1;
          mask[0][2] =   0;
          mask[1][0] =  -1;
          mask[1][1] =   4;
          mask[1][2] =  -1;
          mask[2][0] =   0;
          mask[2][1] =  -1;
          mask[2][2] =   0;
          break;

      case 2:                      /* set mask to be mean filter*/
          mask[0][0] = 0.111;
          mask[0][1] = 0.111;
```

```
         mask[0][2] = 0.111;
         mask[1][0] = 0.111;
         mask[1][1] = 0.111;
         mask[1][2] = 0.111;
         mask[2][0] = 0.111;
         mask[2][1] = 0.111;
         mask[2][2] = 0.111;
         break;

      default:      /* if no mask specified, do nothing*/
         return();
   }

   /* perform the convolution and save scale factors*/
   for(i=1;i<510;++i)
      for(j=1;j<510;++j){

         conv_Img[i][j]=
            Image[i-1][j-1]    * mask[0][0] +
            Image[i-1][j+1]    * mask[0][1] +
            Image[i-1][j]      * mask[0][2] +
            Image[i][j-1]      * mask[1][0] +
            Image[i][j]        * mask[1][1] +
            Image[i][j+1]      * mask[1][2] +
            Image[i+1][j-1]    * mask[2][0] +
            Image[i+1][j]      * mask[2][1] +
            Image[i+1][j+1]    * mask[2][2];

         if(conv_Img[i][j]>max)max=conv_Img[i][j];
        if(conv_Img[i][j]<min)min=conv_Img[i][j];
      }

   /* scale the result to 255 */
   for(i=1;i<510;++i)
      for(j=1;j<510;++j)
         Image(i,j) = 255*(int)(conv_Img[i][j]-min/(max-min));
   }
```

After the mask values are set, the routine processes the convolution within the first set of nested loops. Each result is tested to see if exceeds the maximum value stored in *max*, or is less than the value stored in *min*. These values are saved so that the convolution result may be scaled across the entire range of values computed. Note that the loops start at and index of 1 (instead of zero) and count to 510 (instead of 511). This is to avoid an index out of range error when one is added or subtracted during the convolution calculation. The net effect of this is a single pixel border around the image that does not get convolved. This can be avoided by using conditional statements to detect when the mask is at an edge and supplying zeroes as image values to the calculation.

The routine ends by scaling each of the *conv_img* array values to 255 across the range of values determined from *min* and *max* and replacing the original image values with the scaled convolution. The convolution may not be performed in place because of the dependency of the calculations on the neighborhood of values surrounding each pixel. However, this dependency is only constrained to the size of the mask, in this case 3 x 3. More complex schemes are possible that use far less memory than the one shown here.

The final step in the program is to output the convolution result. This is accomplished in a similar fashion to the way that the image was input to the program. In the simplest case the `Img_out` routine is as follows:

```
/* Output an image to a file */

void Img_out(void){
    int ofile, i, j;

    /* open the file for writing */
    ofile = creat("CONVOUT.PIC", 1);

    /* loop for all pixels, output 1 pixel at a time */
    for(i=0; i<Image_Size; ++i)
        for(j=0; j<Image_Size; ++j)
            write(ofile,Image(i, j),1);

    close(ofile);
}
```

In this version, the pixel is output to the file CONVOUT.PIC in column-row order using a write statement. The pixel is output directly from the image array because *write* accepts the *value* of the variable to output, not the address. The input routines given earlier using *fread* for reading whole rows at each loop iteration or the entire image may be converted to write functions using *fwrite*. The image file may then be viewed on the computer screen by a program capable of displaying a raw image file, or the picture can be sent to a grayscale printer.

Appendix B

C.I.E. Chromaticity Diagram
Electromagnetic Spectrum

C.I.E. Chromaticity Diagram

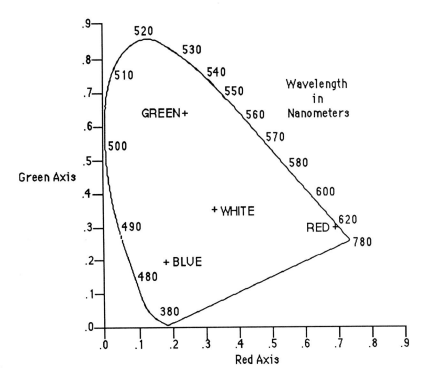

1 = Red + Green + Blue or Blue = 1 − Red − Green

Electromagnetic Spectrum

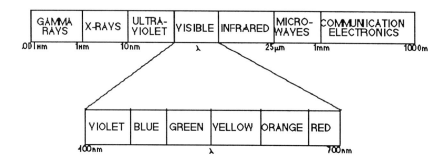

$$f = \frac{3 \times 10^8 \text{ m/s}}{\lambda}$$

where f is the frequency, λ is the wavelength and 3×10^8 m/s is the speed of light.

Appendix C

Compressed Image File Formats (GIF and TIFF)

Graphics Interchange File (GIF) Format

The Graphics Interchange File™ format, or GIF™, is a trademark of the Compuserve Corporation who developed it for the efficient storage and transfer of image data. The format is copyrighted and trademarked, however, use of the standard is free. As computer graphics and imaging increased in popularity in the public domain, an efficient means for storage and transfer of image data was deemed necessary. The GIF format has become a well respected standard for images because the structure of a GIF file is well defined and the data within a GIF file is compressed. The writing of a GIF interpreter is relatively simple and software to perform the functions of decoding and coding GIF files is available on all major computer platforms that have graphic capabilities.

The general file format of a GIF image is given in Figure 1. The *GIF Signature* is a six-character ASCII string that identifies the file as a GIF image. The first three characters of the string will be "GIF" while the last three will be a version identifier. The majority of GIF images will have the string "GIF87a" at their start. The *Screen Descriptor* consists of seven bytes of data that describe the pixel size (height, width and depth) of the image, a flag bit to indicate the prescence of a *Global Color Map*, and the index into the map of the background color. If a Global Color Map is present, it follows the Screen Descriptor and contains three entries for every color possible in the image. The number of possible colors is determined from the number of bits/pixel. If each pixel is one byte, eight bits, deep, then the total number of colors possible is 256 (2^8). Each three-byte entry in the Global Map will define the proportions of Red, Green and Blue intensity required for the color determined by the entries sequence position in the map, from zero to the total number of entries minus one. The Global Color Map allows the user to accurately specify the correct color mappings for a particular image.

The Global Color Map, or Screen Descriptor if no map is present, is followed by any number of *Image Descriptor* blocks. An Image Descriptor begins with an image seperation character, an ASCII ',' (comma) followed by a set of bytes defining the start location of the image in cartesian coordinates with respect to the height and width data given in the Screen Descriptor data, the size in pixels of the image and a flag byte. The flag byte determines whether the *Local Color Map* (whose data follows, if needed) or Global color Map should be used for the image. The flag also indicates whether the data is in sequential or interlaced order and what the pixel depth is in bits. The Raster Data, the actual image data, follows and is compressed using the Lempel-Ziv-Welch (LZW) algorithm. The LZW algorithm is a Huffman type encoding scheme that is capable of compressing and decompressing data streams very rapidly. When no futher image blocks are present, a *GIF Terminator* character, the semicolon (;) indicates the end of the file.

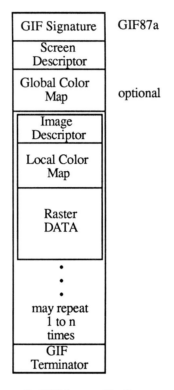

Figure 1. *GIF image file format.*

The GIF format is extensible through the use of *GIF Extension Blocks*. An Extension Block appears as Raster Data, but is introduced with an exclamation (!) character and is not compressed. Unique extensions may be defined by individuals as all GIF interpreters may ignore an extension that they have not been programmed for; however, Compuserve prefers to define and document extensions to provide for a more robust and globally understood standard. Specific information relating to the coding and decoding of GIF data is available through Compuserve.

Tagged Image File Format (TIFF)

The Tagged Image File Format, or TIFF (sometimes just TIF), was jointly developed by the Aldus and Microsoft Corporations primarily for scanned image storage and output. Although the format is heavily used, there is no commitment on the part of either developer to maintain a support structure for the format which is available in the public domain. Manufacturers of scanning equipment and image capture systems use the format heavily, as does the desk top publishing (DTP) industry.

A primary objective in the design of the TIFF format was to provide for extensibility as systems became more sophisticated and were capable of handling more data and more complex image structures. TIFF was not intended to be, nor is, a page description language such as PostScript™; however, the format is fully capable of describing any conceivable variation in digital data. This ability to be easily extended into new forms of data description is at once TIFF's advantage over other formats and disadvantage as well. It is unusual to find a TIFF reader that will accomodate all variations of TIFF files. Some are better than others and this is often a point of frustration with users when they obtain a TIFF image and are unable to read it with the imaging program that they have become accustomed to. In this sense, TIFF is more favorable to image generation systems as opposed to image display and output systems. Once again, TIFF was designed to accomodate variations and evolving improvements in image acquisition hardware. TIFF was also designed to be computer independent as much as possible. The only requirement that the format imposes is that the host support the concept of a file that is defined as a sequence (up to 2^{32}) of 8-bit bytes.

A TIFF file is a sequence of individual fields defined by unique *tags*, hence the name, Tagged Image File Format. The tags may be considered as pointers to defined fields containing the data and data descriptions of the image. It is because of this pointer structure that TIFF incorporates such extensibility. For example, the user may define any type of data compression scheme desired, or may create a unique mapping of the data to better accommodate the data output stream of a device. A TIFF reader interprets each byte in the data stream either as a tag, which tells it what to do with the data the follows, or as specific data that is associated with a description identified by it's tag.

The specifics of TIFF are beyond the scope of this book, however, entire volumes have been devoted to an exacting descriptions of image file formats. One particular text, *Bit-Mapped Graphics*, by Zimmer, is listed in the Annotated Bibliography and contains a complete description of the Tagged Image File Format.

Appendix D

Index of Algorithms and Masks

The Index of Algorithms and Masks is intended to provide rapid access to the algorithms and techniques discussed in the text as well as a quick reference guide to commonly used discrete convolution masks.

Class	Name	Effect/Mask	Section
Color	HSI	Adjust color lookup table using Hue, Saturation and Intensity (HSI) parameters.	7.2
	Pseudocolor	Mapping of colors to graylevel values to enhance visualization.	7.4
	RGB	Change to the mixture of the primary additive colors of light at each pixel.	7.5
Edge Detection	Sobel Masks	$\begin{array}{ccc} -1 & -2 & -1 \\ 0 & 0 & 0 \\ 1 & 2 & 1 \end{array}$ $\begin{array}{ccc} -1 & 0 & 1 \\ -2 & 0 & 2 \\ -1 & 0 & 1 \end{array}$	8.3
	Laplacian Mask	$\begin{array}{ccc} 0 & -1 & 0 \\ -1 & 4 & -1 \\ 0 & -1 & 0 \end{array}$	8.3
	High Pass Mask	$\begin{array}{ccc} 1 & -2 & 1 \\ -2 & 4 & -2 \\ 1 & -2 & 1 \end{array}$	8.5
	Low Pass Mask	$\begin{array}{ccc} 0 & .1 & 0 \\ .1 & .6 & .1 \\ 0 & .1 & 0 \end{array}$	8.5
Enhance-ment	Adaptive	Filtering of images with multiple noise sources, or mixed noise.	11.4-7
	Histogram Equalization	Improves contrast of overly dark/bright image.	5.4
	Histogram Specification	Allows application of a desired histogram to an image.	5.5
	Histogram Stretch	Improves contrast of overly dark/bright image.	5.3
	Smoothing	Reduces spot noise.	8.4
	Sharpening	Clarifies edges.	8.4
	Fourier Filter	Remove image degradation in spatial frequency domain.	10.6
Mensura-tion	Area	Compute pixel count of an object.	6.4
	Centroid	Compute center (x-y coordinates) of an object.	6.4
	Clustering	Find objects in an image.	6.3
Morpho-logy	Closing	Reduce the size of interior contour pertubations in an image.	9.4
	Dilation	Increase the size of an object.	9.3
	Erosion	Decrease the size of an object.	9.3
	Opening	Increase the size of interior contour pertubations in an image.	9.4
	Outlining	Removes interior pixels of an object leaving only the contour.	9.5
	Skeletonizing	Determine the medial axis of an object.	9.6
Segmenta-tion	Thresholding	Find objects and regions using a common grayscale value.	5.6

Glossary

adaptive filters -- filters that change their characteristics as they are applied to an image.

adaptive window edge detected filter -- this filter adaptively changes its window size when an edge is detected to preserve the details of the edge.

aperture -- size of a lens opening, often controlled with a metal iris.

array processor -- specialized computer designed to perform calculations on arrays (or images) rapidly.

aspect ratio -- ratio of height to width of an object either captured by a camera or displayed by a monitor.

autoscaling -- alogrithm that scales an image between a minimum and a maximum gray level value following the application of an algorithm that modifies graylevel.

binary image -- image where pixels have only two values, generally 0 and 1.

brightness -- the gray level value of a pixel within an image that corresponds to energy intensity. The larger the gray level value the greater the brightness.

Cathode Ray Tube (CRT) -- electronic tube that allows display of images and graphics through the electronic positioning of an electron beam; the glass screen of a computer display or monitor.

CCD camera -- solid-state camera using a charge-coupled device sensor.

C-mount -- common lens mounting system used on electronic cameras, 1" in diameter with 32 threads/inch.

closing -- a morphological operation that smooths the geometrical contour of objects within an image. This operation is composed of a morphological dilation operation followed by a morphological erosion operation.

complex numbers -- number system represented by the sum of a pair of real values **a** and **b**, written **a** +**b***j*, where **a** is called the real part(sometimes Re) and **b** the imaginary part (sometimes Im). The term imaginary is used because the second value, **b**, is multiplied by the imaginary operator $j=\sqrt{-1}$. This is simply a convention that allows easy representation of frequency dependent functions. The usefulness of complex numbers is revealed when *phase* and *magnitude spectrums* are derived from the results of Fourier transformations.

composite video -- RS-170 video that includes synchronization signals.

control point -- corresponding points selected between two images so that they can be aligned to each other using a warping process.

contrast -- the amount of gray level variation within an image

convolution -- See *discrete convolution.*

convolution mask -- small subimage, typically 3x3 to 7x7 in size, used as a filter in a discrete convoultion operation. Examples of convolution masks are:

$$\begin{bmatrix} 1 & 2 & 1 \\ 2 & 4 & 2 \\ 1 & 2 & 1 \end{bmatrix} \qquad \begin{bmatrix} 0 & -1 & 1 & -1 & 0 \\ -1 & 2 & -4 & 2 & -1 \\ -1 & -4 & 13 & -4 & -1 \\ -1 & 2 & -4 & 2 & -1 \\ 0 & -1 & 1 & -1 & 0 \end{bmatrix}$$

     3x3 Low Pass (smoothing) Filter   5x5 High Pass (sharpening) Filter

See *discrete convolution.*

cornea -- transparent outer surface of the eye that performs the initial focussing process.

cursor -- graphic object used in display systems to identify the location of a pointing device, such as a mouse, joystick or digitizing pad.

cutting & pasting -- process of outlining an area in an image, removing it (cutting) or adding it (pasting) to either the same image or a different one.

depth of field -- twice the distance an object in focus may move from the object plane and still remain in focus.

digitizer -- electronic circuit that converts analog, or continuous signals into discrete or digital data.

dilation -- a morphological operation that *enlarges* the geometrical size of objects within an image.

dither -- term used to describe computer algorithms that simulate grayscale output on binary devices; see *half-toning*.

discrete -- refers to signals or data that is divided into samples, or fixed quantities.

Discrete Cosine Transform -- mathematical transformation performed on discrete data that resolves additive real sinusoidal components of the data that correspond to the spatial frequency content of the data.

discrete convolution -- process where two images are combined using a shift, multiply and add operation. Typically, one image is substantially smaller than the other and is called the *mask* or window. Masks can be designed to perform a wide range of filtering functions. See *mask, spatial filter*.

Discrete Fourier Transform -- mathematical transformation performed on discrete data that resolves additive complex sinusoidal components of the data that correspond to the spatial frequency content of the data.

double window modified trimmed mean adaptive filter -- filter that uses two windows that adaptively switch from a 3 by 3 *median* to a 5 by 5 *mean* filter.

electromagnetic spectrum -- range of known energy wavelengths (or frequencies) and their corresponding labels.

enhancement -- algorithms and processes that improve an image based on subjective measures.

erosion -- morphological operation that *reduces* the geometrical size of objects within an image.

f-number -- aperture setting of a lens; ratio of the diameter of the aperture to the focal length of the lens; the f is an abbreviation for *field*, not focal length, as the f-number determines the Depth of Field.

f-stop -- see *f-number*.

Fast Fourier Transform (FFT) -- a special formulation of the Fourier Transform (see *Discrete Fourier Transform*) that takes advantage of repetitive forms to increase the speed of computer calculations.

focal length -- point at which the rays converged by a lens meet; may be changed by the aperture setting, see *f-number*.

frame -- term used to describe an image, typically in context with a series of images, such as a single frame in an image sequence.

frame-buffer -- computer memory designed to store an image or set of images that have been captured and digitized by a *frame-grabber*, or *digitizer*.

frame-grabber -- electronic circuit that converts (using digitization) an analog video signal into a digital image, see *digitizer*.

frequency -- measure of periodicity of a data set, or how often the data repeats a pattern in a given measure, such as time or distance. See *periodic*, *spatial frequency*.

gamma -- basic measure of contrast; in film terminology, gamma is the slope of the density vs exposure curve; in electronic display terminology, gamma is the slope of the brightness distribution curve; large gamma indicates a steep slope and high contrast.

ganglia -- grouping of nerves in the retina that combine the signals from the light sensory nerves giving rise to a low-pass filtering effect.

gas-plasma display -- display that uses the electroluminescence of rare gases to create visible output for a computer monitor.

gaussian noise -- a type of noise whose histogram is Gaussian (bell) shaped.

graphic tablet -- computer input device that transforms pen position on a surface into position coordinates.

Graphic Interchange Format™ (GIF) -- file storage format for images developed by Compuserve Information Service, Inc.; uses LZW compression.

graylevel -- value of gray from a black and white (monochrome) image.

grayscale -- range of gray shades, or graylevels, corresponding to pixel values that a monochrome image incorporates.

Hadamard Transform -- transform that resolves a data set into sets of square waves, where the maximum value is 1 and the minimum value is -1. Sometimes called the Walsh-Hadamard transform (see *Walsh Transform*), the Hadamard Transform is distinguished from the Walsh in that the transform matrices may be generated recursively using the lowest order Hadamard matrix,

$$H_2 = \begin{bmatrix} 1 & 1 \\ 1 & -1 \end{bmatrix}$$ and the recursive matrix, $H_{2N} = \begin{bmatrix} H_N & H_N \\ H_N & -H_N \end{bmatrix}$. The H_{2N} matrix is the

Hadamard matrix of order 2N and higher orders are easily generated by applying the recursive relation shown above.

half-toning -- technique for rendering a grayscale effect on a binary (two-tone) output device.

histogram -- distribution of pixel graylevel values. A graph of number of pixels at each graylevel possible in an image. A histogram is a probability distribution of pixels values and may be processed using statistical techniques. These processes result in changes to the brightness and contrast in an image, but are independent of the spatial distribution of the pixels. See *uniform histogram, histogram stretching, histogram equalization, histogram specification.*

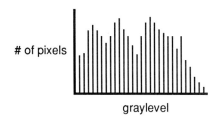

histogram equalization -- process that converts an images histogram to a uniform distribution. This is accomplished by integrating (summing) the histogram over all graylevel values. The effect of equalization is improved contrast in the image.

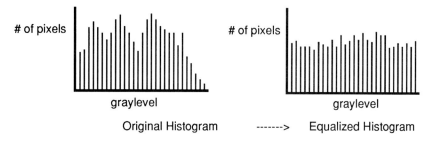

Original Histogram   ------->   Equalized Histogram

histogram specification -- process that changes the shape of a given image histogram to that of another, specified by the user. The process is used when the histogram of one image is desired in another, or during an interactive histogram modification scheme where the user is allowed to change the histogram dynamically to acheive a desired contrast result.

histogram stretching -- process that scales a histogram to the fullest possible range. This is distinguished from histogram equalization, which is the conversion of a histogram to a uniform distribution.

homomorphic filter -- filter that uses logarithm to seperate intensity and reflection components of an image so that each can be modified independently.

Huffman Coding -- coding technique that calculates probability of occurrance for data values and assigns smallest codes to most frequent data.

illumination -- outside source of energy that illuminates a scene or image.

integer numbers -- the set of whole numbers of the following form 1, 2, 301, 1024 etc..

interlacing -- process of skipping every other line in a output or input scheme.

intersection -- the overlapping region of two objects or sets.

Lempel-Ziv-Welch (LZW) Coding -- coding scheme similar to Huffman (see above) where probabilities are recalculated when performance changes.

lens -- transparent device used to bend and focus light rays.

liquid-crystal display -- display that uses the light attentuating effect of amorphous crystals to create visible output for a computer monitor.

magnification -- ratio of the size of an objects image to the actual size of the object.

magnitude spectrum -- spectrum of spatial frequency magnitudes (or strengths) in an image. The *magnitude spectrum* is an image where each pixel represents the magnitude of the spatial frequency at that location from the original image. The spectrum is derived from a complex spatial frequency generating transform, such as the Discrete Fourier. The magnitude(A) at a given pixel location is given by the equation, $A = \sqrt{Re^2 + Im^2}$, where Im is the imaginary portion of the complex transform and Re is the real portion. See *complex numbers, frequency, spectrum.*

mask -- generally refers to a small image used to specify the area of operation to take place on a larger image in an algorithm. Mask also refers to a discrete convolution filter. See *convoultion mask.*

maximum filter -- this filter replaces the pixel being operated on with the maximum graylevel of a set pixels located under a spatial mask.

mean -- the average of a set of data values; e.g., for the set of values:

{ 3, 5, 6, 7, 4, 3, 2, 2 } the mean is $(3 + 5 + 6 + 7 + 4 + 3 + 2 + 2)/8 = 4$.

medial axis transform -- the *skeleton* of an object.

median -- the middle value of a set of *ordered* data values; e.g., for the set of values:

{ 3, 5, 6, 7, 4, 3, 2, 2 } the median is {2 2 3 3 | 4 5 6 7} = 3.5

mensuration -- measurement algorithms.

minimum filter -- this filter replaces the pixel being operated on with the minimum gray level of a set pixels located under a spatial mask. See *maximum filter*.

monochrome -- literally *one color*, also used to describe black and white grayscale images.

monitor -- display used to output images or computer data.

mouse -- computer input device that is moved on a surface and translates physical movement into position data.

multi-level threshold -- the process of thresholding the graylevel values of an image into multiple levels.

negative exponential noise -- a type of noise that is described by a negative exponential histogram.

NTSC -- acronym for National Television Standards Committee; term used to describe RS-170 compatible color video.

nyquist theorem -- sampling theorem that requires that a signal be sampled, or *digitized*, at a rate (the nyquist rate) that is twice the highest frequency present in the sampled signal. When the nyquist rate is used, all components of the sampled signal will be adequately represented.

null set -- a set of objects containing no members.

opening -- morpholgical operation that is used to smooth the geometrical shape of objects within an image. Opening is a morphological erosion followed by a morpholgical dilation operation.

optic nerve -- nerve that carries image data from the eye to the brain.

optimum threshold -- this is the best threshold value for a particular image to reveal the most possible objects.

order statistics -- the process of ordering a set of data from minimum to maximum to obtain a set of statistics.

outliers -- pixels that contain gray level values that do not represent the normal gray level value within a region of an image.

outline -- the contour of objects within an image.

pel -- European term for pixel.

periodic -- when a data set, or signal, repeats itself, the data is said to be *periodic*. The size of the data subset (typically measured in time or distance) that repeats itself is called the *period* of the data set. *Frequency* is the measure of periodicity and is given as periods/time or periods/distance.

phase spectrum -- spectrum of spatial frequency phase (or directions) in an image. The *phase spectrum* is an image where each pixel represents the phase of the spatial frequency at that location from the original image. The spectrum is derived from a complex spatial frequency generating transform, such as the Discrete Fourier. The phase(Θ) angle at a given pixel location is given by the equation, $\Theta = \tan^{-1}(\text{Im}/\text{Re})$, where Im is the imaginary portion of the complex transform and Re is the real portion. See *complex numbers, frequency, spectrum*.

pixel -- slang for picture element, the smallest element of an image; pixels are arranged in row and columns to create an image, frame or picture.

pupil -- aperture of the eye; term used for variable aperture.

profile -- imaging function that plots or displays pixel data along a line within an image to yield a cross section of values.

quantization -- range of values that a pixel can represent.

real numbers -- a set number of the form 3.12, 4.518, 6.323 etc.

real-time -- 30 frames per second, or the number of frames required so that normal motion is not blurred to a human observer.

reconstruction -- algorithms and processes that attempt to construct a two-dimensional image from one-dimensional data functions (CAT scans, Synthetic Aperature Radar, etc.).

reflectance -- portion of incident light that is relected from objects or background in an image.

resolution -- smallest feature (spatial) or graylevel value (quantization) that an image system can resolve.

restoration -- algorithms and processes that attempt to remove a degradation (noise, blurring and defocussing effects) based on an objective criterion.

retina -- spatial light sensor array of the eye.

rubber-band -- when a graphic selection contour or object stretches to follow the input cursor.

RF modulator -- device that converts an RS-170 video signal into a radio frequency signal so that a television can receive it through its tuner.

RS-170 -- video standard of 525 lines, interlaced at 1/30 second.

Run-Length Encoding (RLE) -- simple coding scheme consisting of number pairs where one number represents a pixel value and the other the number of times the value is repeated.

salt and pepper noise -- noise that contains both minimum and maximum outlier pixels. In a 256 gray level image, the pepper noise has gray level value of 0, while the salt noise has a gray level value 255.

sampling -- used to describe spatial resolution of an image.

separability -- two-dimensional (image) transform property where the mathematical operations defining the transform can be divided into two or more parts. This property is advantageous from a computations standpoint. The *Fourier, Cosine, Walsh* and *Hadamard Transforms* are seperable.

set -- a collection of objects combined together that all contain something in common.

signal adaptive median filter -- An adaptive median filter that changes its window size and characteristics depending on the input signal/image.

skeletonization -- algorithm used to find the central axis (skeleton) of an image object.

Sobel -- directional edge detection discrete convolution masks of the following form:

$$\text{vertical}\begin{bmatrix} -1 & 0 & 1 \\ -2 & 0 & -2 \\ -1 & 0 & 1 \end{bmatrix} \qquad \text{horizontal}\begin{bmatrix} -1 & -2 & -1 \\ 0 & 0 & 0 \\ 1 & 2 & 1 \end{bmatrix}$$

solid-state cameras -- electronic cameras that use solid-state arrays as their sensing element, see *CCD camera.*

spatial filter -- image filter that operates on the spatial distribution of pixel values in a small neighborhood. Although a *spatial frequency* filter operates on spatial distributions of pixels, this term is generally reserved for *discrete convolutions* while the latter term is used for filters derived from image transforms, See *discrete convolution.*

spatial frequency -- measure of the periodicity of a data set with respect to a distance measure. Periodic changes in brightness values across an image are defined in terms of spatial frequency, or periods/distance. If the period of a brightness pattern is 20 pixels and the size of a pixel is 1/20th of a mm, then the *spatial frequency* of the data set is 20 pixels/mm. See *periodic, freqency.*

spectrum -- a collection of ordered frequencies describing the frequency content of a data set, or signal. For example, the *electromagnetc spectrum* is the collection of light frequencies that are physically known to science. See *electromagnetc spectrum, magnitude spectrum, phase spectrum.*

square wave -- a rectangularly shaped signal (⌐⌐⌐).

standard image -- 512 by 512 pixels, 8-bits (1 byte) quantization per pixel.

structuring set -- the set of pixels used to describe the structuring function used in the morphological erosion and dilation operations.

Tagged Image File Format (TIFF) -- image storage file format developed by Microsoft and Aldus corporations; most commonly used in desktop publishing applications and with image scanner hardware.

template -- subimage used in image correlation or matching function. Sometimes used to describe discrete convolution mask. See *discrete convolution.*

threshold -- a value used to segment the graylevel values of an image into two different regions. Also called the binarization of an image. For example, if a threshold value of 128 is chosen, then any pixel below this value would be set to 0 and all pixels greater than and equal to this value would be set to 255.

touch-screen -- computer input device that reports the coordinates of where the monitor screen was touched either by a finger or wand.

trackball -- computer input device that moves the cursor based on position of a ball mounted to free rotate in a fixture. As the ball is rotated, the cursor tracks its motion in the same direction.

uniform noise -- a type of noise described by a uniform histogram.

union -- the process of combining two different sets into one set.

variance -- the average value that a set of data values differ from the *mean* of the set. Formally, it is the average value of the *squares* of the deviations from the mean; e.g., for the set of values:

$$\{ 3, 5, 6, 7, 4, 3, 2, 2 \}$$

the mean is 4 , the data set of *differences* from the mean is:

$$\{ -1, -1, 2, 3, 0, -1, -2, -2\},$$

the data set of *squares* of the *differences* is:

$$\{ 1, 1, 4, 9, 0, 1, 4, 4\},$$

and the *mean* of this set, the *variance*, is 3.
See *mean..*

Venn diagrams -- a graphical method of performing various set operations such as union (or) and intersection (and).

video -- signal that carries analog image information.

video output controller -- subunit of an image processing system that controls and routes video signals in the system.

vidicon -- electronic tube that images using a scanned electron beam.

visible spectrum -- portion of the electromagnetic spectrum that is visible to the human eye; color spectrum; see *electromagnetic spectrum.*

WYSIWYG -- What You See Is What You Get; term used to describe computer displays that show what text and graphics will appear when a document is printed.

Walsh Transform -- transform that resolves a data set into sets of square waves, where the maximum value is 1 and the minimum value is -1. Sometimes called the Walsh-Hadamard transform (see *Hadamard Transform*), the Walsh Transform is distinguished from the Hadamard in that the transform has a fast form implementation similar to that used by the *Fast Foruier Transform*. The Walsh-Hadamard transforms have substantial advantages in computation over other transforms in that no complex or floating-point numbers are required.

warp -- to perform a geometric distortion operation on an image using a computer algorithm.

weber ratio -- ratio of background intensity to foreground intensity in human visual perception; this ratio remains close to 20% over a large range of brightness values.

zoom -- process by which an image is magnified by a computer algorithm.

Annotated Bibliography

Image Processing

R. C. Gonzalez and P. Wintz, *Digital Image Processing*, Addison-Wesley, 1987.
   Excellent general coverage of image processing; used in many introductory college courses in image processing.

E. L. Hall, *Computer Image Processing and Recognition*, Academic Press, 1979.
   Excellent general coverage of image processing, more mathematically rigorous than Gonzalez and Wintz, but less current; good treatment of photometry and radiometry.

I. Pitas & A. N. Venetsanopoulos, *Nonlinear Digital Filters*, Kluwer Academic, 1990.
   Complete coverage of Adaptive and Morphological Filters and theory behind them; requires some background in probability and statistics.

W. K. Pratt, *Digital Image Processing*, John Wiley & Sons, 1978.
   Sometimes called the "Encyclopaedia of Image Processing" because of its extensive coverage of the discipline; used in many college courses in image processing.

A. Rosenfeld and A. C. Kak, *Digital Picture Processing*, Academic Press, 1982.
   Advanced texts (two volumes) treating images as stochastic processes; requires communications theory with strong math background; excellent treatment of reconstruction theory andalgorithms; Volume 1 covers basic image processing, Volume 2 explores image understanding.

Machine Vision

D. H. Ballard & Brown, *Computer Vision*, L. J. Galbiati, *Machine Vision and Digital Image Processing Fundamentals*, Prentice-Hall, 1990.
   Basic text covering macine vision applications and algorithms; chapter on bar code evaluation.

R. Nevatia, *Machine Perception*, Prentice-Hall, 1982.
   Basic text with good coverage of classic recognition algorithms and edge detection.

J. T. Tou and R. C. Gonzalez, *Pattern Recognition Principles*, Addison-Wesley, 1974.
    Classic pattern recognition with excellent sections on basic clustering and mensuration techniques.

Computer Graphics

J. D. Foley & A. Van Damm, *Fundamentals of Interactive Computer Graphics*, Addison-Wesley, 1984.
    Classic computer graphics textbook used in college courses on the subject.

E. Angel, *Computer Graphics*, Addison-Wesley, 1990.
    Clearly written coverage of basic graphics techniques; example algorithms in C language.

S. Rimmer, *Bit--Mapped Graphics*, Windcrest, 1990.
    Completely covers personal computer graphic image formats. Illustrates how to write C and assembler code to read and write popular image file formats.

Image Algebra

E. R. Doughetry & C. R. Gardina, *Image Processing-Continuous to Discrete,* Vol. 1, Prentice-Hall, 1987.
    Not specifically *Image Algebra*, however, the treatment and approach to image processing in this text is an algebraic one.

Index

24 bit color systems, 91